Elements of Lite[illegible]

Third Course

Holt Assessment: Literature, Reading, and Vocabulary

- Entry-Level Test and End-of-Year Test
- Collection Diagnostic Tests
- Selection Tests
- Collection Summative Tests
- Answer Key

HOLT, RINEHART AND WINSTON
A Harcourt Education Company
Orlando • Austin • New York • San Diego • Toronto • London

STAFF CREDITS

EDITORIAL

Project Director
Laura Wood

Managing Editor
Marie Price

Associate Managing Editor
Elizabeth LaManna

Writers and Editors
Thomas Browne
e2 Publishing Services, llc

Editorial Staff
Text Editor, Shelley Mack Hoyt; *Copyeditors*, Emily Force, Julia Thomas Hu, Nancy Shore; *Senior Copyeditors*, Christine Altgelt, Elizabeth Dickson, Leora Harris, Anne Heausler, Kathleen Scheiner; *Copyediting Supervisor*, Mary Malone; *Copyediting Manager*, Michael Neibergall; *Editorial Coordinator*, Erik Netcher; *Editorial Support*, Danielle Greer

ART, DESIGN, AND PHOTO

Design
Jeff Robinson

PRODUCTION/ MANUFACTURING

Senior Production Coordinators, Belinda Barbosa Lopez, Michael Roche; *Production Manager*, Carol Trammel; *Senior Production Manager*, Beth Prevelige

Printed in the United States of America

ISBN 0-03-068521-4

1 2 3 4 5 6 179 05 04 03

Table of Contents

Collection 4 Comparing Themes • Synthesizing Sources

Collection 5 Irony and Ambiguity • Evaluating an Argument

Collection 6 Symbolism and Allegory • Synthesizing Sources

Collection 7 Poetry

Collection 8 Evaluating Style • Evaluating Arguments: Pro and Con

Collection 9 Biographical and Historical Approach • Using Primary and Secondary Sources

Collection 10 Epic and Myth • Evaluating an Argument

Collection 11 Drama • Synthesizing Sources

Collection 12 Consumer and Workplace Documents: The World of Computer Game Development

Overview of ELEMENTS OF LITERATURE Assessment Program

Two assessment booklets have been developed for ELEMENTS OF LITERATURE.

(1) Assessment of student mastery of selections and specific literary, reading, and vocabulary skills in the **Student Edition:**

- ***Holt Assessment: Literature, Reading, and Vocabulary***

(2) Assessment of student mastery of workshops and specific writing, listening, and speaking skills in the **Student Edition:**

- ***Holt Assessment: Writing, Listening, and Speaking***

Diagnostic Assessment

Holt Assessment: Literature, Reading, and Vocabulary contains two types of diagnostic tests:

- The Entry-Level Test is a diagnostic tool that helps you determine (1) how well students have mastered essential prerequisite skills needed for the year and (2) to what degree students understand the concepts that will be taught during the current year. This test uses multiple tasks to assess mastery of literary, reading, and vocabulary skills.
- The Collection Diagnostic Tests help you determine the extent of students' prior knowledge of literary, reading, and vocabulary skills taught in each collection. These tests provide vital information that will assist you in helping students master collection skills.

Holt Online Essay Scoring can be used as a diagnostic tool to evaluate students' writing proficiency:

- For each essay, the online scoring system delivers a holistic score and analytic feedback related to five writing traits. These two scoring methods will enable you to pinpoint the strengths of your students' writing as well as skills that need improvement.

Ongoing, Informal Assessment

The **Student Edition** offers systematic opportunities for ongoing, informal assessment and immediate instructional follow-up. Students' responses to their reading; their writing, listening, and speaking projects; and their work with vocabulary skills all serve as both instructional and ongoing assessment tasks.

Overview of ELEMENTS OF LITERATURE Assessment Program *(continued)*

- Throughout the **Student Edition,** practice and assessment are immediate and occur at the point where skills are taught.
- In order for assessment to inform instruction on an ongoing basis, related material repeats instruction and then offers new opportunities for informal assessment.
- Skills Reviews at the end of each collection offer a quick evaluation of how well students have mastered the collection skills.

Progress Assessment

Students' mastery of the content of the **Student Edition** is systematically assessed in two test booklets:

- ***Holt Assessment: Literature, Reading, and Vocabulary*** offers a test for every selection. Multiple-choice questions focus on comprehension, the selected skills, and vocabulary development. In addition, students write answers to constructed-response prompts that test their understanding of the skills.
- ***Holt Assessment: Writing, Listening, and Speaking*** provides both multiple-choice questions for writing and analytical scales and rubrics for writing, listening, and speaking. These instruments assess proficiency in all the writing applications appropriate for each grade level.

Summative Assessment

Holt Assessment: Literature, Reading, and Vocabulary contains two types of summative tests:

- The Collection Summative Tests, which appear at the end of every collection, ask students to apply their recently acquired skills to a new literary selection. These tests contain both multiple-choice questions and constructed-response prompts.
- The End-of-Year Test helps you determine how well students have mastered the skills and concepts taught during the year. This test mirrors the Entry-Level Test and uses multiple tasks to assess mastery of literary, reading, and vocabulary skills.

Holt Online Essay Scoring can be used as an end-of-year assessment tool:

- You can use ***Holt Online Essay Scoring*** to evaluate how well students have mastered the writing skills taught during the year. You will be able to assess student

Overview of ELEMENTS OF LITERATURE Assessment Program *(continued)*

mastery using a holistic score as well as analytic feedback based on five writing traits.

Monitoring Student Progress

Both ***Holt Assessment: Literature, Reading, and Vocabulary*** and ***Holt Assessment: Writing, Listening, and Speaking*** include skills profiles that record progress toward the mastery of skills. Students and teachers can use the profiles to monitor student progress.

***One-Stop Planner*® CD-ROM with ExamView® Test Generator**

All of the questions in this booklet are available on the ***One-Stop Planner*® CD-ROM with ExamView® Test Generator.** You can use the ExamView Test Generator to customize any of the tests in this booklet. You can then print a test unique to your classroom situation.

Holt Online Assessment

You can use ***Holt Online Assessment*** to administer and score the diagnostic and summative tests online. You can then generate and print reports to document student growth and class results. For your students, this online resource provides individual assessment of strengths and weaknesses and immediate feedback.

FOR THE TEACHER

About This Book

Holt Assessment: Literature, Reading, and Vocabulary accompanies **ELEMENTS OF LITERATURE.** The booklet includes copying masters for diagnostic tests, selection tests, and summative tests to assess students' knowledge of prerequisite skills, their comprehension of the readings in the **Student Edition,** and their mastery of the skills covered in each collection.

Entry-Level Test

The **Entry-Level Test** is a diagnostic tool that enables you to evaluate your students' mastery of essential skills at the start of the year. This objective, multiple-choice test contains several reading selections followed by questions assessing students' comprehension of their reading and their knowledge of select literary skills. Other sections of the test evaluate students' command of vocabulary skills.

Collection Tests

The copying masters in ***Holt Assessment: Literature, Reading, and Vocabulary*** are organized by collection. There are three types of tests for each collection:

- A **Collection Diagnostic Test** is included for every collection. These multiple-choice tests cover literary terms and devices as well as reading and vocabulary skills. These tests will enable you to assess students' prior knowledge of the skills taught in each collection.
- A **Selection Test** accompanies every major selection in the **Student Edition.** Each Selection Test includes objective questions that assess students' comprehension of the selection, mastery of literary skills as they apply to the selection, and acquisition of vocabulary words. In addition, students write a brief essay in response to a constructed-response prompt that asks them to formulate answers independently using their newly acquired skills.
- A **Collection Summative Test** follows the selection tests for each collection. This test asks students to apply their new skills to a selection that does not appear in the **Student Edition.** Students are asked to read a brief selection and then respond to multiple-choice questions and constructed-response prompts that assess their comprehension of the selection and vocabulary, reading, and literary skills.

End-of-Year Test

The **End-of-Year Test** is a summative tool that assesses students' mastery of the skills and concepts taught during the year. Like the Entry-Level Test, this test uses a multiple-choice format to assess students' comprehension of several reading selections and their mastery of literary and vocabulary skills.

About This Book *(continued)*

Answer Sheets and Answer Key

Answer Sheets are provided for the Entry-Level Test and the End-of-Year Test. If you prefer, students may mark their answers on the tests themselves. For all collection tests, students should write their answers on the tests. The **Answer Key** provides answers to objective questions. It also provides model responses to constructed-response prompts.

Skills Profile

The **Skills Profile** lists the skills assessed by the tests in this booklet. You can use the Skills Profile to create a developmental record of your students' progress as they master each skill.

Administering the Tests

The format of the Entry-Level Test and the End-of-Year Test, with their accompanying answer sheets, replicates that of most standardized tests. You can use these tests to help familiarize your students with the types of standardized tests they will take in the future.

To administer these tests, prepare a copy of the appropriate test and answer sheet for each student. Some sections of the tests have sample items. Before students begin these sections, you may want to select the correct answer for the sample items with the class. Then, answer any questions students have about the samples. When students demonstrate that they understand how to do the items, have them begin these sections. Students may record their answers on the answer sheets or on the tests.

To administer the collection tests, prepare a copy of each test for your students. Students should mark their answers on the tests themselves. When administering Selection Tests that cover poetry, you may want to allow students to use the textbook, since these tests often require a response to the precise wording, rhythm, or meter of a particular poem. You also have the option of making any Selection Test an open-book test.

***One-Stop Planner*® CD-ROM with ExamView® Test Generator**

The tests in this booklet are included on the ***One-Stop Planner*® CD-ROM with ExamView® Test Generator.** Use the ExamView Test Generator to customize and print a test tailored to the needs of your students.

Holt Online Assessment

With ***Holt Online Assessment*** you can administer and score the diagnostic and summative tests online. Use this online tool to generate and print reports to record student mastery and class performance.

NAME ______________________ CLASS ______________ DATE ______________

Entry-Level Test

Reading and Literary Analysis

DIRECTIONS The following story is about a girl and her grandmother. Read the story and answer questions 1 through 10.

from *My Grandma*
by
Letty Cottin Pogrebin

The trouble started when my friend Katy found Grandma's false teeth floating in a glass on the bathroom sink. I guess I was so used to seeing them that I didn't even notice them anymore. But Katy noticed. She shouted, "Yuuuck! Gross!" and started laughing hysterically, and pretending to talk to them and making them talk back. I had to get down on my knees and *beg* her to shut up so my grandmother wouldn't hear and get her feelings hurt.

After that happened, I started to realize there were a *million* things about Grandma that were embarrassing. Like the way she grabs my face in her palms and murmurs *"Shaine maidl"* which means "beautiful girl" in Yiddish. What would Katy say if she saw *that*!

Or how Grandma always says her *B'rachas* before she eats. *B'rachas* are Hebrew blessings that thank God for things. All I can say is my Grandma must really be hungry because what she eats isn't exactly worth a thank-you note. Chopped herring is gross enough but white bread soaking in warm milk could make a regular person throw up.

And that's just the problem. My friends are regular people. So when Katy or Jill or Angie are around, I have to worry about what Grandma's going to do next.

Once she took me and Jill out to Burger King, even though she doesn't eat there herself because they don't have kosher meat. Instead of ordering our hamburgers well done, she told the person behind the counter "They'll have two Whoppers well-to-do." Jill burst out laughing, but I almost died.

After a while, I started wishing I could hide my Grandma in a closet. It got so bad I even complained to my parents. My parents said they understood how I felt, but I had to be careful not to make Grandma feel unwelcome in our house.

"She's had a very tough life," said my Dad.

"Try to make the best of it," said my Mom.

I was trying, *believe* me, I was trying.

GO ON

Then, on Wednesday, something happened that changed everything. My teacher made an announcement that our school was going to be a part of a big Oral History Project. We were supposed to help find interesting old people and interview them about their lives so kids in the future will understand how things used to be.

I was trying to think if I knew anyone interesting when Angie nudged me from across the aisle.

"Volunteer your grandmother!" she whispered. "*She's* interesting!"

So that's how I ended up here. The whole school is in the auditorium for a big assembly and I'm up here on stage interviewing my own Grandma.

We have microphones clipped to our shirts and TV cameras pointed at us and a bunch of professors are standing off to the side in case I need help asking questions.

Which I don't.

After all this time, nobody knows my Grandma's stories better than I do. I just say the right thing to get her started.

Like when I say "Grandma, why did you leave the Old Country?" she goes right into how the Nazis took over her town.

I've heard all that before. But then she starts telling this incredible story that is brand new to me:

"My parents, they sold all their furniture to buy passage to America. In the meantime, they hid me in a broken-down barn under a pile of straw.

"Can you believe it?" Grandma says looking right at me. "When I was only a little older than you are now, I was running from the Nazis. Me and my parents and my grandparents got into a big old ship, and people were getting sick during the trip and some of them even died. But we had a happy ending when we saw the Statue of Liberty."

While my Grandma talks, I see all my friends and teachers are listening to her as if she's a great hero. And suddenly I feel so proud of my Grandma, I could burst.

I can hardly wait to ask her the next question.

"How did it feel when you saw the Statue of Liberty, Grandma?"

"Very nice," she says. "When that lady she held up her lamp for us to come in nice and safe, I *knew* everything would be okay. I *knew* it."

Next she talks about her life in America and I hear her saying something else that she never put in any of her stories before. She's telling us that she loved her family very much, but she has to admit one thing: that she used to be ashamed of her grandmother.

GO ON

"For twenty years that woman was in this country, but she wouldn't learn English never," says my Grandma about her Grandma. "Such a shame she was to me in front of my American girlfriends."

I can't believe my ears. I feel a little stabbing pain in my heart. And right there on the stage I make a *B'racha* to thank God for never letting my Grandma know I was ashamed of her, too.

1 The internal conflict regarding Grandma is that the narrator—

A secretly wants to be more like Grandma

B wants Grandma to love her but fears rejection

C is embarrassed by Grandma's words and actions

D worries that she isn't living up to Grandma's expectations

2 The first half of the story MOSTLY serves to—

A explain events leading up to the time of the assembly

B tell about Grandma's experiences in the Old Country

C explain why the school is part of an Oral History Project

D predict how the narrator's life will change after the assembly

3 At first, the narrator MOSTLY bases her opinion of Grandma on—

A Mom's insight

B Grandma's stories

C her own impressions

D her friends' reactions

4 Read this sentence from the story.

I had to get down on my knees and *beg* her to shut up so my grandmother wouldn't hear and get her feelings hurt.

What character trait does this reveal about the narrator?

A bravery

B compassion

C determination

D curiosity

5 What effect does point of view have on the story?

A Readers see things only through Grandma's eyes.

B Readers do not know the feelings of the characters.

C Readers learn the narrator's private thoughts and feelings.

D Readers see things only as the narrators' friends see them.

GO ON

6 Which event MOST influences the narrator's change in perspective?

A the decision to nominate Grandma for the Grammy

B the decision to choose Grandma for the Oral History Project Award

C the story about Grandma that the narrator had not heard

D the success of Grandma's assembly presentation

7 What did the Statue of Liberty symbolize to Grandma when she first saw it?

A safety

B honor

C courage

D pride

8 What does the narrator find out that she has in common with her grandmother?

A They were both born in the same country.

B They prefer to eat the same types of food.

C They both felt ashamed of their grandmothers.

D They shared similar childhood experiences.

9 At the end of the story, readers can infer that—

A the narrator will be more understanding of Grandma from now on

B the narrator's relationship with Grandma will not change at all

C the narrator's friends will continue to make fun of Grandma

D Grandma will learn that the narrator is unhappy with her

10 Which of the following BEST expresses a theme of the story?

A importance of honesty in families

B rewards of volunteerism in the community

C value of friendships at school

D complexity of generational relationships

Reading and Literary Analysis *(continued)*

DIRECTIONS The following article is about telescopes. Read the article and answer questions 11 through 19.

Exploring the Night Sky

Stargazing can be a fascinating hobby. The wonders of our universe are waiting to be observed in the night sky, but our eyes are not powerful enough to capture the light necessary to fully see these objects. Telescopes are designed to collect an amount of light many times greater than the amount the naked eye can gather. A variety of telescopes are available for use, but choosing the right type is essential.

Before choosing any telescope, keep in mind that the *aperture,* or diameter of the main lens or mirror, is the most important characteristic to consider. The larger the aperture is, the more light it collects, and the brighter and sharper the images you see will be.

People can choose from three basic types of telescopes: the refractor, the reflector, and the catadioptric. The oldest and most common telescope available is a *refractor* telescope. The refractor uses a big lens at the front to bend, or refract, light to a focus. First-time stargazers frequently purchase refractors because they provide crisp images and are ideal for viewing the Moon and other planetary objects. These amateurs are also attracted by the fact that refractors require little maintenance and have tight seals to keep dust out of the lenses. However, refractor telescopes have disadvantages as well. Because refractors often have smaller apertures than other types, they fail to collect enough light to allow viewing of deep-space objects outside our solar system. Also, slight imperfections in the lenses can cause the images seen in some refractors to suffer from *chromatic aberration,* a faint-colored halo or prismlike color error. Good-quality refractors can also cost more per inch of aperture than other kinds of telescopes.

Another popular type of telescope available is commonly called a *reflector.* A reflector telescope uses a large curved mirror instead of a lens to gather and focus light. Reflectors are often purchased because they provide the most features in relation to cost. These simple yet high-quality telescopes deliver bright images and are ideal for viewing deep-sky objects such as galaxies, nebulae, and star clusters. Reflectors have some drawbacks, however; they are somewhat fragile, and they require regular maintenance for the best possible images.

ENTRY-LEVEL TEST

GO ON

The most recently developed telescope available is the *catadioptric*, or compound, telescope. The catadioptric uses both lenses and mirrors to gather and focus light in a compact tube. People usually purchase catadioptric telescopes because they are compact and less difficult than other telescopes to use—not because of improved visual performance. Some have special options such as advanced tracking and electronics that allow users to locate sky targets reliably. However, catadioptric telescopes cost more than a reflector of the same aperture, the focusing mechanism can be imprecise, and the scope can be taken apart only by the manufacturer.

Backyard astronomers have many tools available to assist in exploring the night sky. You might already own a piece of equipment that many astronomers insist on using to begin their nightly sightseeing tours. A simple pair of binoculars can open up a universe of unseen images to you, such as the craters of the Moon and some of the satellites of Jupiter. The viewing possibilities are truly astronomical.

11 What is the primary purpose of this passage?

A to inform
B to persuade
C to entertain
D to debate

12 Who is the intended audience?

A professional astronomers
B telescope manufacturers
C telescope lens designers
D beginning stargazers

13 The first paragraph MAINLY serves to—

A explain types of telescopes available
B establish interest in the topic of telescopes
C define terms associated with telescopes
D list features of one type of telescope

14 Which question is answered in this passage?

A Does a lens or a mirror gather light better in a telescope?
B How do you determine the power, or magnification, of a telescope?
C What is the main feature to consider when buying a telescope?
D Which type of telescope is purchased most frequently?

15 The ideas in paragraphs 3, 4, and 5 are MOSTLY arranged to show—

A steps in a process
B problems and solutions
C advantages and disadvantages
D opposing sides of an argument

GO ON

16 **The author's attitude toward the topic of telescopes is one of—**

A frustration and distrust

B boredom and indifference

C enthusiasm and interest

D disapproval and criticism

17 **Which resource would BEST provide the cost of the telescopes described in the passage?**

A a book on various constellations

B an advertisement from a local store

C a magazine article on the world's largest telescope

D an online resource that specializes in astronomy

18 **The author of the passage believes telescope purchases should be based MAINLY on—**

A clarity of images

B cost of the telescope

C priorities of each user

D maintenance requirements

19 **Which statement is the MOST accurate evaluation of the information in the article?**

A The author presents a balanced view showing both good and bad features of each type of telescope.

B The author presents biased information that favors one type of telescope over the others.

C The author offers facts, but they cannot be verified by checking other sources.

D The author offers information that is not relevant to choosing a telescope.

GO ON

Reading and Literary Analysis *(continued)*

DIRECTIONS The following poem was written by Don Marquis, a newspaper columnist. He wrote poems that he pretended were written by a cockroach named archy. The cockroach supposedly typed the poems and left them on the boss's desk. Since archy was so small, he could not reach both the shift key and a letter at the same time, so he could not make capital letters. He was also very careless about punctuation. Read the poem and answer questions 20 through 30.

The Lesson of the Moth

by Don Marquis

i was talking to a moth
the other evening
he was trying to break into
an electric light bulb
and fry himself on the wires

why do you fellows
pull this stunt i asked him
because it is the conventional
thing for moths or why
if that had been an uncovered
candle instead of an electric
light bulb you would
now be a small unsightly cinder
have you no sense
plenty of it he answered
but at times we get tired
of using it
we get bored with the routine
and crave beauty
and excitement
fire is beautiful
and we know that if we get
too close it will kill us
but what does that matter
it is better to be happy
for a moment
and be burned up with beauty
than to live a long time
and be bored all the while
so we wad all our life up
into one little roll
and then we shoot the roll
that is what life is for
it is better to be a part of beauty
for one instant and then cease to
exist than to exist forever
and never be a part of beauty
our attitude toward life
is come easy go easy
we are like human beings
used to be before they became
too civilized to enjoy themselves

and before i could argue him
out of his philosophy
he went and immolated himself
on a patent cigar lighter
i do not agree with him
myself i would rather have
half the happiness and twice
the longevity

but at the same time i wish
there was something i wanted
as badly as he wanted to fry himself

archy

20 **What kind of poem is "The Lesson of the Moth"?**

A sonnet
B haiku
C ballad
D free verse

21 **The poet's style in this poem can BEST be described as—**

A formal
B flowery
C conversational
D old-fashioned

22 **The first stanza of the poem is satirical because the speaker—**

A exaggerates the moth's behavior
B admires the moth's behavior
C regrets the moth's behavior
D envies the moth's behavior

23 **With what does the moth equate beauty?**

A knowledge
B boredom
C pleasure
D civilization

24 **With which statement would the moth be MOST likely to agree?**

A Common sense brings happiness.
B Boredom is worse than death.
C A long life is all-important.
D Life is not worth living.

25 **What does the moth mean when it says that a moth's attitude toward life is "come easy go easy"?**

A Life should be carefree.
B Change should be feared.
C Death should be resisted.
D Humans are pleasure seekers.

26 **Which statement BEST paraphrases the last stanza of the poem?**

A The speaker longs for truth.
B The speaker longs for freedom.
C The speaker longs for a purpose.
D The speaker longs for a routine.

27 **The writer's style in this poem is distinguished MOSTLY by the consistent use of—**

A end rhymes
B run-on lines
C regular meter
D onomatopoeia

28 **Which words suggest that the speaker envies the moth?**

A "before i could argue him out of his philosophy"
B "i do not agree with him"
C "myself i would rather have half the happiness"
D "i wish there was something i wanted as badly as he wanted"

GO ON

29 **By the end of the poem, the speaker's attitude toward the moth becomes more—**

A respectful and less critical
B impatient and angry
C sympathetic and sad
D cynical and disgusted

30 **The theme of "The Lesson of the Moth" most likely reflects the poet's—**

A politics
B history
C religion
D philosophy

NAME ______ CLASS ______ DATE ______

Entry-Level Test

Vocabulary

DIRECTIONS Choose the word or group of words that means the same, or about the same, as the underlined word. Then, mark the answer you have chosen.

SAMPLE A

To prolong something is to—

- A erase it
- B extend it
- C desire it
- D replace it

31 Someone who is imprudent is—

- A modest
- B unwise
- C dignified
- D mischievous

32 An obstruction is a kind of—

- A confession
- B reward
- C examination
- D barrier

33 To condone something is to—

- A overlook it
- B punish it
- C admire it
- D regret it

34 Someone who is impartial is—

- A noble
- B friendly
- C unbiased
- D fearless

35 Retribution is another word for—

- A respect
- B loyalty
- C protection
- D punishment

36 Something that is diverting is—

- A entertaining
- B reassuring
- C disturbing
- D confusing

ENTRY-LEVEL TEST

GO ON

DIRECTIONS Read the sentence in each box. Then, choose the answer in which the underlined word is used in the same way. Mark the answer you have chosen.

SAMPLE B

He moved his lips, but he did not make a sound.

A My doctor says I am in sound health.
B The soldier will sound the alarm if he sees the enemy.
C We could hear the sound of the distant bells.
D Our plan is based on sound reasoning.

It will take courage to tackle that problem.

A Let's grab our fishing tackle and go to the lake.
B It's a difficult job, but someone must tackle it.
C The movers used a tackle to lift the heavy piano.
D The tackle positioned himself between the guard and the end.

A thicket of snarled vines kept us from going forward.

A His matted and snarled hair was difficult to comb.
B "Get out of my way!" the rude salesclerk snarled.
C The threatening dog snarled at me and bared his teeth.
D I'm afraid I've snarled the whole plan into a mass of confusion.

We tried to peer through the dense fog.

A The British peer took his seat in the House of Lords.
B That woman is a peer of mine from medical school.
C Members of my peer group will review my essay.
D As I peer into the microscope, I see the minute organisms.

Through thick clouds, a small patch of blue sky could be seen.

A I stitched a patch onto my torn jacket.
B A patch of snow remained on the grass.
C The telephone operator will patch your call through to me.
D The patient absorbed antibiotics through a patch on his skin.

ENTRY-LEVEL TEST

NAME ______ CLASS ______ DATE ______ SCORE ______

COLLECTION 1 DIAGNOSTIC TEST

LITERATURE
INFORMATIONAL TEXT
VOCABULARY

Plot and Setting

On the line provided, write the letter of the *best* answer to each of the following items. *(100 points; 10 points each)*

______ **1.** A struggle or clash that drives the plot is known as —

A theme

B point of view

C conflict

D characterization

______ **2.** Which part of a plot usually contains the *most* tension?

F Basic situation

G Complication

H Climax

J Resolution

______ **3.** What is **chronological order**?

A The order in which objects are arranged in space

B The logical order in which ideas are presented

C A sequence that goes from question to answer

D The time order in which things happen

______ **4.** **Foreshadowing** is —

F giving away the ending of a story

G having a surprise twist at the end of a story

H scaring the reader in a way the reader enjoys

J hinting at what will happen later in a story

______ **5.** Which of the following elements is *not* part of the **setting** of a story?

A A character's nickname

B The weather

C The time period

D The location

______ **6.** Which of the following images would create a scary **mood**?

F The opening of a creaky door

G A bird chirping in the early morning

H The smell of baking bread

J Two swans on a lake

______ **7.** When you are doing research, newspapers can be useful **sources** because they —

A are always more accurate than encyclopedias

B provide up-to-date information

C contain specialized information not found in reference books

D never present people's personal opinions

______ **8.** If you wanted to use a **search engine** to learn about animals that may become extinct, which **search term** would be *most* useful?

F Animal behavior

G The National Zoo in Washington, D.C.

H Veterinarians

J Endangered species

______ **9.** Adding a **prefix** to a word —

A changes the word's meaning

B makes the word easier to pronounce

C makes the word plural

D changes the word's part of speech

______ **10.** Unlike its **denotation,** a word's **connotations** are based on —

F facts

G subjective feelings

H experts' research

J the root of the word

NAME ______ CLASS ______ DATE ______ SCORE ______

SELECTION TEST **Student Edition page 5** LITERARY RESPONSE AND ANALYSIS

The Most Dangerous Game Richard Connell

COMPREHENSION *(40 points; 4 points each)*
On the line provided, write the letter of the *best* answer to each of the following items.

______ **1.** General Zaroff first comes to his island after —
- **A** swimming to it when his ship sank
- **B** being stranded on it by his crew
- **C** buying it in order to build his château there
- **D** inheriting it from his father

______ **2.** Rainsford comes to the island because he —
- **F** swims to it after accidentally falling overboard
- **G** wishes to write an article about Zaroff
- **H** wants to prove that Zaroff can't successfully hunt him
- **J** wants to bring the evil Zaroff to justice

______ **3.** What is Zaroff's *main* reason for preferring to hunt human beings rather than animals?
- **A** There is no other big game on his island.
- **B** He doesn't like to kill innocent creatures.
- **C** He hates humanity and wants to take revenge against it.
- **D** Hunting men is more of a challenge than hunting beasts.

______ **4.** Zaroff especially welcomes Rainsford because the general —
- **F** is glad to meet another expert hunter
- **G** wants news about the outside world
- **H** has no other humans to hunt
- **J** wishes to share his secret with the world

______ **5.** Rainsford first realizes he is going to be the prey when —
- **A** he sees the blood and an empty cartridge in the bush
- **B** Zaroff claims to hunt game that is more dangerous than the Cape buffalo
- **C** Zaroff claims to have invented a new kind of game to hunt
- **D** Zaroff tells him to join the hunt or become Ivan's sport

______ **6.** The *best* evidence that Zaroff is aware of his own viciousness and cruelty is that he —
- **F** makes fun of Rainsford for being afraid
- **G** explains how he obtains the men he hunts
- **H** says that all Cossacks are savage and that he, Zaroff, is a Cossack
- **J** claims that it is not murder to kill sailors because they are "scum"

______ **7.** Which of the following statements *best* describes how Zaroff justifies his hunting of human beings?

A Animal life is more precious than human life.

B Only the strong deserve to survive.

C Individual freedom is more important than laws.

D Human beings are not morally responsible for one another.

______ **8.** Who is dead by the end of the story?

F Rainsford

G Rainsford and Zaroff

H Rainsford, Ivan, and two of the captive sailors

J Zaroff, Ivan, and one of Zaroff's best dogs

______ **9.** Rainsford finally gets the better of Zaroff when Rainsford —

A swims to Zaroff's château and surprises him

B kills Ivan, leaving Zaroff defenseless

C catches Zaroff in a tiger trap made from a bent sapling

D signals to a passing boat that helps him escape

______ **10.** The *main* conflict in "The Most Dangerous Game" is between —

F two different opinions of what the most dangerous animal is

G a human being and human evil

H a person and the doubts and fears within himself

J a human being and the forces of nature

LITERARY FOCUS *(20 points; 5 points each)*

On the line provided, write the letter of the *best* answer to each of the following items.

______ **11.** The last sentence of the story is, "He had never slept in a better bed, Rainsford decided." What important piece of plot information does that sentence give you?

A Zaroff has lost the final duel.

B Rainsford has safely reached his homeland.

C Rainsford has a history of sleep problems.

D Rainsford cares too much about luxuries.

______ **12.** Which of the following events occurs first?

F Ivan threatens Rainsford.

G Zaroff welcomes Rainsford.

H Zaroff hunts Rainsford.

J Whitney warns Rainsford.

______ **13.** **Foreshadowing** is a —

A look back at what happened before the story began

B hint about what is to come in the plot

C scene that is out of chronological order

D struggle between inner and outer forces

______ **14.** Which of the following statements is the *best* example of foreshadowing in the story?

F Whitney's tales of Ship-Trap Island foreshadow danger.

G The fact that Rainsford smokes a pipe foreshadows his death.

H The fact that Ivan does not speak foreshadows the story of Ivan's youth.

J Rainsford's construction of traps foreshadows that he is an expert hunter.

VOCABULARY DEVELOPMENT *(20 points; 2 points each)*

Match the definition on the left with the Vocabulary word on the right. On the line provided, write the letter of the correct Vocabulary word.

______ **15.** removing or lessening fears	**a.** disarming
______ **16.** sticking out	**b.** imprudent
______ **17.** unwise	**c.** impulse
______ **18.** sudden desire to do something	**d.** receding
______ **19.** overcame	**e.** surmounted
______ **20.** calm	**f.** invariably
______ **21.** without changing	**g.** protruding
______ **22.** entertaining	**h.** diverting
______ **23.** extended	**i.** unruffled
______ **24.** becoming more distant	**j.** prolonged

CONSTRUCTED RESPONSE *(20 points)*

25. On a separate sheet of paper, retell the important events of "The Most Dangerous Game" in the order in which the story shows them. Include events that are important to the plot. Leave out details that are not important to the plot.

NAME ______ CLASS ______ DATE ______ SCORE ______

SELECTION TEST **Student Edition page 27** **INFORMATIONAL READING**

Can Animals Think? Eugene Linden

COMPREHENSION *(50 points; 10 points each)*

On the line provided, write the letter of the *best* answer to each of the following items.

______ **1.** Orky, Meladi, Tawan, and Fu Manchu have one thing in common: They all —

A trick their owners

B are orangutans

C learn to use sign language

D use intelligence creatively

______ **2.** Suppose you were researching cooperation between animals and humans. Which incident provides your *best* supporting data?

F Orky makes a platform to help workers rescue his baby.

G Fu Manchu repeatedly picks the lock of the door.

H Meladi hides her orange in order to get another one.

J Scientists disagree about the meaning of Washoe's signs.

______ **3.** Which choice is a *5W–How?* question about animal intelligence?

A Are whales intelligent?

B Fu Manchu escapes from his cage by climbing down air louvers and unlocking the door.

C What specific signs of intelligence have animals given?

D Rate the intelligence of these animals: orangutans, whales, chimpanzees, and humans.

______ **4.** Fu Manchu repeatedly fools his keepers. What conclusion would a scientist come to?

F Orangutans are smarter than people.

G Fu Manchu gets lucky three times in a row.

H Fu Manchu is deliberately using deception.

J Fu Manchu is the smartest orangutan in the world.

______ **5.** Suppose you are researching the ways scientists study animal intelligence. Which question has the right scope to generate useful information?

A How intelligent is author Eugene Linden?

B What is thought?

C Which methods of testing animal intelligence work best?

D Will animals of the future be smarter than animals of today?

VOCABULARY DEVELOPMENT *(50 points; 10 points each)*

On the line provided, write the letter of the choice that is the *best* synonym for the Vocabulary word.

______ **6.** balmy

F mild

G round

H rough

J bent

______ **7.** intangible

A unforgettable

B untouchable

C unforgivable

D undeniable

______ **8.** awry

F perfect

G new

H hazy

J wrong

______ **9.** devious

A tricky

B incorrect

C unseen

D clever

______ **10.** beguile

F start

G charm

H finish

J glance

NAME ______ CLASS ______ DATE ______ SCORE ______

Dog Star Arthur C. Clarke

COMPREHENSION *(40 points; 4 points each)*

On the line provided, write the letter of the best answer to each of the following items.

______ **1.** When the story begins, where is the narrator?

A At his home on earth
B In his bunk on the moon
C In a spaceship, leaving earth behind
D In the Mount Palomar observatory, watching the stars

______ **2.** It seems odd that the narrator rescues Laika, because the narrator —

F never liked animals
G lives in a small space
H already has a pet
J will soon go to the moon

______ **3.** During a visit to Berkeley, a crucial event occurs when Laika —

A scares away a burglar
B offends the narrator's hosts
C warns the narrator of disaster
D helps the narrator discover a new star

______ **4.** When change comes over the narrator as a result of his love for Laika, the narrator changes by —

F coming to love dogs and animals in general
G giving up astronomy and taking up biology
H becoming more interested in human beings
J becoming less interested in human beings

______ **5.** Which is *not* a reason why the narrator doesn't take Laika to the moon?

A It is too expensive to take her there.
B It costs too much to feed her on the moon.
C Pets are not allowed on the moon.
D Laika is too old and sick to go.

______ **6.** What trait does the narrator seem to lack?

F Love
G Sociability
H Common sense
J A good memory

______ **7.** The dream about Laika has a major effect on the narrator because it —

A saves his life

B convinces him to get a new dog

C reminds him of Laika

D helps him solve a scientific problem

______ **8.** By the end of the story, of what is the narrator sure?

F He did experience a miracle.

G He did not experience a miracle.

H He must get a new dog to replace Laika.

J No other dog could ever do what Laika did.

______ **9.** Which quotation from the story states the *most* probable cause of the narrator's dream?

A "an unselfish, undemanding love I have found nowhere else on this or any other world."

B "The human mind has strange and labyrinthine ways . . . it knew the signal that would most swiftly rouse me. . . ."

C "As far back as the nineteen–sixties it was realized that Earth was no place for an astronomical observatory."

D "from the beginning she was my dog, and would obey no one else."

______ **10.** What is the *most* unusual thing about the plot of "Dog Star"?

F The narrator is from earth.

G It involves a human being and an animal.

H Most of it occurs during a flashback.

J At the time the story was written, it was about the future.

LITERARY FOCUS *(20 points; 5 points each)*

On the line provided, write the letter of the *best* answer to each of the following items.

______ **11.** The *main* purpose of a **flashback** is to —

A show what happened at an earlier point in the story

B make a printed story seem more like a movie

C answer the questions *who? what? where? why?* and *how?*

D introduce the main character to the other characters

______ **12.** Which part of "Dog Star" is a flashback?

F Only the first paragraph

G The entire story

H The descriptions of the moon

J Only the story of finding and raising Laika

______ **13.** Of the following items, the *last* event to occur is when the narrator —

A adopts a stray dog

B dreams about his dog

C survives a disaster on the moon

D survives a disaster on earth

______ **14.** At the beginning of the story, the narrator is awakened by a dream. Near the end of the story, the narrator presses an alarm button. Approximately how much time takes place in between?

F Five seconds

G Five days

H Five years

J Five hours

VOCABULARY DEVELOPMENT *(20 points; 4 points each)*
Complete each sentence with the *best* Vocabulary word in the list below.

desolating	**stellar**	**terrestrial**	**luminous**
astronomers	**misanthropic**	**default**	**labyrinthine**

15. I am interested only in ______________ things, not in things concerning outer space or other worlds.

16. Outer space is full of thrilling ______________ events, such as exploding stars and solar flares.

17. There is nothing quite so ______________ as being stranded, alone, on a strange, deserted planet.

18. On the other hand, if you're the ______________ type and prefer to be apart from other humans, you might enjoy being on a planet all by yourself.

19. The English language is a huge, complex, mysterious, ______________, and dazzling world in itself.

NAME ______ CLASS ______ DATE ______ SCORE ______

CONSTRUCTED RESPONSE *(20 points)*

20. Flashbacks can be used for each of the following purposes: (a) to explain the background of a story, (b) to create an emotional effect by showing the impact of the past on the characters, (c) to create suspense, surprise, or mystery, and (d) to explore character. State how the use of a flashback in "Dog Star" does all four things. Cite specific examples from the story.

Far-out Housekeeping on the ISS Ron Koczor

COMPREHENSION *(100 points; 10 points each)*

On the line provided, write the letter of the *best* answer to each of the following items.

______ **1.** According to this article, what change will be marked by the orbit of the International Space Station, Expedition 1?

- **A** Food preparation aboard space stations will be more efficient.
- **B** From that time on, there will always be humans in space.
- **C** Human beings will follow a set of procedures for housekeeping in space.
- **D** People on space stations will not need as much support from people on earth.

______ **2.** What is a major difference between Hollywood spacefarers and real astronauts?

- **F** Life for real astronauts is filled with adventure.
- **G** Real astronauts rarely encounter dangerous situations.
- **H** Real astronauts often have to do chores and follow day-to-day routines.
- **J** Hollywood spacefarers have opportunities for rest and relaxation.

______ **3.** This article contains firsthand information from all of the following sources *except* —

- **A** Hollywood producers
- **B** Daniel Burbank
- **C** Vicki Kloeris
- **D** Dr. Edward Lu

______ **4.** All of the following details support the idea that living on a space station is risky *except* —

- **F** space is a hostile environment
- **G** neither of the astronauts interviewed would give up the experience of working in space
- **H** people on a space station depend on people on the ground for necessary supplies
- **J** there is little margin of error in space; a small error can lead to disaster

______ **5.** When you click on the words *All Food,* you —

- **A** are connected to more information about food in space
- **B** hear the article read aloud
- **C** see pictures of astronauts taking out the trash
- **D** zoom in on the picture of the ISS taken from the space shuttle *Atlantis*

______ **6.** Which of the following statements about food aboard the space station is *false*?

F Most of the food will come in pouches or cans.

G Some of the food will be fresh.

H Some of the food will be dehydrated.

J Some of the food will require refrigeration.

______ **7.** One of the biggest problems faced by crews aboard space shuttles is —

A phoning home

B isolation

C fear

D boredom

______ **8.** How is the waste problem on the space station to be solved?

F *Progress* and the shuttle haul trash back to earth.

G Ninety-five percent of trash is recycled aboard the space station.

H All trash from the shuttle is incinerated over the ocean.

J Only food and fuel containers are recycled.

______ **9.** Crews aboard the space station will be able to do all of the following activities for relaxation *except* —

A go for long evening walks

B play checkers or chess

C watch movies

D listen to music

______ **10.** Which of the following resources listed under "Web Links" would be the *best* source for answering questions about the most recent advances in life-support systems?

F Water on the Space Station

G Breathing Easy on the Space Station

H Microscopic Stowaways on the Space Station

J Environmental Control and Life Support Systems

NAME ______ CLASS ______ DATE ______ SCORE ______

SELECTION TEST **Student Edition page 51**

LITERARY RESPONSE AND ANALYSIS

A Christmas Memory Truman Capote

COMPREHENSION *(40 points; 4 points each)*

On the line provided, write the letter of the *best* answer to each of the following items.

______ **1.** Buddy and his friend keep their money —

- **A** at Mr. Haha Jones's house
- **B** in the local bank's Christmas club
- **C** buried in the pecan orchard
- **D** under a floorboard beneath the bed

______ **2.** Buddy and his friend give fruitcakes to everyone *except* —

- **F** the relatives they live with
- **G** a bus driver
- **H** people who visit them only once
- **J** President Roosevelt

______ **3.** Which of the following statements *best* describes Buddy's friend?

- **A** Fashion is her passion.
- **B** She has strong feelings about God.
- **C** Big cities fascinate her.
- **D** She spends a lot of time at the movies.

______ **4.** Buddy compares his friend to a bantam hen because she is —

- **F** always poking her "beak" into things
- **G** not very intelligent
- **H** small and sprightly
- **J** as flighty as a bird

______ **5.** When it comes to his other relatives, Buddy —

- **A** barely acknowledges their existence
- **B** feels very close to them
- **C** is jealous of the attention they pay to his cousin
- **D** feels that they offer him a lot of support

______ **6.** Which adjective *best* applies to Buddy's friend?

- **F** unstable
- **G** generous
- **H** elegant
- **J** cruel

______ **7.** Which of the following items is *not* an activity that binds the two friends together?

A Flying kites

B Traveling

C Making decorations

D Drinking whiskey

______ **8.** Toward the end of the story, Buddy is separated from his friend. Why?

F He runs away from home.

G His friend is sent to the hospital to suffer her last illness.

H A letter from President Roosevelt invites Buddy's friend to the White House.

J Buddy is sent to military school by his relatives.

______ **9.** Which sentence tells you that Buddy's friend has died?

A "A morning arrives . . . when she cannot rouse herself to exclaim: 'Oh my, it's fruitcake weather!'"

B "The other Buddy died in the 1880s, when she was still a child."

C "I wrapped her in a Fine Linen sheet and rode her in the buggy down to Simpson's pasture where she can be with all her Bones."

D "I'll wager at the very end a body realizes the Lord has already shown Himself."

______ **10.** Which image from the story appeals to the sense of smell?

F "sweet, oily, ivory meat mounts in the milk-glass bowl."

G "A straw cartwheel corsaged with velvet roses out-of-doors has faded. . . ."

H "a hateful heap of bitter-odored pennies."

J "words tumbling together into a wrathful tune. . . ."

LITERARY FOCUS *(20 points; 5 points each)*

On the line provided, write the letter of the *best* answer to each of the following items.

______ **11.** Which custom is a major part of the setting and mood of "A Christmas Memory"?

A Kissing under the mistletoe

B Listening for Santa Claus's sleigh

C Making and giving gifts

D Inviting friends to a Christmas party

______ **12.** What is the difference between **tone** and **mood**?

F They are synonyms; there is no real difference.

G Tone expresses how an author feels; mood is how an author makes the reader feel.

H Tone appeals to the sense of hearing; mood appeals to the sense of sight.

J Mood can be created through setting, but tone cannot.

______ **13.** How are flapjacks and hominy grits part of the setting of "A Christmas Memory"?

A They show the traits and attitudes of the two main characters.

B The fact that they are described makes them part of the setting.

C They help show the customs of characters in a certain time and place.

D The images of these foods are so detailed, a reader can almost taste them.

______ **14.** All of the following places are part of the setting of "A Christmas Memory" *except* a(n) —

F forest

G riverside cafe

H attic

J church

VOCABULARY DEVELOPMENT *(20 points; 4 points each)*
Fill in the blanks in the sentences below by choosing a Vocabulary word from the following list.

inaugurating	**dilapidated**	**paraphernalia**	**sacrilegious**	**carnage**
prosaic	**disposition**	**exhilarates**	**suffuse**	**noncommittal**

15. The smells of baking and the freshly cut trees ______________ the old kitchen.

16. Buddy's friend has a strong faith and never says anything ______________.

17. Buddy's friend might be considered ______________ by some people, but he thinks she is the most special person on earth.

18. The ______________ baby buggy serves them well.

19. Killing flies to earn money results in a ______________ of bugs.

NAME CLASS DATE SCORE

CONSTRUCTED RESPONSE *(20 points)*

20. Choose a favorite passage from "A Christmas Memory." Identify its setting, and state what you think the mood of the passage is. Referring to specific images, explain how the setting helps create that mood.

COLLECTION 1 SUMMATIVE TEST

Plot and Setting

This test asks you to use the skills and strategies you have learned in this collection. Read "The Boy Who Drew Cats," and then answer the questions that follow it.

The Boy Who Drew Cats
by Lafcadio Hearn

A long, long time ago, in a small country village in Japan, there lived a poor farmer and his wife, who were very good people. They had a number of children, and found it very hard to feed them all. The elder son was strong enough when only fourteen years old to help his father; and the little girls learned to help their mother almost as soon as they could walk.

But the youngest, a little boy, did not seem to be fit for hard work. He was very clever—cleverer than all his brothers and sisters; but he was quite weak and small, and people said he could never grow very big. So his parents thought it would be better for him to become a priest than to become a farmer. They took him with them to the village-temple one day, and asked the good old priest who lived there if he would have their little boy for his acolyte, and teach him all that a priest ought to know.

The old man spoke kindly to the lad, and asked him some hard questions. So clever were the answers that the priest agreed to take the little fellow into the temple as an acolyte, and to educate him for the priesthood.

The boy learned quickly what the old priest taught him, and was very obedient in most things. But he had one fault. He liked to draw cats during study-hours, and to draw cats even where cats ought not to have been drawn at all.

Whenever he found himself alone, he drew cats. He drew them on the margins of the priest's books, and on all the screens of the temple, and on the walls, and on the pillars. Several times the priest told him this was not right; but he did not stop drawing cats. He drew them because he could not really help it. He had what is called "the genius of an artist," and just for that reason he was not quite fit to be an acolyte;—a good acolyte should study books.

One day after he had drawn some very clever pictures of cats upon a paper screen, the old priest said to him severely: "My boy, you must go away from this temple at once. You will never make a good priest, but perhaps you will become a great artist. Now let me give you a last piece of advice, and be sure you never forget it. *Avoid large places at night—keep to small!*

The boy did not know what the priest meant by saying, *"Avoid large places—keep to small."* He thought and thought, while he was tying up his little bundle of clothes to go away; but he could not understand those words, and he was afraid to speak to the priest any more, except to say goodby.

He left the temple very sorrowfully, and began to wonder what he should do. If he went straight home he felt sure his father would punish him for having been disobedient to the priest; so he was afraid to go home. All at once he remembered that at the next village, twelve miles away, there was a very big temple. He had heard there were several priests at that temple; and he made up his mind to go to them and ask them to take him for their acolyte.

Now that big temple was closed up but the boy did not know this fact. The reason it had been closed up was that a goblin had frightened the priests away, and had taken possession of the place. Some brave warriors had afterward gone to the temple at night to kill the goblin; but they had never been seen alive again. Nobody had ever told these things to the boy—so he walked all the way to the village, hoping to be kindly treated by the priests.

When he got to the village, it was already dark, and all the people were in bed; but he saw the big temple on a hill at the other end of the principal street, and he saw there was a light in the temple. People who tell the story say the goblin used to make that light, in order to tempt lonely travelers to ask for shelter. The boy went at once to the temple, and knocked. There was no sound inside. He knocked and knocked again; but still nobody came. At last he pushed gently at the door, and was quite glad to find that it had not been fastened. So he went in, and saw a lamp burning—but no priest.

He thought some priest would be sure to come very soon, and he sat down and waited. Then he noticed that everything in the temple was gray with dust, and thickly spun over with cobwebs. So he thought to himself that the priests would certainly like to have an acolyte, to keep the place clean. He wondered why they had allowed everything to get so dusty. What most pleased him, however, were some big white screens, good to paint cats upon. Though he was tired, he looked at once for a writing pad, and found one and ground some ink, and began to paint cats.

He painted a great many cats upon the screens; and then he began to feel very, very sleepy. He was just on the point of lying down to sleep beside one of the screens, when he suddenly remembered the words, *"Avoid large places—keep to small!"*

The temple was very large; he was all alone; and as he thought of these words—though he could not quite understand them—he began to feel for the first time a little afraid; and he resolved to look for a *small place* in which to sleep. He found a little cabinet, with a sliding door, and went into it, and shut himself up. Then he lay down and fell fast asleep.

Very late in the night he was awakened by a most terrible noise—a noise of fighting and screaming. It was so dreadful that he was afraid even to look through a chink in the little cabinet; he lay very still, holding his breath for fright.

The light that had been in the temple went out; but the awful sounds continued, and became more awful, and all the temple shook. After a long time silence came; but the boy was still afraid to move. He did not move until the light of the morning sun shone into the cabinet through the chinks of the little door.

Then he got out of his hiding place very cautiously, and looked about. The first thing he saw was that all the floor of the temple was covered with blood. And then he saw, lying dead in the middle of it, an enormous, monstrous rat—a goblin-rat—bigger than a cow!

But who or what could have killed it? There was no man or other creature to be seen. Suddenly the boy observed that the mouths of all the cats he had drawn the night before were red and wet with blood. Then he knew that the goblin had been killed by the cats which he had drawn. And then also, for the first time, he understood why the wise old priest had said to him, *"Avoid large places at night—keep to small."*

Afterward that boy became a very famous artist. Some of the cats which he drew are still shown to travelers in Japan.

VOCABULARY SKILLS *(25 points; 5 points each)*

For each sentence below, select the word or phrase that provides the *best* meaning for the underlined word. Write the letter of the meaning in the space provided.

______ **1.** If you are an acolyte, you are a(n) —

- **A** farmer
- **B** attendant or follower
- **C** artist
- **D** ordained priest

______ **2.** Someone who is disobedient —

- **F** fails to follow orders
- **G** pays strict attention to the rules
- **H** follows his own conscience
- **J** respects the rights of others

______ **3.** When you take possession of a place, you —

- **A** move away from it
- **B** remove goblins from it
- **C** take ownership of it
- **D** frighten the people who live in it

______ **4.** If you have resolved to do something, you have —

- **F** solved a problem
- **G** decided against something
- **H** voted for a resolution
- **J** reached a decision to act in a certain way

______ **5.** If you move cautiously, you move —

- **A** very quickly
- **B** with great care
- **C** quite slyly
- **D** very slowly

From *75 Short Masterpieces: Stories from the World's Literature,* edited by Roger B. Goodman, Bantam Books, 1961.

COMPREHENSION *(25 points; 5 points each)*

On the line provided, write the letter of the *best* answer to each of the following items.

______ **6.** Why do the parents ask the priest to take in their youngest son?

- **F** The boy doesn't get along with the other children.
- **G** His parents are angry with him because he draws cats.
- **H** The boy is too small and weak to be a good farmer.
- **J** The boy has told his parents that he wants to be a priest.

______ **7.** All of the following items describe the boy *except* —

- **A** clever
- **B** quick to learn
- **C** artistic
- **D** studious

______ **8.** The boy doesn't go home after he is turned out by the priest because the boy —

- **F** is afraid his father will punish him
- **G** cannot give up his dream of becoming a priest
- **H** has been accepted by other priests in another town
- **J** wants to explore the world

______ **9.** Once in the temple the boy looks for a small space in which to sleep because he —

- **A** doesn't want to take up too much room
- **B** knows that a goblin cannot get into a small space
- **C** remembers the words of the old priest
- **D** hopes no one will notice him

______ **10.** Which detail reveals the fate of the monstrous rat?

- **F** The boy understands the meaning of the words *"Avoid large places—keep to small."*
- **G** The mouths of the cats the boy drew are red.
- **H** The boy's drawings of cats are still shown to travelers in Japan.
- **J** During the night the boy hears awful sounds from the temple.

READING SKILLS AND STRATEGIES

Using Chronological Order *(20 points; 2 points each)*

11. Place the events of the story in chronological order. In the blank, write *1* by the event that happens first, *2* by the event that happens second, and so on.

______ The priest tells the boy to avoid large places.

______ The priest rebukes the boy for drawing pictures.

______ The boy becomes a famous artist.

______ The boy is awakened by fighting and screaming.

______ The farmer and his wife ask the priest to take in their son.

______ The boy finds that the mouths of the cats are covered with blood.

______ The priest educates the boy for the priesthood.

______ In the empty temple the boy draws pictures of cats.

______ The boy looks for a small place in which to sleep.

______ The boy travels to the next village in the hope that the priests will take him in.

Predicting *(10 points; 5 points each)*

On the line provided, write the letter of the *best* answer to each of the following items.

______ **12.** What is a logical prediction to make after reading that the temple has been closed up because a goblin had frightened the priests away?

- **F** Some brave warriors will return and frighten the goblin away.
- **G** The boy will encounter the goblin in the temple.
- **H** The priests will keep the boy from the temple.
- **J** The boy will draw the goblin.

______ **13.** All of the following details are significant in helping you make predictions in this story *except* the —

- **A** words of the old priest
- **B** boy's need to draw cats
- **C** story about the light in the temple
- **D** fact that the boy went to be trained by a priest

NAME ______ CLASS ______ DATE ______ SCORE ______

LITERARY FOCUS: CONSTRUCTED RESPONSE *(20 points)*

14. The **setting** of this story plays a very important role. The author tells you details about the old temple that help you predict the true nature of the setting. In the left-hand column of the chart below, list the details you know that the boy doesn't know. Then, in the right-hand column, list details that finally make him suspicious that something odd is going on. Finally, on the lines below the chart, explain the meaning of the old priest's warning.

Details You Know That Boy Doesn't Know	Details That Finally Make Boy Suspicious

The Old Priest's Warning

NAME ______ CLASS ______ DATE ______ SCORE ______

COLLECTION 2 DIAGNOSTIC TEST

LITERATURE
INFORMATIONAL TEXT
VOCABULARY

Character

On the line provided, write the letter of the *best* answer to each of the following items. *(100 points; 10 points each)*

______ **1.** Describing a character's fancy style of dress is an example of revealing **character** through —

A setting
B appearance
C speech
D contrast

______ **2.** Characters reveal themselves *most* vividly through their —

F actions
G names
H ages
J places of birth

______ **3.** By using **indirect characterization,** writers —

A directly describe a character's personality
B provide little information about characters
C prevent readers from forming their own opinions about characters
D show, rather than tell, readers what a character is like

______ **4.** Characters with **internal conflicts** —

F struggle with opposing desires or emotions
G are incapable of taking action
H do not clash with other people
J face threats from their family or community

______ **5.** When writers convey the reasons for a character's actions, they are describing the character's —

A outcome
B autobiography
C motivation
D exposition

______ **6.** A **dynamic character** is *best* described as a character who —

F tells the story
G performs most of the actions in a story
H changes and develops
J opposes the main character

______ **7.** A book that describes events in which the writer did *not* participate is called a —

A secondary source
B bibliography
C primary source
D generalization

______ **8.** What is the difference between **facts** and **opinions**?

F Facts are used in nonfiction, but opinions appear only in fiction.
G Facts are objective, but opinions are subjective.
H Opinions are less complex than facts.
J Opinions are inaccurate, while facts are accurate.

______ **9.** A **synonym** —

A means the opposite of another word
B has the same or almost the same meaning as another word
C is a figure of speech
D is a word that has multiple meanings

______ **10.** In a **word analogy** —

F a sentence contains clues to the meaning of a word
G several words have related meanings
H two words share the same origin
J the relationship between the words in one pair matches the relationship between the words in a second pair

Thank You, M'am Langston Hughes

COMPREHENSION *(50 points; 5 points each)*
On the line provided, write the letter of the *best* answer to each of the following items.

______ **1.** Which words *best* describe Mrs. Jones?
- **A** meek and shy
- **B** foolish and trusting
- **C** tough and ruthless
- **D** wise and kind

______ **2.** Which of the following terms *b*est describes Mrs. Jones's residence?
- **F** Large apartment
- **G** Noisy rooming house
- **H** Quiet suburban home
- **J** Exclusive penthouse

______ **3.** What will Roger *probably* do as a result of his encounter with Mrs. Jones?
- **A** Ask her for a job.
- **B** Stop purse-snatching.
- **C** Try to get revenge.
- **D** Buy something other than shoes.

______ **4.** By the end of the story, Roger seems to want Mrs. Jones to —
- **F** trust him
- **G** punish him
- **H** release him
- **J** take care of him

______ **5.** How is Roger's attempt to steal Mrs. Jones's pocketbook thwarted?
- **A** Mrs. Jones uses her knowledge of martial arts to trip him.
- **B** The police stop him after he has grabbed the purse.
- **C** The combined weight of the purse and his body throws him off balance.
- **D** Mrs. Jones sees what he is about to do and talks him out of it.

______ **6.** Readers can conclude that Mrs. Jones —
- **F** is able to forgive Roger
- **G** wants to adopt Roger
- **H** thinks Roger should earn the money for shoes
- **J** wants Roger to visit her often

______ **7.** After Mrs. Jones brings Roger home, she —

A watches him suspiciously, as if he were a thief

B disciplines him as if he were her own child

C treats him cruelly, as if he were her enemy

D coddles him, as if he were a helpless puppy

______ **8.** At the end of the story, —

F Roger steals Mrs. Jones's dinner

G Roger offers to repay Mrs. Jones

H Mrs. Jones keeps Roger prisoner

J Mrs. Jones wishes Roger good-night

______ **9.** To show that she does not expect Roger to rob her again, Mrs. Jones —

A turns her back on him while she cooks

B tells him he shouldn't have snatched her purse

C asks if there is anyone at his house to feed him

D asks him to go to the store

______ **10.** Mrs. Jones wants Roger to learn how to —

F trust people

G get a job

H behave himself

J be tough

LITERARY FOCUS *(20 points; 5 points each)*

On the line provided, write the letter of the *best* answer to each of the following items.

______ **11.** A character's **traits** are the —

A words the character says

B way the character treats others

C things that make the character an individual

D words that the authors uses to describe the character

______ **12.** Mrs. Jones says, "I have done things, too, which I would not tell you, son." This statement *most likely* means that Mrs. Jones —

F is lying about her past

G is a private person

H once stole something

J has held a variety of jobs

______ **13.** "When I get through with you, sir, you are going to remember Mrs. Luella Bates Washington Jones," Mrs. Jones says. From this announcement you can see that Mrs. Jones —

- **A** has a powerful personality
- **B** is courteous
- **C** looks up to Roger
- **D** is afraid of Roger

______ **14.** By the end of the story, you know that Roger —

- **F** has a criminal mind
- **G** is a quiet, polite boy at heart
- **H** thinks the world owes him something
- **J** is ambitious

CONSTRUCTED RESPONSE *(30 points)*

15. When Roger asks, "You gonna take me to jail?" Mrs. Jones replies, "Not with that face, I would not take you nowhere." What does Mrs. Jones's response tell you about her? Support your inferences by citing other things she says and does.

NAME ______________________ CLASS ______________________ DATE ______________ SCORE ______________

SELECTION TEST **Student Edition pages 97, 98, 100**

INFORMATIONAL READING

Teaching Chess, and Life Carlos Capellan
Community Service & You T. J. Saftner
Feeding Frenzy Peter Ames Carlin *and* Don Sider

COMPREHENSION *(50 points; 10 points each)*

On the line provided, write the letter of the *best* answer to each of the following items.

______ **1.** Which of the following statements is *true*?

A "Teaching Chess, and Life" is a primary source because Carlos Capellan writes about his own experiences.

B "Community Service & You" is a primary source because T. J. Saftner surveys the experiences of many volunteers.

C "Feeding Frenzy" is a primary source because it uses quotes from the article's subject.

D "Feeding Frenzy" is a primary source because it comes from the magazine *People*.

______ **2.** Which of the following items was probably *not* one of the author's purposes for writing "Teaching Chess, and Life"?

F To inspire young people to play chess

G To inspire teachers to become mentors

H To inform students about after-school clubs

J To encourage students to work for *The New York Times*

______ **3.** Which detail from "Community Service & You" is an opinion rather than a fact?

A Volunteer jobs can either be long-term or short-term.

B Sometimes it's a good idea to work without pay.

C One thousand youngsters participated in cleaning up a river in 1995.

D Stephanie Star volunteers at a battered women's shelter.

______ **4.** David Levitt asked a packaging company for eight cases of plastic bags because —

F they might come in handy someday

G he needed them for a science project

H Florida law requires special packaging for secondhand food

J he always buys things in large quantities

______ **5.** David Levitt helped draw people's attention to the —

A importance of extracurricular activities

B idea that surplus food can be used to feed the hungry

C value of knowing your public officials

D fact that proper packaging prevents food from spoiling

VOCABULARY DEVELOPMENT *(50 points; 10 points each)*
On the line provided, write the letter of the *best* answer to each of the following items.

______ **6.** In Greek mythology, Mentor is the name of Odysseus's trusted counselor. Complete this sentence with the word that fits *best:* Under the mentorship of Professor Howard, we prepared for —

F recess
G our swim
H the party
J the exam

______ **7.** What is the literal meaning of *legislation*?

A laws
B Congress
C judges
D argument

______ **8.** Literally *bureaucratic* means "relating to rigid government routine." Figuratively it might mean —

F referring to anything about government
G having to do with all kinds of rigid routines
H having to do with the piece of furniture called a bureau
J referring to something that is democratic

______ **9.** Which word has a meaning most similar to the meaning of *endeavors*?

A laws
B fears
C advice
D attempts

______ **10.** Which of the following items is *least* intimidating to most people?

F Seeing a new hit movie
G Doing income taxes
H Facing an uncaged tiger
J Getting married

Helen on Eighty-sixth Street Wendi Kaufman

COMPREHENSION *(40 points; 4 points each)*

On the line provided, write the letter of the *best* answer to each of the following items.

______ **1.** "Helen on Eighty-sixth Street" is about a —

A Greek goddess who appears on a New York City sidewalk
B woman who believes she is Helen of Troy
C girl in a school play about Helen of Troy
D war between the Greeks and Trojans

______ **2.** Where is Vita's father while the events of the story are taking place?

F Living in the apartment
G Traveling to unknown places
H Married to his second wife
J Directing the school play

______ **3.** What do the dog Argus, the cat Marlowe, the birds John and John, and the sixth-grader Helen all have in common?

A Vita calls them animals.
B They all suffer disappointment.
C They are annoying.
D Their names are allusions to literary figures.

______ **4.** Mr. Dodd thinks that, as an actress, Vita —

F is the best actress in the sixth grade
G is worthy of stardom
H has little or no talent
J needs training to develop her gifts

______ **5.** Which is the *best* description of Vita's mother?

A Grieving but trying to get on with her life
B Merry and outgoing, always looking for fun
C So bitter that she is unable to help her own daughter
D Totally focused on her work and career

______ **6.** What is Old Farfel's relationship to Vita's mother?

F She knows him because he is her daughter's school principal.
G He works with her and wants to become her boyfriend.
H He has been pestering her despite her protests.
J The poor man is trying to free himself from her clutches.

______ **7.** How is a restaurant takeout cup made into a mythological allusion in this story?

A The cup is blue, and so is Vita's mood.

B The cup becomes a prop for the class play.

C Ancient Greeks invented the paper cup.

D The cup has a picture of an ancient Greek temple on it.

______ **8.** Vita burns the letters because she —

F wants to make a sacrifice in order to get three wishes

G doesn't want Helen to act in the play

H suffers from an unhealthy desire to start fires

J wants to keep her mother from reading them

______ **9.** When Vita's mother says, "No more burnt offerings when I'm not home," readers learn that she —

A is clueless about Vita's life

B probably made "burnt offerings" at Vita's age

C knows more than Vita thought she did

D worries about leaving Vita alone

______ **10.** By the end of the story, Vita has *not* —

F gotten two of her wishes

G shown she is a gifted actress

H learned that her mother and Mr. Farfel have parted company

J seen her father return after his long voyage

LITERARY FOCUS *(20 points; 5 points each)*

On the line provided, write the letter of the *best* answer to each of the following items.

______ **11.** Which line is part of Vita's narration?

A "It never hurts to have a little help."

B "I made all these things happen with my offering."

C "Ah, the face that launched a thousand ships."

D "It is I, the hated Helen, scourge of Troy."

______ **12.** To *best* describe Vita's traits, you might say that she —

F is athletic and musical

G makes the best of every situation

H is imaginative and emotional

J is confident about her appearance

______ **13.** Vita describes the letter she wants to write to her father. Then she describes the letter she actually does write. What inference can you make?

- **A** The letter she writes is a lie, intended to make her look good.
- **B** The things she wants to say are too painful to actually write.
- **C** She is ashamed of her writing skills.
- **D** She wants to fool her mother.

______ **14.** What can you infer from Vita's description of her final line?

- **F** Mr. Dodd is angry with her for disobeying his directions.
- **G** She has forgotten the exact words but is able to fake it.
- **H** She freezes and cannot say the line.
- **J** She is deeply moved by her own interpretation of the line.

VOCABULARY DEVELOPMENT *(20 points; 4 points each)*

Complete each sentence with the *best* Vocabulary word in the list below.

embodies	**odyssey**	**litany**	**incantation**	**stifled**
polytheism	**ramparts**	**supplication**	**enunciate**	**scourge**

15. The word ______________ comes from the title of an ancient Greek epic about a wandering hero.

16. "Please," she said in a tone of ______________; "please let me play the lead."

17. She began to say, "That's not fair!" but after the word *that*, she ______________ the rest.

18. When you perform in a play, it is important to ______________ all the words loudly and clearly.

19. Helen was called the ______________ of Troy because she caused its downfall.

CONSTRUCTED RESPONSE *(20 points)*

20. Re-read the five paragraphs beginning, "At home Old Farfel is visiting again," and ending, "he's beginning to come around all the time." What does this passage in Vita's narrative tell you about Old Farfel? What does it tell you about Vita? On a separate sheet of paper, write a paragraph that explains your answer. Use quotations from the passage to support your ideas.

NAME ______ CLASS ______ DATE ______ SCORE ______

SELECTION TEST **Student Edition page 119** **LITERARY RESPONSE AND ANALYSIS**

Marigolds Eugenia W. Collier

COMPREHENSION *(40 points; 4 points each)*

On the line provided, write the letter of the *best* answer to each of the following items.

______ **1.** John Burke sits in a chair all day because he —
- **A** is ill and tired
- **B** has a mental disability
- **C** is too lazy to get up
- **D** wants to make Miss Lottie care for him

______ **2.** When Lizabeth hears her father cry, the emotion she feels is —
- **F** fear
- **G** embarrassment
- **H** anger
- **J** guilt

______ **3.** The two events that contribute *most directly* to the end of Lizabeth's innocence are —
- **A** throwing rocks at the marigolds and then pulling them up
- **B** chanting at Miss Lottie and then pulling up the marigolds
- **C** hearing her father cry and then pulling up Miss Lottie's marigolds
- **D** hearing her father cry and going out at four o'clock in the morning

______ **4.** Lizabeth begins to have compassion when she —
- **F** joins the boys in throwing stones at Miss Lottie's marigolds
- **G** is able to feel Miss Lottie's pain and despair
- **H** admires the marigolds
- **J** comforts her brother

______ **5.** The story shows that during the Depression —
- **A** families that had at least one working parent were well-off
- **B** many jobs were available if you knew where to look
- **C** everyone worked hard, knowing it would pay off in the end
- **D** finding the strength to cope with poverty and lack of work was difficult

______ **6.** Miss Lottie grows marigolds in order to —
- **F** make the neighbors envious
- **G** sell them
- **H** win respect
- **J** create a small patch of beauty

______ **7.** Which of the following emotions *best* describes what Lizabeth feels for Miss Lottie at the end of the story?

A Fear

B Admiration

C Indifference

D Jealousy

______ **8.** Lizabeth's youthful destructiveness *cannot* be explained by her —

F parents' problems

G confusion over being both woman and child

H fear of John Burke

J family's poverty

______ **9.** When the boys throw stones, Lizabeth hesitates at first. What makes her join in?

A She remembers how much she hates Miss Lottie.

B The boys threaten to beat her up.

C She doesn't want to seem scared.

D She finds the perfect stone for throwing.

______ **10.** The last line of the story, "And I too have planted marigolds," implies that the adult Lizabeth —

F has also tried to create beauty amid suffering

G is a professional gardener

H teaches others about the health benefits of plants

J wants to be just like Miss Lottie

LITERARY FOCUS *(20 points; 5 points each)*

On the line provided, write the letter of the *best* answer to each of the following items.

______ **11.** A character's **motivation** is the character's —

A reason for an action

B personality

C conflict with another character

D inner struggle

______ **12.** Which of the following events is an example of external conflict?

- **F** Lizabeth's mother comforts her father.
- **G** Lizabeth feels like she's both a child and a woman.
- **H** John Burke sits in a chair all day.
- **J** Kids throw rocks at Miss Lottie's flowers.

______ **13.** Which statement reflects an internal conflict in the story?

- **A** Lizabeth's mother works as a domestic.
- **B** Lizabeth's father has no work prospects.
- **C** Lizabeth hesitates before throwing rocks at the marigolds.
- **D** Joey leaves the house at four in the morning

______ **14.** In the final interaction between Lizabeth and Miss Lottie, —

- **F** Miss Lottie whips Lizabeth for destroying her garden
- **G** Miss Lottie stares at Lizabeth wordlessly
- **H** Miss Lottie demands that Lizabeth pay for the flowers
- **J** Lizabeth begs Miss Lottie's forgiveness

VOCABULARY DEVELOPMENT *(20 points; 4 points each)*
On the line before each sentence, write the Vocabulary word that has a similar meaning to the italicized word or phrase. You will have choices left over.

arid	**futile**	**impoverished**	**poignantly**	**clarity**
placidly	**inciting**	**malicious**	**contrition**	

______________ **15.** Lizabeth recalls the memory with great *clearness,* as if it had just happened.

______________ **16.** John Burke sat *calmly and quietly* in his chair, rocking and daydreaming.

______________ **17.** Lizabeth and her brother Joey grew up in a very *poor* family.

______________ **18.** Some years the soil was *too dry* for flowers to grow well.

______________ **19.** Lizabeth wished she could make up with Miss Lottie, but her wish was *in vain.*

NAME ______________________ CLASS ______________________ DATE ______________ SCORE ____________

CONSTRUCTED RESPONSE *(20 points)*

20. Analyze how Lizabeth's interactions with other children, her parents, and Miss Lottie affect the story's plot as it unfolds.

COLLECTION 2 SUMMATIVE TEST

Character

This test asks you to use the skills and strategies you have learned in this collection. Read the following excerpt from a short story entitled "The Day Before They Came." Then, answer the questions that follow it.

FROM The Day Before They Came

by Mary Soon Lee

The morning before the aliens came, Molly Harris busied herself preparing her son's lunchbox. Since it was a Friday, Justin would be going to school in person for his social skills classes. Molly put a generous handful of cherries into the lunchbox. Even the vat-grown cherries cost more than she could really afford, but she wanted Justin to have a treat to swap with the other second-graders.

Most of the younger mothers Molly knew worried when their kids went to school, checking the germ count hourly, scared their children might come home with a bruise, or a scrape, or a runny nose. But Molly had been 53 when Justin was born, and she remembered when classroom violence meant knives and guns, the way her heart had thudded during the weekly bomb drill.

So instead of worrying about Justin on Fridays, Molly worried about him on Monday through Thursday. She would peek into his bedroom as she moved around the apartment. No matter how absorbed Justin looked, the tip of his tongue sticking out as the computer led him through a problem, Molly couldn't convince herself that it was right for a child to spend hours on end netted-in.

A terrible din erupted from Justin's bedroom: screeches and bleats, neighs and howls and squawks. Molly slapped her hands over her ears. She had bought Justin the Noah's Ark alarm clock for his sixth birthday, a year ago.

The din subsided for a moment, but Molly wasn't fooled. She kept her hands pressed to her ears as the alarm clock exploded into the deep bass trumpet of the elephants. In the silence that followed, Molly wiped her hands on her apron, then reached for the peanut butter jar.

Sounds of hasty splashing came from the bathroom, followed by bare feet running toward her. Two thin brown arms, somehow sticky despite the bathroom expedition, wrapped themselves around Molly's waist.

"Morning, Mom."

"Good morning, Justin." She stared down at the top of her son's head, pressed tight against her stomach, his fine black hair tousled.

"It's my birthday tomorrow."

"Really? I don't believe you."

Justin let go of her, and rolled his eyes exaggeratedly. "Yes, you do. You do, you do."

"I do," said Molly, wishing he had hugged her a little longer. "Tomorrow's your birthday and we're going to the water park. But today you have to go to school."

"Uh huh." Justin poured the milk onto his cereal, holding the milk carton with both hands, and managing not to spill any.

Breakfast took less than five minutes, and then Justin clattered down the staircase ahead of her, down the four flights to the porch to wait for the school bus.

The bus came early. One quick hug, and Justin scrambled on board.

The afternoon before the aliens came, Molly went birthday shopping. The city tax paid for glass roofs over the downtown streets. Molly told herself she approved of such a sensible precaution against the ultraviolet, but the enclosed air seemed stale despite the constant whir of fans, and the filtered sunlight seemed somehow flatter.

Molly spent half an hour choosing new swimming trunks for Justin. She couldn't decide between a pair covered with dapper penguins and another pair with plain blue and yellow stripes. Six months ago she would have bought the penguins without hesitation, but perhaps Justin would think them too childish now.

She tried to remember what his best friend, Adam, had worn the last time she took the two of them to the water park. Something simple she thought. She paid for the blue and yellow striped trunks, secretly yearning for the penguins.

Outside again, the air temperature fixed at the calculated summer optimum, warm but not hot. Perversely Molly wished the system would break down, even for an hour or two, just long enough for a mini heat wave. She paused for a minute, remembering playing on the beach one summer holiday. The sun had burnt the back of Molly's neck, too hot, too bright. Her face had stung from blowing sand. And yet everything sparkled, the very air buoyant, as if she breathed in tablespoons of undiluted joy.

People surged past Molly as she stood there on the downtown street. She pulled herself together with a shrug. She would have loved to take Justin to the beach, but no use dwelling on it now.

She set off again, heading for the AI store. She knew how much Justin wanted a pair of AI shoes, but even though most of his class had them by now, he had only asked for them once. When Molly had told him they cost too much for her to buy, he bit his lip and never asked again.

So two months ago, Molly had canceled her subscription to the interactives, making do with ordinary TV, and she thought she had saved enough to buy Justin his shoes.

Entering the AI store, Molly blinked. The floor, ceiling, and walls were velvet black. Glowing holograms danced to either side, marking the corridors. Molly took one cautious step forward.

"Can I be of assistance?" A caterpillar-shaped mechanical appeared in front of her. The mechanical raised the front of its long body until its head was level with her chest, its silvered skin gleaming.

"I'm looking for AI shoes."

"Please follow me." The mechanical started down a corridor, turning its head to check she was following. It stopped by a vast array of shoes. "First select a shoe style, and then I will demonstrate our selection of AI personalities."

Molly nodded, trying to look as if she came to shops like this every day. Sandals and ballet shoes, ice-skates and boots and babies' bootees stretched before her. After a long pause, she pointed at a pair of orange sneakers. "How much are those ones?"

"Eighty dollars, without any program installed. Did you have a particular AI personality in mind for the shoes?"

"No. They're for my son. He's turning seven."

"Perhaps an educational supplement?" The mechanical lifted its forelegs to a small keyboard, and typed in a command.

The left sneaker twitched. "What's two times twenty-six?" asked the orange shoe.

Molly said nothing. The mechanical made throat-clearing noise, though she knew it didn't really have a throat. "Fifty-two," said Molly.

"That's right!" said the shoe. "What a clever girl!"

The right shoe twitched beside it. "Two times twenty-six is fifty-two, and do you know how many states there are in America?"

"Fifty-two," said Molly. She looked at the mechanical. "I wanted something a little more fun."

The mechanical keyed in another command.

"Let's all sing to the sing-along-song," sang the two orange sneakers.

Molly shook her head. "Definitely not."

She declined the next dozen offerings. The cops and robbers program amused her, but she had overheard Justin and Adam discussing how old-fashioned police games were. Finally she settled on a program with no gimmicks at all. The left shoe and the right shoe just chatted away as if they were children; the left shoe, Bertie, was a little bossier, the right shoe, Alex, seeming shyer.

The mechanical wrapped up the shoes in orange tissue paper inside an orange box, explained how to switch off Alex and Bertie's voices, and assured her the program automatically deactivated during school hours.

Molly clutched the gift-wrapped shoe box to her all the way home on the bus, picturing Justin's reaction the next morning.

VOCABULARY SKILLS *(25 points; 5 points each)*

On the line provided, write the letter of the correct answer to each question.

______ **1.** Something that might be described as having *subsided* is a —

A dull old penny that was polished bright and shiny

B rainstorm that gradually let up

C race-car driver who zoomed ahead of the pack

D clock that chimes every fifteen minutes

______ **2.** An *expedition* is a(n) —

F wilderness or forest

G journey or excursion

H promise or vow

J attempt or effort

______ **3.** A part of the word *precaution* tells you that a precaution is taken —

A after it will do any good

B only by the leader of a group

C before a possible event occurs

D in secret

_____ **4.** If you *hesitate*, you do *not* —

F delay

G pause

H hold back

J hurry

_____ **5.** The word *yearning* implies a —

A lack of feeling

B keen desire or wish

C distrust or uncertainty

D willingness to cooperate

COMPREHENSION *(25 points; 5 points each)*

On the line provided, write the letter of the *best* answer to each of the following items.

_____ **6.** Who or what are "they" in the title "The Day Before They Came"?

F Creatures from another planet

G Family members from across the ocean

H A long-awaited pair of shoes

J Twin robots who do the housework

_____ **7.** How is Justin's school different from present-day schools?

A It has no teachers.

B It has no students.

C Students don't have to attend if they don't want to.

D Students work at home four days a week.

_____ **8.** Which of the following activities is *not* done in Justin's time?

F Shopping in stores

G Celebrating birthdays

H Swimming at the beach

J Watching television

_____ **9.** In Justin's time, parents are especially worried about —

A germs

B bombs

C alien invaders

D lack of proper food

_______ **10.** In this story, who are Alex and Bertie?

- **F** Justin's brothers
- **G** Justin's classmates
- **H** Artificial personalities
- **J** Video-game characters

READING SKILLS AND STRATEGIES: CONSTRUCTED RESPONSE *(30 points; 10 points each)*

Making Inferences

11. The world in which Justin and his mother live is different in many ways from the one in which you live. Think about the differences and the similarities between the characters' world and yours. Then, make an inference about the history or "current events" of their world. On a separate sheet of paper, state your inference and support it with evidence from the story.

Understanding Allusions

12. The story contains an allusion, or reference, to the biblical story of Noah's Ark. In the story, God warns Noah that the world is about to be destroyed by a flood. God tells Noah to build an ark, or large boat, in order to save Noah's family and the animals of the world. Based on this allusion, on a separate sheet of paper, write a prediction about what might happen to the characters in the story "The Day Before They Came."

Making Inferences About Motivation

13. What do you think most strongly motivates Molly Harris in "The Day Before They Came"? Choose one of the possibilities below. On the lines provided, write the letter of your choice. Then, use evidence from the story to defend your choice.

- **A** Love for her son
- **B** Nostalgia for her youth and for the past
- **C** Wonder at the strange world she lives in
- **D** A desire to live more simply and sanely

____

____

____

____

____

____

NAME ______ CLASS ______ DATE ______ SCORE ______

LITERARY FOCUS: CONSTRUCTED RESPONSE *(20 points)*

14. Fill out the character profile below for the character of Molly Harris. Be sure to provide evidence that supports your descriptions of Molly's inner and outer life.

Character Profile

Name: Molly Harris

Age: ______

Job or profession: ______

Where and when she lives: ______

Her inner life (thoughts and feelings): ______

Her outer life (actions and words): ______

NAME ______ CLASS ______ DATE ______ SCORE ______

COLLECTION 3 DIAGNOSTIC TEST

LITERATURE
INFORMATIONAL TEXT
VOCABULARY

Narrator and Voice

On the line provided, write the letter of the *best* answer to each of the following items. *(100 points; 10 points each)*

______ **1.** To tell a story from the **point of view** of one character, authors —

A limit the number of characters in the story
B do not provide information about other characters
C tell about the thoughts and feelings of all the characters
D use the first-person pronoun *I* to write the story

______ **2.** A **narrator** in a story —

F does not always tell the truth
G can be fully trusted by the reader
H is always the main character
J describes the past, present, and future

______ **3.** What is **tone**?

A An author's choice of words
B An author's characteristic writing style
C An author's attitude toward a subject, character, or the audience
D The way one character interacts with other characters

______ **4.** What is a **surprise ending**?

F An unexpected but logical ending to a story
G An ending that is not related to the rest of the plot
H An ending that can be interpreted in several ways
J An ending that presents a solution to a mystery

______ **5.** **Irony** occurs when—

A a character lies to other characters
B there is a contrast between what is expected and what actually happens
C characters have a disagreement
D a writer shows that a character is wrong

______ **6.** What is the **main idea** of a nonfiction text?

- **F** The body of an essay
- **G** The writer's subject
- **H** The first point a writer makes in a text
- **J** The writer's most important point

______ **7.** Restating a passage in your own words is called —

- **A** paraphrasing
- **B** making inferences
- **C** analyzing
- **D** brainstorming

______ **8.** To support a point, nonfiction writers often use —

- **F** transitions
- **G** chronological order
- **H** evidence
- **J** images

______ **9.** Which of the following sentences uses a **definition** as a **context clue** to hint at the meaning of the underlined word?

- **A** The children who roamed the neighborhood and stole things were called marauders by the community.
- **B** He had trouble climbing the precipitous slope.
- **C** When she heard about the incident, she sent the family her condolences.
- **D** At the end of the meeting, there was no sign of reconciliation between the two sides.

______ **10.** The part of a word that establishes the word's core meaning is the —

- **F** suffix
- **G** prefix
- **H** derivation
- **J** root

The Interlopers Saki

COMPREHENSION *(40 points; 4 points each)*

On the line provided, write the letter of the *best* answer to each of the following items.

_____ **1.** The conflict between Gradwitz and Znaeym is over —

- **A** what animals can be hunted in the forest
- **B** which of the two men has more money
- **C** which man owns a piece of land
- **D** clearing the field that borders the properties of the two men

_____ **2.** At the beginning of the story, —

- **F** both Gradwitz and Znaeym are in the forest
- **G** only Gradwitz is in the forest
- **H** only Znaeym is in the forest
- **J** no one is in the forest

_____ **3.** When the two men meet, they —

- **A** immediately begin to fight
- **B** trade insults
- **C** both run for help
- **D** are knocked down and pinned under a tree branch

_____ **4.** As the men talk, —

- **F** a storm begins to blow
- **G** they start to develop a friendship
- **H** Gradwitz's men appear in the distance
- **J** Znaeym's men appear in the distance

_____ **5.** Gradwitz and Znaeym agree to —

- **A** finish the hunt together
- **B** call for help together
- **C** clear a small section of the land
- **D** settle their problems in court

_____ **6.** When the men see figures in the distance, the men assume that they —

- **F** will become friends
- **G** will remain enemies
- **H** are going to be rescued
- **J** will have allies to help them

______ **7.** This story is *mainly* about a —

- **A** pair of bitter enemies who settle a feud
- **B** storm that causes extensive damage
- **C** hunting trip that ends unexpectedly
- **D** wealthy family that protects its property

______ **8.** The story's ending is a surprise because the reader —

- **F** expects the figures to be men
- **G** expects the two men will not meet in the woods
- **H** expects the men to kill each other
- **J** has come to root for Gradwitz rather than Znaeym

______ **9.** Which term *best* describes the story's ending?

- **A** Gory
- **B** Melodramatic
- **C** Joyful
- **D** Ironic

______ **10.** Surprise endings are —

- **F** rarely memorable
- **G** illogical and unexpected
- **H** logical but unexpected
- **J** a trick

LITERARY FOCUS *(20 points; 5 points each)*

On the line provided, write the letter of the *best* answer to each of the following items.

______ **11.** The omniscient point of view can *best* be described as —

- **A** all-knowing
- **B** philosophical
- **C** metaphorical
- **D** restricted

______ **12.** The author selected this viewpoint to —

- **F** avoid having to jump between each character's mind
- **G** stir up sympathy for Gradwitz alone
- **H** see inside the minds of Gradwitz and Znaeym at the same time
- **J** give readers a limited vantage point to increase the story's suspense

______ **13.** The narrator's voice is *best* described as —

A innocent and inexperienced

B understanding and sympathetic

C all-knowing and objective

D cynical and sarcastic

______ **14.** What tone is created by the narrator's voice in this story?

F Fearful and amazed

G Ironic

H Terrifying

J Hostile

VOCABULARY DEVELOPMENT *(20 points; 4 points each)*
On the line provided, write the Vocabulary word that has the closest meaning to the italicized word or phrase in each sentence.

precipitous **acquiesced** **marauders** **languor** **succor**

______ **15.** Volunteers provided *relief* to the victims.

______ **16.** After noting the patient's *weariness*, the doctor recommended a good night's sleep.

______ **17.** At the end of the trail, the men faced a *very steep* rock wall.

______ **18.** After considering Gradwitz's offer, Znaeym *accepted*.

______ **19.** The two men could band together to fight off any *plunderers* roaming in search of food.

CONSTRUCTED RESPONSE *(20 points)*

20. Explain how the story would have changed if Saki had used the first-person point of view. On the lines provided, write a paragraph that explains your answer. Support your ideas with details from the story.

______

______

______

______

The Necklace Guy de Maupassant

COMPREHENSION *(40 points; 4 points each)*

On the line provided, write the letter of the *best* answer to each of the following items.

______ **1.** The narrator suggests that Mathilde's problem is that she —
- A needs a job to give her self-worth
- B was born into the wrong social class
- C does not know how to spend her vast wealth
- D does not really love her husband

______ **2.** Mathilde envies the social class and wealth of others because —
- F she was born wealthy but wants to be even wealthier
- G she feels that she deserves a more beautiful life
- H her husband is very demanding
- J her friends encourage her to be a social climber

______ **3.** Mathilde borrows a necklace from Mme. Forestier because —
- A she does not have fine jewelry
- B all of her jewels are in storage
- C she does not want to wear real diamonds and risk losing them
- D Mme. Forestier offers one, and Mathilde feels bad about refusing her kindness

______ **4.** Why don't the Loisels tell Mme. Forestier that the necklace has been lost?
- F They fear Mme. Forestier will mock them.
- G They do not care what anyone thinks of them.
- H The minister advises M. Loisel not to tell the truth.
- J They are ashamed to admit their carelessness.

______ **5.** In order to get the money to replace the necklace, the Loisels —
- A borrow all of it
- B steal it
- C borrow some, reduce their standard of living, and work hard
- D work hard but do not reduce their standard of living

______ **6.** Mathilde seems happiest when she —
- F attends the big party
- G gets the party invitation
- H replaces the necklace
- J finally pays off her debt

______ **7.** Mme. Forestier responds to Mathilde's final revelation with —

A cruel mockery

B compassion and generosity

C a scream of terror

D amazement

______ **8.** At the end of the story, it is plain that —

F the Loisels will soon become wealthy

G the Loisels have learned an important lesson about thrift

H the Loisels have suffered needlessly

J Mme. Forestier will help the Loisels

______ **9.** Which of the following statements *best* summarizes "The Necklace"?

A A woman who wants to make a good impression goes to a dance.

B An expensive necklace is lost and needs to be replaced.

C A woman buys an expensive dress and borrows a diamond necklace.

D In pursuit of recognition, a woman is driven to financial ruin.

______ **10.** If you were summarizing "The Necklace," you would mention a(n) —

F rifle

G necklace made of fake diamonds

H Oriental tapestry

J expensive fur coat

LITERARY FOCUS *(20 points; 5 points each)*

On the line provided, write the letter of the *best* answer to each of the following items.

______ **11.** This story is told from the —

A third-person-limited point of view

B omniscient point of view

C first-person point of view

D second-person point of view

______ **12.** This point of view focuses on —

F two objective characters

G one of the characters

H all the characters

J the main characters only

NAME ________ CLASS ________ DATE ________ SCORE ________

______ **13.** This point of view allows the reader to —

- **A** see what Mme. Forestier really thinks of Mathilde
- **B** understand the details of M. Loisel's life as a clerk
- **C** know why Mathilde is unhappy with her life
- **D** know what each character thinks of Mathilde

______ **14.** The narrator is basically —

- **F** biased against social climbers
- **G** cruel toward the Loisels
- **H** very sympathetic toward Mathilde
- **J** neutral

VOCABULARY DEVELOPMENT *(20 points; 4 points each)*

Match each word with its definition. On the line provided, write the letter of the definition.

______ **15.** incessantly	**a.** poor person
______ **16.** disconsolate	**b.** continually
______ **17.** vexation	**c.** intense admiration
______ **18.** pauper	**d.** disturbance
______ **19.** adulation	**e.** very unhappy

CONSTRUCTED RESPONSE *(20 points)*

20. Explain how the author's choice of point of view affected the story's tone and plot. On the lines provided, write a paragraph that explains your answer. Support your ideas with details from the story.

____

____

____

____

____

____

____

____

NAME ______ CLASS ______ DATE ______ SCORE ______

SELECTION TEST **Student Edition page 173** **LITERARY RESPONSE AND ANALYSIS**

The Cask of Amontillado Edgar Allan Poe

COMPREHENSION *(40 points; 4 points each)*

On the line provided, write the letter of the *best* answer to each of the following items.

______ **1.** According to Montresor, he decides to seek revenge against Fortunato because Fortunato —

A attacked him with his fists

B injured him more than a thousand times

C insulted him

D stole some valuable wine from him

______ **2.** According to Montresor, revenge would not be successful if he were —

F punished for taking his revenge

G not punished for taking his revenge

H recognized by his victim

J compelled to murder

______ **3.** The story takes place in —

A Amontillado during Carnival time

B the present right after Christmas

C America during Carnival time

D Italy during Carnival time

______ **4.** Fortunato's weak point is his —

F habit of dressing in silly costumes

G pride about his knowledge of fine wines

H jealousy of Luchesi

J poor sense of direction

______ **5.** Which evidence *best* supports the claim that Montresor is insane?

A He wears a strange costume.

B Thoughts of Fortunato's death make him smile.

C He pays full price for a cask of wine.

D He does not ask Luchesi to test the wine.

______ **6.** Which of the following things does Montresor do?

F Explain how Fortunato has insulted him

G Let Fortunato know how upset he is with him

H Never let the readers know how Fortunato has insulted him

J Be rude to Fortunato from the very beginning of the story

______ **7.** Dramatic irony occurs when —

A the reader knows that Montresor plans revenge, but Fortunato does not know
B Fortunato dresses as a jester
C the narrator urges Fortunato to try the wine
D the crime is committed in the crypt

______ **8.** Montresor kills Fortunato by —

F walling him up
G stabbing him
H poisoning him
J beating him to death with iron rods

______ **9.** Based on Montresor's actions throughout the story, the reader can conclude that he is —

A rational and open-minded
B patient and forgiving
C good-natured and sociable
D treacherous and unbalanced

______ **10.** What can you conclude about Montresor's feelings toward those who have allegedly wronged him?

F Holding grudges is a waste of time.
G One must not let injustice dominate reason.
H Wrongdoers must be punished, and the wrong must be avenged.
J If the injustice is intentional, retaliation is justified.

LITERARY FOCUS *(20 points; 5 points each)*

On the line provided, write the letter of the *best* answer to each of the following items.

______ **11.** An **unreliable narrator** may be described as one who —

A deliberately does not tell the whole truth
B makes untrue statements but is always corrected by another character
C lies throughout the story but admits the truth at the end
D is unreliable until the story's climax

______ **12.** One reason why we know that Montresor is an unreliable narrator is he —

F is drunk
G does not reveal anything about the past
H is wealthy and snobbish
J is feverish and unable to think clearly

______ **13.** The narrator's persona is clearly—

A elderly

B sane

C insane

D friendly

______ **14.** The story's tone is *best* described as —

F immature and unaware

G friendly and warm

H relaxed throughout

J mounting hysteria

VOCABULARY DEVELOPMENT *(20 points; 4 points each)*
On the line before each sentence, write the Vocabulary word with the *closest* meaning to that of the italicized word or phrase.

impunity **retribution** **recoiling** **impose** **precluded**

______ **15.** Fortunato's drunkenness *made impossible in advance* his realization of his fate.

______ **16.** The catacombs ensured Montresor's *freedom from punishment.*

______ **17.** Montresor viewed Fortunato's death as suitable *punishment.*

______ **18.** "I don't wish to *intrude* on your time!" lied Montresor.

______ **19.** *Moving backward* as if in horror, Montresor frowned.

CONSTRUCTED RESPONSE *(20 points)*

20. In "The Cask of Amontillado," Montresor seems so intent upon revenge that readers might question his state of mind. Explain whether you think Montresor is a reliable narrator or an unreliable narrator. On the lines provided, write a paragraph that explains your answer. Support your ideas with details from the story.

______

______

______

Poe's Final Days *from* Edgar A. Poe: Mournful and Never-Ending Remembrance Kenneth Silverman

Poe's Death Is Rewritten as Case of Rabies, Not Telltale Alcohol *The New York Times*

If Only Poe Had Succeeded When He Said Nevermore to Drink Burton R. Pollin *and* Robert E. Benedetto

Rabies Death Theory R. Michael Benitez, M.D.

COMPREHENSION *(50 points; 5 points each)*

On the line provided, write the letter of the *best* answer to each of the following items.

______ **1.** What is the *main* idea of the biography by Kenneth Silverman?

A The precise cause of Poe's death remains a mystery.

B Poe died of rabies.

C Poe died of alcohol poisoning.

D Poe was a misunderstood, tortured genius.

______ **2.** The tone of Silverman's biography is *best* described as —

F angry

G sympathetic

H neutral

J contemptuous

______ **3.** How is *The New York Times* article similar to Silverman's biography?

A Both trace all the main events in Poe's life.

B Both argue that Poe died of rabies.

C Both have an unbiased tone.

D Neither believe that Poe was a great writer.

______ **4.** Pollin and Benedetto argue that Poe —

F died from rabies

G was a victim of his own self-destructive behavior

H had severe symptoms of starvation

J was a genius who met with a tragic death

______ **5.** Dr. Benitez defends himself against Pollin and Benedetto's charges by —

A proving that Poe was bitten and scratched by his rabid cat

B arguing that diagnosing rabies is difficult

C citing evidence from Poe's relatives and friends

D describing his own experience as a doctor

______ **6.** Dr. Benitez says that —

F there was a pet vaccine for rabies in Poe's time

G all rabies victims remember getting bitten by a rabid animal

H doctors did not know how people caught rabies in Poe's time

J it can take as long as a year for infected people to develop a full-blown case of rabies

______ **7.** What evidence would make Dr. Benitez's argument more convincing?

A Data on rabies from the Centers for Disease Control and Prevention

B Facts about the rabies vaccine

C Information about Poe's short stories

D His personal examination of Poe's remains

______ **8.** Which document presents the *most* information about Poe?

F *The New York Times* article, "Poe's Death Is Rewritten as Case of Rabies, Not Telltale Alcohol"

G Pollin and Benedetto's letter, "If Only Poe Had Succeeded When He Said Nevermore to Drink"

H Dr. Benitez's letter, "Rabies Death Theory"

J Silverman's biography, *Edgar A. Poe: Mournful and Never-Ending Remembrance*

______ **9.** All four selections are similar in that they—

A explore the possible cause of Poe's death

B discuss Poe's literary achievements

C show how Poe's life was bitterly unhappy

D share the same voice and tone

______ **10.** Which summary *best* synthesizes the information in these four sources?

F Few people really care how Poe died.

G Rabies kills more people than we realize.

H There is no general agreement about what caused Poe's death.

J Poe clearly died of alcoholism.

NAME ______________ CLASS ______________ DATE ______________ SCORE ______________

VOCABULARY DEVELOPMENT *(50 points; 10 points each)*

Complete each of the following analogies with the Vocabulary word that fits *best*. Select the Vocabulary words from the list below.

spectral **stupor** **maligned** **insensible** **imposing**

11. AWAKE : RATIONAL :: UNCONSCIOUS : ______________

12. OCEAN LINER : IMPRESSIVE :: MONUMENT : ______________

13. TRANCE : DAZE :: DULLNESS : ______________

14. PERSON : SOLID :: GHOST : ______________

15. APPLAUDED : SLANDERED :: PRAISED : ______________

NAME CLASS DATE SCORE

COLLECTION 3 SUMMATIVE TEST

Narrator and Voice

This test asks you to use the skills and strategies you have learned in this collection. Read the following passage from a nonfiction book, and then answer the questions that follow it.

FROM **Among Schoolchildren**
by Tracy Kidder

Mrs. Zajac wasn't born yesterday. She knows you didn't do your best work on this paper, Clarence. Don't you remember Mrs. Zajac saying that if you didn't do your best, she'd make you do it over? As for you, Claude, God forbid that you should ever need brain surgery. But Mrs. Zajac hopes that if you do, the doctor won't open up your head and walk off saying he's almost done, as you just said when Mrs. Zajac asked you for your penmanship, which, by the way, looks like you did it and ran. Felipe, the reason you have the hiccups is, your mouth is always open and the wind rushes in. You're in fifth grade now. So, Felipe, put a lock on it. Zip it up. Then go get a drink of water. Mrs. Zajac means business, Robert. The sooner you realize she never said everybody in the room has to do the work except for Robert, the sooner you'll get along with her. And . . . Clarence. Mrs. Zajac knows you didn't try. You don't just hand in junk to Mrs. Zajac. She's been teaching an awful lot of years. She didn't fall off the turnip cart yesterday. She told you she was an old-lady teacher.

She was thirty-four. She wore a white skirt and yellow sweater and a thin gold necklace, which she held in her fingers, as if holding her own reins, while waiting for children to answer. Her hair was black with a hint of Irish red. It was cut short to the tops of her ears, and swept back like a pair of folded wings. She had a delicately cleft chin, and she was short—the children's chairs would have fit her. Although her voice sounded conversational, it had **projection**. She had never acted. She had found this voice in the classrooms.

Mrs. Zajac seemed to have a frightening amount of energy. She strode across the room, her arms swinging high and her hands in small fists. Taking her stand in front of the green chalkboard, discussing the rules with her new class, she repeated sentences, and her lips held the shapes of certain words, such as "homework," after she had said them. Her hands kept very busy. They sliced the air and made **karate** chops to mark off boundaries. They extended straight out like a traffic cop's, halting **illegal** maneuvers yet to be perpetrated. When they rested momentarily on her hips, her hands looked as if they were in holsters. She told the children, "One thing Mrs. Zajac expects from each of you is that you do your best." She said, "Mrs. Zajac gives homework. I'm sure you've all heard. The old meanie gives homework." Mrs. Zajac. It was in part a role. She worked her way into it every September.

At home on a late summer day like these, Chris Zajac wore shorts or blue jeans. Although there was no dress code for teachers here at Kelly School, she always went to work in skirts or dresses. She dressed as if she were applying for a job, and hoped in the back of her mind that someday, heading for job interviews, her students would remember her example. Outside school, she wept easily over small and large **catastrophes** and at sentimental movies, but never cried in front of students, except once a few years ago when the news came over the intercom that the Space Shuttle had exploded and Christa McAuliffe had died—and then she saw in her students' faces that the sight of Mrs. Zajac crying had frightened them, and she made herself stop and then explained.

At home, Chris laughed at the antics of her infant daughter and egged the child on. She and her first-grade son would sneak up to the radio when her husband wasn't looking and change the station from classical to rock-and-roll music. "You're regressing, Chris," her husband would say. But especially on the first few days of school, she didn't let her students get away with much. She was not amused when, for instance, on the first day, two of the boys started dueling with their rulers. On nights before the school year started, Chris used to have bad dreams: her principal would come to observe her, and her students would choose that moment to climb up on their desks . . . or they would simply wander out the door. But a child in her classroom would never know that Mrs. Zajac had the slightest doubt that students would obey her.

The first day, after going over all the school rules, Chris spoke to them about effort. "If you put your name on a paper, you should be proud of it," she said. "You should think, 'This is the best I can do and I'm proud of it and I want to hand this in.'" Then she asked, "If it isn't your best, what's Mrs. Zajac going to do?"

Many voices, most of them female, answered softly in **unison**, "Make us do it over."

"Make you do it over," Chris repeated. It sounded like a chant.

VOCABULARY SKILLS *(25 points; 5 points each)*
Each of the underlined words below has also been underlined in the selection. Re-read those passages in which the underlined words appear, and then use context clues and your prior knowledge to help you select an answer. On the line provided, write the letter of the word or words that *best* answer each question.

______ **1.** A voice that has projection —

A cannot be heard easily

B is harsh

C is soft and sweet

D carries to all corners of a room

______ **2.** Karate is —

F a river in Japan

G a forested mountain

H a set of laws

J a type of self-defense

______ **3.** Something that is illegal is —

- **A** against the law
- **B** desirable
- **C** free
- **D** valuable

______ **4.** Catastrophes are —

- **F** disasters
- **G** dramas
- **H** musical events
- **J** games

______ **5.** To speak in unison means to speak —

- **A** different words at the same time
- **B** the same words at the same time
- **C** loudly
- **D** meaningless words

COMPREHENSION *(25 points; 5 points each)*
On the line provided, write the letter of the *best* answer for each of the following items.

______ **6.** Which of the following descriptions of Mrs. Zajac's movements does *not* use figurative language?

- **F** Making "karate chops to mark off boundaries"
- **G** Extending her hands as if to halt "illegal maneuvers"
- **H** Swinging her arms, her hands in "small fists"
- **J** Placing her hands on her hips as if her hands "were in holsters"

______ **7.** Tracy Kidder's tone, or attitude, toward Mrs. Zajac is *best* described as —

- **A** admiring
- **B** angry
- **C** scornful
- **D** pitying

______ **8.** Of the following details about Mrs. Zajac, the one that is *most* subjective is that she —

- **F** wore a skirt and sweater
- **G** wore a gold necklace
- **H** had black hair
- **J** had a frightening amount of energy

______ **9.** Who is speaking in the first paragraph?

A The principal

B Mrs. Zajac

C The author, Tracy Kidder

D A student

______ **10.** Mrs. Zajac tries to set a good example for her class by —

F being easy on her students on the first day

G wearing a skirt or dress to class every day

H showing all her emotions in front of her students

J letting her students know her dreams

READING SKILLS AND STRATEGIES: CONSTRUCTED RESPONSE *(30 points; 10 points each)*

Monitoring Your Reading

11. Summarize the first paragraph of this passage from *Among Schoolchildren* in your own words.

______

______

______

______

______

______

Summarizing: A Plot Formula

12. Complete the following chart based on your reading of the first paragraph of *Among Schoolchildren.*

Mrs. Zajac wanted . . .	but when . . .	she then . . .

NAME ______________________ CLASS ______________________ DATE ______________ SCORE ______________

Drawing Conclusions

13. What details could support the conclusion that Mrs. Zajac is a dedicated teacher? List at least three details.

____

____

____

LITERARY FOCUS: CONSTRUCTED RESPONSE *(20 points)*

14. The author's voice, persona, and choice of a narrator affect characterization and the tone, plot, and credibility of a text. Complete the following chart by analyzing how Tracy Kidder used these elements in this passage from *Among Schoolchildren.*

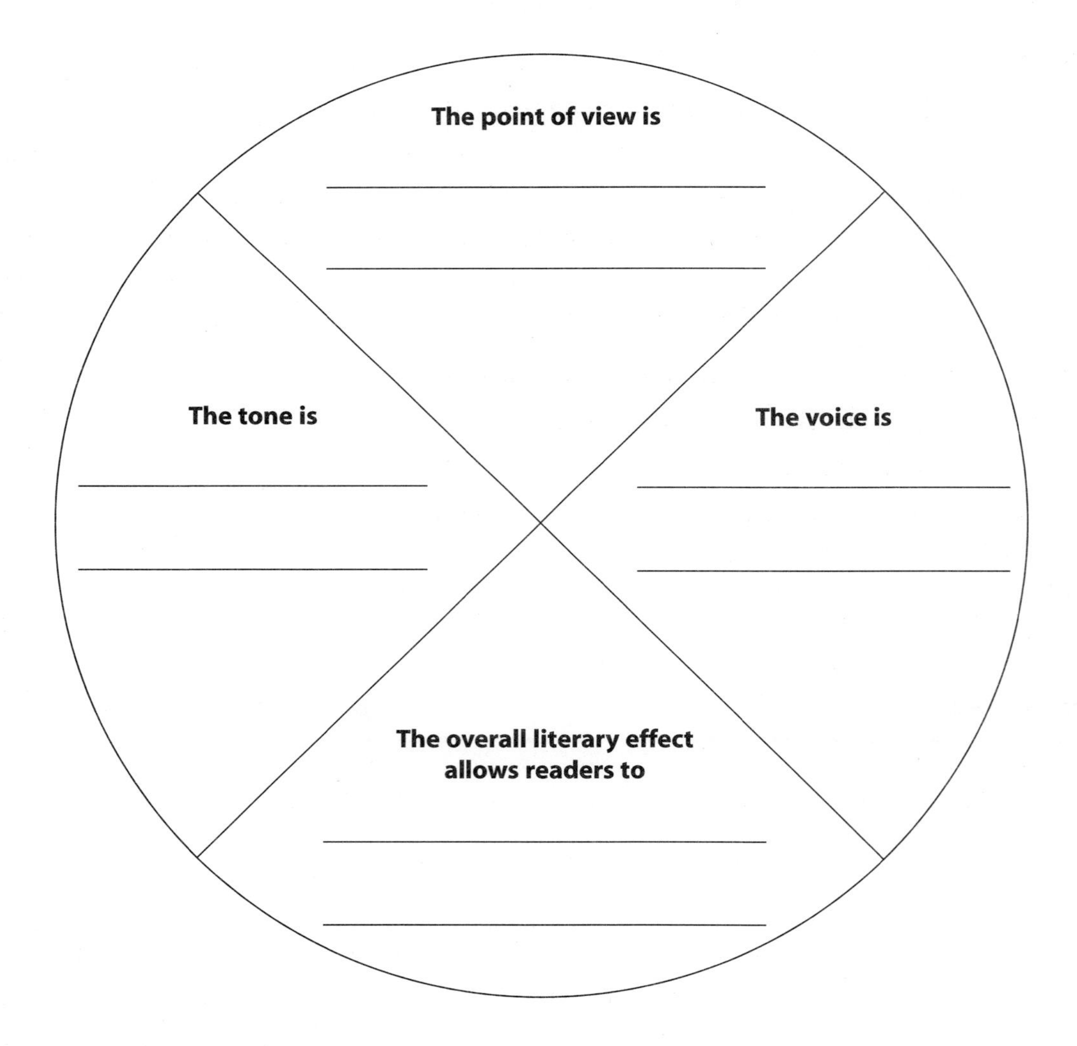

NAME ______________________ CLASS ______________ DATE ____________ SCORE ________

COLLECTION 4 DIAGNOSTIC TEST

Comparing Themes

LITERATURE
INFORMATIONAL TEXT
VOCABULARY

On the line provided, write the letter of the *best* answer to each of the following items. *(100 points; 10 points each)*

______ **1.** Which of the following statements about **theme** is *false*?

- **A** The theme of a story is a central idea, or insight, about life.
- **B** The title of a story may provide a clue to the story's theme.
- **C** The term *theme* refers to the subject of a story.
- **D** Writers may convey a story's theme through what a character learns.

______ **2.** The **theme** of a literary work —

- **F** is always unique
- **G** may recur in literature from different cultures and historical periods
- **H** is not subject to interpretation
- **J** is usually stated in the opening of the work

______ **3.** What is a **symbol**?

- **A** An object that is given human characteristics
- **B** A person, an animal, or an object that has meaning in itself and stands for something beyond itself as well
- **C** A reference to a person, a statement, or an event from literature, history, art, or mythology
- **D** An example provided by a writer to make a point

______ **4.** Writers reveal the **motivation** of their characters to —

- **F** explain the characters' backgrounds
- **G** resolve conflicts in stories
- **H** convey the reasons for the characters' actions
- **J** create universal characters

______ **5.** A **narrative poem** —

- **A** praises a person
- **B** tells a story
- **C** follows a set pattern of rhyme
- **D** focuses on the speaker's personal feelings

______ **6.** *Both* **metaphors** and **similes** —

F compare two unlike things

G are types of images

H are words that a writer uses for the way they sound

J hint at future events in a story's plot

______ **7.** When you research a subject using several nonfiction **sources,** you should do all of the following steps *except* —

A determine the purpose of each work

B consider each author's audience

C compare and contrast the main ideas in the works

D describe the plot of each work

______ **8.** When you draw a **conclusion,** you —

F make a judgment or form an opinion based on evidence

G make a prediction, or an educated guess

H present an opposing view

J support an argument

______ **9.** What is a word's **denotation**?

A The word's dictionary definition

B The history and origin of the word

C The way in which a writer uses the word

D The emotions associated with the word

______ **10.** In a **word analogy,** the words in a pair often —

F sound alike

G are antonyms

H are different tenses of the same verb

J have the same spellings but different meanings

NAME ______ CLASS ______ DATE ______ SCORE ______

SELECTION TEST **Student Edition page 212**

LITERARY RESPONSE AND ANALYSIS

The Sniper Liam O'Flaherty

COMPREHENSION *(40 points; 4 points each)*

On the line provided, write the letter of the *best* answer to each of the following items.

______ **1.** When the story opens, its mood is —

A neutral

B tense

C eerie

D tranquil

______ **2.** The Republican sniper is *best* described as —

F immature and childish

G devoted to his cause

H terrified of death

J happy and lighthearted

______ **3.** The sniper's job is to —

A protect local citizens

B guard his superior officers

C seize the armored car

D shoot the enemy

______ **4.** He puts out his cigarette because —

F he is hungry and wants to eat

G it does not taste good

H it makes him a target

J he wants to save it for later

______ **5.** When the sniper is shot in the arm, he —

A calmly examines the wound and tends to it

B lights another cigarette to calm himself

C panics and cries out

D moves to a less obvious roof

______ **6.** You can infer from his actions that the sniper —

F is experienced in warfare

G has never seen action before

H is older than he appears

J has never been injured before

______ **7.** The sniper drops his left hand over the roof and lets the rifle drop to the street in order to —

A give himself time to dress his wound
B trick the enemy into thinking he is dead
C reload his spare gun
D take a few minutes to think of his next step

______ **8.** How does the sniper feel when he *first* realizes that he has killed his enemy?

F remorseful
G joyful
H mildly pleased
J unconcerned

______ **9.** At the end of the story, the sniper has experienced all of the following conflicts *except* an —

A external conflict with his enemies
B external conflict with danger
C external conflict with the authorities
D internal conflict with his conscience

______ **10.** The surprise at the end of this story is that the —

F war ended the previous week
G sniper has killed his mother
H sniper dies from his own bullet
J sniper has killed his brother

LITERARY FOCUS *(20 points; 5 points each)*

On the line provided, write the letter of the *best* answer to each of the following items.

______ **11.** The topic of this story is —

A Ireland
B murder
C civil war
D danger

______ **12.** The sniper's external conflict is resolved when the —

F sniper kills his brother

G sniper is killed by the enemy sniper

H war ends

J old lady turns the sniper in to the authorities

______ **13.** Why might Liam O'Flaherty have related this experience in a story rather than a play?

A Plays are told through dialogue, and "The Sniper" relies on description.

B "The Sniper" is not dramatic enough to be a play.

C "The Sniper" takes place at night, and the audience couldn't see the action.

D Plays never have narrators, and "The Sniper" depends on a first-person narrator.

______ **14.** "The Sniper" is remarkable as a short story for its lack of —

F humor

G metaphor

H description

J dialogue

Vocabulary Development *(20 points, 4 points each)*

Match each Vocabulary word with its definition. On the line provided, write the letter of the word or words that *best* define each Vocabulary word.

______ **15.** beleaguered

______ **16.** ascetic

______ **17.** fanatic

______ **18.** ruse

______ **19.** silhouetted

a. outlined

b. trick

c. surrounded and under attack

d. person with an excessive devotion to a cause

e. self-disciplined; severe

Constructed Response *(20 points)*

20. Do you think the story would be better told as a novel? On a separate sheet of paper, write a paragraph that explains your answer. Support your ideas with details from the story.

NAME ____________ CLASS ____________ DATE ____________ SCORE ____________

SELECTION TEST **Student Edition page 222** **LITERARY RESPONSE AND ANALYSIS**

Cranes Hwang Sunwŏn *translated by* Peter H. Lee

COMPREHENSION *(40 points; 4 points each)*

On the line provided, write the letter of the *best* answer to each of the following items.

______ **1.** The story takes place in —

A Korea in the present
B Japan in the distant past
C China in the present
D Korea in the past

______ **2.** Who is Tŏkchae?

F A prisoner
G The narrator
H A police officer
J An old man who owns a chestnut tree

______ **3.** How does the writer foreshadow the ending?

A Sŏngsam volunteers to take Tŏkchae with him.
B Sŏngsam refuses to give Tŏkchae a puff of his cigarette.
C Sŏngsam does not recognize Tŏkchae.
D Tŏkchae's father has died alone.

______ **4.** Sŏngsam's memory of the incident with the chestnuts reveals all of the following details *except* —

F he and Tŏkchae trusted each other
G he and Tŏkchae were close friends
H Tŏkchae always looked out for himself first
J Tŏkchae is generous and thoughtful

______ **5.** What was Tŏkchae's mission for the league?

A To make everyone become a Communist
B To become rich at the expense of others
C To kill all the villagers
D Nothing in particular

______ **6.** What is Tŏkchae's relationship to his father?

F Close
G Distant
H Filled with resentment
J Confused

_______ **7.** What can you infer Sŏngsam feels about Tŏkchae's relationship to his father?

A Confusion over his betrayal

B Admiration for his former friend

C Anger over his desertion

D Resentment at having to take care of the old man

_______ **8.** What *finally* happened to the crane the boys made into a pet and then freed?

F It died of grief.

G It tried to fly, but it was too weak to take off.

H A hunter shot it when it finally took off.

J It flew away.

_______ **9.** Why does Sŏngsam make Tŏkchae flush the cranes?

A To give him the opportunity to escape

B To shoot him in the back

C To avoid having his blood on his hands

D Because they are hungry and need the food

_______ **10.** The last line of the story suggests that —

F both Tŏkchae and Sŏngsam will fly away to America

G the cranes have been extinct since the 1950s

H Tŏkchae will escape, and Sŏngsam will not be blamed

J Tŏkchae will betray Sŏngsam, and both will die

LITERARY FOCUS *(20 points; 5 points each)*

On the line provided, write the letter of the *best* answer to each of the following items.

_______ **11.** "The Sniper" and "Cranes" are similar in that each story has —

A only two characters

B the same setting

C a surprise ending

D flashbacks to the main character's childhood

_______ **12.** Both the Republican sniper and Sŏngsam —

F experience an internal conflict because of war

G are killed at the end of the story

H are confident and sure of their actions

J obey the authorities rather than their conscience

____ **13.** It seems likely that the authors of both "The Sniper" and "Cranes" —

A have experienced war
B grew up in cities
C raised animals as pets
D have been prisoners of war

____ **14.** The themes of both stories describe —

F how war can unite families and friends
G the importance of having close friends
H the hardship of the battlefield
J how war can destroy families and friendships

VOCABULARY DEVELOPMENT *(20 points; 4 points each)*
Write a synonym or antonym for each Vocabulary word, as directed.

15. averted *antonym:* ____

16. obstruction *synonym:* ____

17. constitutes *synonym:* ____

18. mainstay *synonym:* ____

19. refuge *antonym:* ____

CONSTRUCTED RESPONSE *(20 points)*

20. Explain how both "The Sniper" and "Cranes" describe characters with divided loyalties. On a separate sheet of paper, write a paragraph that explains your answer. Support your ideas with details from the stories.

A Country Divided *from* One Belfast Boy Patricia McMahon
Lives in the Crossfire *from* Children of "the Troubles" Laurel Holliday
Internment Margaret McCrory
Peace Isn't Impossible George J. Mitchell

COMPREHENSION *(50 points; 10 points each)*

On the line provided, write the letter of the *best* answer to each of the following items.

_____ **1.** According to Patricia McMahon, Catholics living under British rule in Northern Ireland were restricted in many ways. However, Catholics did have one freedom: They —

A could vote if they owned land

B were allowed to leave Ireland

C could be elected to public office

D were allowed to speak the Irish language

_____ **2.** "Lives in the Crossfire" helps you understand "A Country Divided" in that "Lives in the Crossfire" —

F shows how one child deals with the civil war

G presents a far more hopeful viewpoint of Ireland's future

H adds examples from daily life to general historical information

J explains why the conflict first started

_____ **3.** The author's purpose in "Internment" is to —

A praise one family's courage in a war they don't understand

B argue that other countries must step in to help restore peace in Ireland

C show the grief and fear caused by the continued violence

D convince people to help poor families escape from Northern Ireland

_____ **4.** What is the *main* point of "Peace Isn't Impossible"?

F The IRA is standing in the way of peace.

G Tony Blair is an outstanding prime minister.

H There will never be peace in Northern Ireland.

J Now is the time to achieve peace in Northern Ireland.

_____ **5.** What inference can you make from the information in these four selections?

A Ireland will always be at war with itself.

B Few people outside Ireland care about the events there.

C The Irish people are very hard-working and determined.

D Many people want an end to the civil war in Northern Ireland.

VOCABULARY DEVELOPMENT *(50 points; 10 points each)*
Complete each sentence with the *best* word from the word box.

coerced **divergent** **designate** **absorb** **reunification**

6. The Belfast police ____________ the main street as a safe road to travel.

7. The tourists cannot accept and ____________ the amount of damage they see all around.

8. The ____________ of Ireland would make the entire island one country.

9. However, people may still take ____________ paths and go in separate directions.

10. Should people be ____________ into working together?

NAME ______ CLASS ______ DATE ______ SCORE ______

SELECTION TEST **Student Edition pages 246, 256, 262, 265** LITERARY RESPONSE AND ANALYSIS

Liberty Julia Alvarez
Exile Julia Alvarez
An American Story Anthony Lewis
Ex-Refugee Is Nominated for Justice Post Dena Bunis *and* Anh Do

COMPREHENSION *(40 points; 4 points each)*

On the line provided, write the letter of the *best* answer to each of the following items.

______ **1.** The narrator of "Liberty" is *best* described as —

A obedient and shy

B immature and spoiled

C sneaky and wild

D loving and curious

______ **2.** The puppy does all of the following things *except* —

F bite the two men who menace the narrator

G eat all of Mami's orchids

H knock things off the coffee table with his tail

J tear up the flower garden in a search for buried treasure

______ **3.** Mister Victor moves in with the family to —

A protect them until they can immigrate to America

B make sure they don't escape to America

C keep them from revealing state secrets

D help them with the household chores

______ **4.** What does the narrator's aunt mean when she says, "You're going to find liberty when you get to the United States"?

F The aunt is taking the dog to the United States.

G Only America is free.

H The family will be free in the United States.

J Mami will relax once the family gets to America.

______ **5.** The title of the poem "Exile" suggests that —

A America is the home of the displaced and unwanted

B the family feels out of place in America

C the family will return to their homeland as soon as possible

D Americans treat the family very poorly

______ **6.** In "Exile," Papi tells his children they are going to the beach because —

F he doesn't want to alarm the children

G they did go to the beach for a week

H he had planned to go to the beach but received visas at the last moment

J they are taking a boat to escape to America

______ **7.** The family feels uneasy about being in America because —

A they feel they do not fit in

B they are very poor

C people treat them very badly

D the American beach is not as nice as they expected

______ **8.** According to the news article, Dinh's family went by boat to —

F Washington, D.C.

G Vietnam

H New York City

J Malaysia

______ **9.** The news article states that Dinh's mother, Nguyen, destroyed their boat because she —

A was terrified of the ocean

B was forced to do so by her husband

C had lost her mind because of tremendous stress

D did not want the family to be forced to leave by sea

______ **10.** All four selections —

F are told from the first-person point of view

G concern Hispanic Americans who fight corrupt governments

H describe the bravery of people forced to leave their countries

J are set in the distant past

LITERARY FOCUS *(20 points; 5 points each)*

On the line provided, write the letter of the *best* answer to each of the following items.

______ **11.** The story "Liberty" and the poem "Exile" both —

A describe how people have trouble adjusting to a new country

B have narrators that must leave a pet behind

C describe the experience of immigrating to America

D are told from the third-person point of view

______ **12.** Unlike the story "Liberty," the poem "Exile" is *mainly* designed to —

- **F** show the poet's strong emotions and feelings
- **G** reveal an insight about life and human experience
- **H** directly state the theme
- **J** support its ideas with facts and examples

______ **13.** By describing Viet Dinh's experience in an article, Anthony Lewis —

- **A** helps readers feel Viet Dinh's gratitude for being an American
- **B** makes readers think about the reality and result of Viet Dinh's experiences
- **C** makes readers thankful that they live do not live in Vietnam
- **D** helps readers experience events along with Viet Dinh

______ **14.** What theme do all four selections have in common?

- **F** The deep loss people feel when they leave their birth countries
- **G** The difficulty of adjusting to a new country
- **H** The reasons why everyone wants to come to America
- **J** A description of the experiences of immigrants to America

Vocabulary Development *(20 points; 4 points each)*

Match each Vocabulary word with its definition. On the line provided, write the letter of the word or phrase that *best* defines each Vocabulary word.

______ **15.** elect
______ **16.** hyperactive
______ **17.** distracted
______ **18.** putrid
______ **19.** admonitions

a. scoldings
b. unable to concentrate on something
c. choose
d. abnormally active
e. disgusting

Constructed Response *(20 points)*

20. Explain why Alvarez recounts her experiences in a story and a poem whereas Lewis tells the story of Viet Dinh as an article. Explain how the choice of genre affects each selection. On a separate sheet of paper, write a paragraph that explains your answer. Support your ideas with details from the three selections.

COLLECTION 4 SUMMATIVE TEST

Comparing Themes

This test asks you to use the skills and strategies you have learned in this collection. Read the following two passages, and then answer the questions that follow them. The first passage is part of an autobiography. The second passage is a poem.

The Best Gift of My Life

FROM But I'll Be Back Again

by Cynthia Rylant

I think my idea of heaven when I was a kid was Christy Sanders's home. She lived in a new brick house with carpeting in it and a bar in the kitchen you could eat on and a picture window in the living room. Her dad wore suits and her mother was queen of the PTA. Christy's house always smelled like those chocolate-covered marshmallow cookies you can get at the grocery. Everything in it was new and it matched and it worked.

In the apartment my mother and I shared, there were old gas heaters you had to light with a match and which threatened to blow you up every time you did. We didn't have carpet. We had old green-and-brown linoleum with cigarette burns in it. Every morning, there would be at least one spider in the bathtub, and it would take every ounce of nerve I had to look in and check. Once, a really big spider crawled out from under our old couch and I was too scared to step on him; instead I dropped a Sears catalog on his head and left it there for a week, just to make sure he was dead.

If you looked out our front window, you would have seen Todd's warehouse and junkyard. It was a long metal building enclosed by a high chain-link fence, and on the outside were rusting barrels and parts of bulldozers and all manner of rotten equipment. There was some talk that the ghost of Mr. Todd's old father walked around the warehouse at night, but I was too worried about spiders in my bathtub to give it much thought.

Wanting Christy Sanders's brick house was just a symptom of the overall desire I had for better things. I read a lot of magazines, and I wanted to live in houses with yellow drapes and backyard pools. I was ashamed of where I lived and felt the world would judge me unworthy because of it. I wouldn't even go to the library in the nearby city because I felt so unequal to city kids. Consequently, I lived on comic books for most of my childhood, until I moved into drugstore paperback romances as a teenager.

As long as I stayed in Beaver, I felt I was somebody important. I felt smart and pretty and fun. But as soon as I left town to go anywhere else, my sense of being somebody special evaporated into nothing, and I became dull and ugly and poor. The feeling would stick with me for years, and when I went away to college and met students who had grown up in big Northern cities and could breeze through the world talking like they owned it, I realized that no matter how much I studied or how many college degrees I got, there was one thing I might never fully learn: I might never fully learn that it would be all right for me to have a house that smelled like chocolate-covered marshmallow cookies.

One year the New Orleans Symphony Orchestra came to play in our junior high school gymnasium. What that orchestra was doing in my little town I cannot imagine, for surely they were all fresh out of London and New York and Los Angeles and didn't need any extra publicity in Beaver, West Virginia.

But the visit of that orchestra was something I have never forgotten. I was not familiar with any real sort of culture. No one I knew played classical records. I had never been to a museum of any kind. In fact, it would not be until I went to college in Charleston, West Virginia, that I set foot in a library or an art museum.

The New Orleans Symphony was for me like a visit from God himself, so full of awe and humility was I. We sat on the hard bleachers our bottoms usually warmed for junior varsity games, and we watched these elegant people who seemed long and fluid, like birds, play their marvelous instruments. Their music bounced off the blue-and-gold picture of our school tiger on the wall and the time clock and the heavy velvet curtains we used for school plays, and the gym was transformed into a place of wonder for me.

The conductor was a slender, serious man with a large nose and a lot of dark hair swept back from his forehead. I watched him and I wanted to live in his pink house in New Orleans, surrounded by maids carrying iced tea and peanuts, sleeping each night in a white canopy bed, greeting at the door of our home such notable musicians as Elvis Presley, Paul McCartney, and The Monkees.

Watching the conductor and his beautiful orchestra, I felt something in me that wanted more than I had. Wanted to walk among musicians and artists and writers. Wanted a life beyond Saturdays at G. C. Murphy's department store and Sundays with the Baptist Youth Fellowship.

I wanted to be someone else, and that turned out to be the worst curse and the best gift of my life. I would finish out my childhood forgetting who I really was and what I really thought, and I would listen to other people and repeat their ideas instead of finding my own. That was the curse. The gift was that I would be willing to try to write books when I grew up.

Daily
by Naomi Shihab Nye

These shriveled seeds we plant,
corn kernel, dried bean,
poke into loosened soil,
cover over with measured fingertips
These T-shirts we fold
into perfect white
squares
These tortillas we slice and fry to crisp strips
This rich egg scrambled in a gray clay bowl

This bed whose covers I straighten
smoothing edges till blue quilt fits brown blanket
and nothing hangs out
This envelope I address
so the name balances like a cloud
in the center of the sky
This page I type and retype
This table I dust till the scarred wood shines
This bundle of clothes I wash and hang and wash again
like flags we share, a country so close
no one needs to name it
The days are nouns: touch them
The hands are churches that worship the world

VOCABULARY SKILLS *(25 points; 5 points each)*
Each of the underlined words below is also underlined in the selection. Re-read those passages in which the underlined words appear, and then use context clues and your prior knowledge to select an answer. On the line provided, write the letter of the word or words that *best* complete each sentence.

______ **1.** Linoleum is used as a —
- **A** snack food
- **B** floor covering
- **C** window covering
- **D** cleaning tool

______ **2.** All of the following elements are part of an orchestra *except* —
- **F** violins
- **G** flowers
- **H** flutes
- **J** musicians

______ **3.** Which of the following activities would the writer consider culture?
- **A** Sleeping
- **B** Swimming
- **C** Visiting museums
- **D** Playing basketball

______ **4.** When you feel awe, you are —

F proud
G bored
H horrified
J amazed

______ **5.** Being elegant means that you are —

A loud and noisy
B young and restless
C fashionable and wealthy
D graceful and dignified

COMPREHENSION *(25 points; 5 points each)*
On the line provided, write the letter of the *best* answer to each of the following items.

______ **6.** The author of "The Best Gift of My Life" admires Christy Sanders's life for all of the following reasons *except* that —

F everything in her house is new and matches
G her house smells good
H her parents are artists who have an exciting lifestyle
J her mother is important in the community

______ **7.** You can infer from the story of the spider that —

A the author's mother does not work outside the home
B the author is left alone a great deal and has many fears
C Mr. Todd acts like a father to the author
D the author rarely sees spiders

______ **8.** Because of her home and family the author feels —

F ashamed of herself and insecure
G confident and ready to conquer the world
H eager to join a symphony orchestra
J unwilling to get married and start her own family

______ **9.** Listening to the New Orleans Symphony Orchestra —

A bothers the writer because the musicians seem snobbish
B seems like a waste of time to the writer and her classmates
C makes the writer want to play a musical instrument
D awakens in the writer a desire for a better life

NAME ______ CLASS ______ DATE ______ SCORE ______

______ **10.** The poem "Daily" shows that —

F poor cleaning women are forced to work hard

G women are oppressed by chores

H the writer hates to do things around the house

J ordinary household chores are sacred

READING SKILLS AND STRATEGIES: CONSTRUCTED RESPONSE *(30 points; 10 points each)*

Making Inferences About Motivation

11. What motivates the narrator of "The Best Gift of My Life" to act the way she does? Complete the following chart to make inferences about her motivation.

Goal	Motivation	Outcome
Wants to live in a home like Christy Sanders's		
Wants culture in her life		
Wants to be someone important		

Comparing and Contrasting Themes

12. Complete the following chart to show how the themes of "The Best Gift of My Life" and "Daily" are either the same or different.

	"The Best Gift of My Life"	"Daily"
Main character		
Character's motives		
What character learns		
Theme		

NAME	CLASS	DATE	SCORE

Connecting Literature to Current Events

13. Writers often base their stories and poems on real-life events. What is the real-life event in "The Best Gift of My Life"? Explain how this event affects the writer.

____

____

____

____

____

____

LITERARY FOCUS: CONSTRUCTED RESPONSE *(20 points)*

14. The writer's choice of **genre** shapes the theme in a work of literature. Complete the following chart to see how Cynthia Rylant and Naomi Shihab Nye develop their themes through the literary form they used.

	"The Best Gift of My Life"	"Daily"
Genre		
Purpose		
Theme: stated or implied?		
How genre is used to develop the theme		
Theme		

NAME ______ CLASS ______ DATE ______ SCORE ______

COLLECTION 5 DIAGNOSTIC TEST

LITERATURE
INFORMATIONAL TEXT
VOCABULARY

Irony and Ambiguity

On the line provided, write the letter of the *best* answer to each of the following items. *(100 points; 10 points each)*

______ **1.** **Situational irony** occurs when —

A there is a struggle between characters

B there is a contrast between what we expect will happen and what actually occurs

C an element of a story seems illogical

D the ending of a story is predictable

______ **2.** When characters say one thing but mean the opposite, they are using —

F verbal irony

G metaphors

H personification

J dialect

______ **3.** A story contains **dramatic irony** when —

A the ending is tragic

B the characters are highly sensitive

C the reader knows more than the characters know

D elements of the story seem exaggerated

______ **4.** A **contradiction** occurs when two statements —

F have slightly different interpretations

G have opposite meanings

H are unrelated

J come from different sources

______ **5.** **Tone** is the —

A reader's attitude toward a subject

B characters' attitude toward the narrator

C reader's attitude toward the characters

D writer's attitude toward a subject or character

______ **6.** The function of a **symbol** is to —

F provide conflict

G entertain the reader

H add suspense to the plot

J stand for something beyond itself

______ **7.** The purpose of an **argument** is to —

A explain how to do something

B point out the reader's lack of knowledge

C inform the reader

D convince the reader of something

______ **8.** What is a **generalization**?

F A type of comparison used to clarify a point

G An overused expression

H A broad statement that applies to many situations

J An educated guess

______ **9.** If a doctor were writing an article for a medical journal, he or she would probably use —

A technical language

B slang

C literary terms

D flowery language

______ **10.** **Context clues** can include all of the following items *except* —

F synonyms

G antonyms

H homophones

J examples

The Gift of the Magi O. Henry

COMPREHENSION *(40 points; 4 points each)*

On the line provided, write the letter of the *best* answer to each of the following items.

_____ **1.** Della is sobbing at the beginning of the story because she —

A always misses her family at Christmas
B can't find a job
C hates her shabby flat
D has no money for the holidays

_____ **2.** Which of the following terms *best* describes Jim and Della's marriage?

F fiery
G difficult
H loving
J boring

_____ **3.** Della's biggest treasure is her —

A watch
B hair
C jewels
D height

_____ **4.** Della visits Mme. Sofronie because Della wants to —

F pawn Jim's watch
G sell her hair
H know the future
J rent a flat

_____ **5.** What does Della buy after leaving Mme. Sofronie?

A Food for dinner
B A set of combs
C A watch chain
D A curling iron

_____ **6.** Which word *best* describes Jim's first reaction to Della after she returns from Mme. Sofronie?

F terrified
G disappointed
H heartbroken
J stunned

______ **7.** Della cries when she sees the combs because she had —

A wanted a watch fob
B not spent as much on Jim's gift
C not expected anything so nice
D cut off her hair

______ **8.** When Jim gets Della's present, he —

F gets angry
G roars with laughter
H smiles knowingly
J storms out of the room

______ **9.** After Jim receives his present, Della learns that he —

A has sold his watch
B didn't buy a present for her
C has lost his job
D dislikes her short hair

______ **10.** According to the author, the Magi are —

F a group of foolish children
G couples who live in flats
H people who give selflessly
J three men who receive gifts

LITERARY FOCUS *(20 points; 5 points each)*

On the line provided, write the letter of the *best* answer to each of the following items.

______ **11.** The *situational* irony in this story comes from the fact that the ending is —

A unexpected
B predictable
C confusing
D mysterious

______ **12.** The surprise ending is that —

F Della learns the truth
G Della decides to have a baby
H Jim loves Della the way she is
J Jim has sold his watch

______ **13.** The *dramatic* irony in this story comes from the fact that —

A we feel sympathy for the characters

B Jim is witty and urbane

C we are aware of the situation before Della is

D Della has a theatrical personality

______ **14.** The story's irony is based on the fact that life is —

F unpredictable

G difficult

H unfair

J complicated

VOCABULARY DEVELOPMENT *(20 points; 4 points each)*

On the line provided, write the letter of the *best* definition for each underlined Vocabulary word.

______ **15.** Della did not know why Jim's <u>scrutiny</u> made her so uncomfortable.

A activity

B observation

C gossip

D recklessness

______ **16.** Della's <u>nimble</u> fingers opened the parcel in no time flat.

F quick

G contrary

H conceited

J anxious

______ **17.** Della's beautiful hair would make the rarest jewels <u>depreciate</u> in value.

A increase

B yield

C decline

D progress

______ **18.** At first, Jim was <u>discreet</u> about his secret.

F judgmental

G prudently silent

H loyal

J good-hearted

______ **19.** Della spent the day ransacking the stores for Jim's present.

A opening

B looting

C using

D searching

CONSTRUCTED RESPONSE *(20 points)*

20. Why is "The Gift of the Magi" a good example of situational irony? What effect does this type of irony have on the reader? Support your ideas with details from the text.

______

______

______

______

______

______

______

______

______

______

NAME ________________ CLASS ________________ DATE ________________ SCORE ________________

The Lady, or the Tiger? Frank R. Stockton

COMPREHENSION *(40 points; 4 points each)*

On the line provided, write the letter of the *best* answer to each of the following items.

______ **1.** The setting for "The Lady, or the Tiger?" takes place in a(n) —

- **A** castle in medieval France
- **B** fictional kingdom
- **C** actual lost civilization
- **D** city in ancient Rome

______ **2.** The king does *not* —

- **F** despise his daughter's lover
- **G** enjoy jury trials
- **H** like to play with people's lives
- **J** have absolute power

______ **3.** According to the king's system of justice, each prisoner has to —

- **A** fight a vicious tiger
- **B** confess or be killed
- **C** die for his crimes
- **D** open one of two doors

______ **4.** A person's guilt or innocence is decided by —

- **F** the king's daughter
- **G** a military tribunal
- **H** a royal court
- **J** his or her own choice

______ **5.** The king's daughter is —

- **A** passive
- **B** empathetic
- **C** jealous
- **D** curious

______ **6.** The king's daughter knows —

- **F** which door is which
- **G** of the prisoner's plans for escape
- **H** the combination of the lock
- **J** where to find an underground tunnel

______ **7.** The king's daughter knows that the lady is —

A a foreigner

B fierce competition

C quite ugly

D her oldest friend

______ **8.** The young man "knew in his soul" that his lover would —

F beg the king for mercy

G tell him which door to pick

H turn her back on him

J marry someone else

______ **9.** The king's daughter might point to the "tiger's" door because she —

A knows her lover will be killed anyway

B is flustered and confused under pressure

C hopes to please her father and inherit the kingdom

D thinks her lover will be better dead than married to another

______ **10.** What happens at the end?

F The lover chooses the tiger.

G The king's daughter saves his life.

H It's up to us to decide.

J We find out which door held the tiger.

LITERARY FOCUS *(20 points; 5 points each)*

On the line provided, write the letter of the *best* answer to each of the following items.

______ **11.** Which of the following examples does *not* contain verbal irony?

A The narrator comments on the "perfect fairness" of the king's justice system.

B It was the duty and privilege of the person on trial to open one of the doors.

C The king refuses to let facts interfere with the principles of justice.

D The tiger was the "fiercest and most cruel" that could be found.

______ **12.** The narrator only implies that the —

F king is a semibarbarian

G king's daughter is insecure

H young man is honest and forthright

J king sees the error of his ways

______ **13.** The ending of the story is ambiguous because we don't know —

- **A** what the king's daughter decides to do
- **B** the identity of the lady behind the door
- **C** whether the king will show mercy
- **D** what the imprisoned man is thinking

______ **14.** The author of this story uses irony to —

- **F** confuse the reader
- **G** encourage the reader to think
- **H** tell us what might happen next
- **J** help us identify with the characters

VOCABULARY DEVELOPMENT *(20 points; 4 points each)*

On the lines provided, write the *best* Vocabulary word for each item.

exuberant **impartial** **dire** **retribution** **deliberation**

15. The king believed that chance was completely fair and ______________.

16. The king imprisoned the man as ______________ for the horrible crime he had committed.

17. The situation was so ______________ that the princess was up half the night worrying about what to do.

18. From the dungeon the prisoner could hear the wild and ______________ cries of the assembled crowd.

19. The princess acted quickly; she wasted no time in endless ______________.

CONSTRUCTED RESPONSE *(20 points)*

20. Why is the ending of "The Lady, or the Tiger?" so effective? How does this ambiguity affect the reader? Include references to the story to support your ideas.

____

____

NAME ____________ CLASS ____________ DATE ____________ SCORE ____________

A Defense of the Jury System Thomas M. Ross, Esq.

COMPREHENSION *(50 points; 10 points each)*
On the line provided, write the letter of the best answer to each of the following items.

_____ **1.** The author makes a generalization when he states, —

A "Much of the criticism of the jury system is unjustified"

B it "has been said that democracy is the worst form of government—except all the others"

C "a fast-food company was forced to pay $2.7 million in damages"

D "One congressman remarked, 'Most people say this doesn't make a lot of sense'"

_____ **2.** The author's belief that the jury system is essentially fair could be described as a(an) —

F emotional appeal

G analogy

H logical appeal

J opinion

_____ **3.** A **reason** —

A explains why an opinion is held

B provides factual evidence

C contains loaded words

D usually takes the form of a statistic

_____ **4.** The tone of this article could *best* be described as —

F biased

G scholarly

H emotional

J fair-minded

_____ **5.** The author uses an analogy when he compares the jury system to —

A ill-informed voters

B unjustified criticism

C civil lawsuits

D democracy

VOCABULARY DEVELOPMENT *(50 points; 10 points each)*
On the lines provided, write the *best* Vocabulary word for each item.

irrational **advocates** **affluent** **superficial** **obscure**

My opponent generally **[6]** ____________________ positions I find totally

[7] ____________________ and illogical. The fact that he represents only

[8] ____________________ people and special-interest groups concerns me greatly.

I believe his grasp of the real world is shallow and **[9]** ____________________.

He attempts to **[10]** ____________________ the real issues by pretending they don't exist.

NAME ______ CLASS ______ DATE ______ SCORE ______

SELECTION TEST **Student Edition page 315** LITERARY RESPONSE AND ANALYSIS

The Road Not Taken Robert Frost

COMPREHENSION *(50 points; 5 points each)*

On the line provided, write the letter of the *best* answer to each of the following items.

______ **1.** In the line "Oh, I kept the first for another day!," "the first" refers to —

A the narrator's choice

B the poem

C fate

D the road

______ **2.** Frost uses the image of two diverging roads to symbolize —

F sorrow and regret

G life's choices

H the love of nature

J the spirit of independence

______ **3.** According to the poet, the second road has "the better claim" because it —

A was a familiar path

B had never been used

C was covered with leaves

D had been less traveled upon

______ **4.** This poem might have special relevance for you if you are —

F planning a move to the country

G deciding which college to attend

H concerned about the environment

J studying for a big exam

______ **5.** What does the narrator decide to do?

A Take the second road

B Save the decision for another day

C Take the well-traveled road

D Wait until an answer occurs to him

______ **6.** Which of the following statements is the *closest* interpretation of the line "Yet knowing how way leads on to way"?

F You can know something yet not know it.

G It's easy to get lost.

H One path takes you to the next.

J You can never go home again.

______ **7.** According to the narrator, the two roads looked —

- **A** about the same
- **B** very different
- **C** equally charming
- **D** muddy and unpleasant

______ **8.** What does the narrator imply about the choice he made?

- **F** It was sudden.
- **G** He knew he was taking a risk.
- **H** It was the right decision.
- **J** It led to more confusion.

______ **9.** Looking back on his decision, the narrator feels —

- **A** regretful
- **B** relieved
- **C** embarrassed
- **D** meditative

______ **10.** The narrator envisions that in later years he will —

- **F** feel sad
- **G** tell his story
- **H** see his error
- **J** write about the episode

LITERARY FOCUS *(20 points; 5 points each)*

On the line provided, write the letter of the *best* answer to each of the following items.

______ **11.** The statement "And sorry I could not travel both / And be one traveler . . ." is an example of —

- **A** dramatic irony
- **B** situational irony
- **C** verbal irony
- **D** ambiguity

______ **12.** The meaning of the poem is ambiguous because —

- **F** we don't know if it's autobiographical
- **G** it can mean different things to different people
- **H** the narrator is indecisive
- **J** the poem was written for an educated audience

_____ **13.** The last line of the poem might be characterized as —

A a contradiction

B ambiguous

C ironic

D subtle

_____ **14.** The narrator says that this small "choice" —

F was the wrong choice

G was necessary at the time

H allowed him to become a poet

J made a big difference

CONSTRUCTED RESPONSE *(30 points)*

15. "The Road Not Taken" is about the choices in life we make—or don't make. The poem is especially provocative because its meaning is so ambiguous. Choose one example of ambiguity in the poem, and explain its significance, using details from the text.

NAME ______ CLASS ______ DATE ______ SCORE ______

COLLECTION 5 SUMMATIVE TEST

Irony and Ambiguity

This test asks you to use the skills and strategies you have learned in this collection. Read the following poem entitled "El Olvido." Then, answer the questions that follow it.

El Olvido
by Judith Ortiz Cofer

It is a dangerous thing
to forget the climate of your birthplace,
to choke out the voices of dead relatives
when in dreams they call you
by your secret name.
It is dangerous
to spurn the clothes you were born to wear
for the sake of fashion; dangerous
to use weapons and sharp instruments
you are not familiar with; dangerous
to disdain the plaster saints
before which your mother kneels
praying with embarrassing fervor
that you survive in the place you have chosen to live:
a bare, cold room with no pictures on the walls,
a forgetting place where she fears you will die
of loneliness and exposure.
Jesús, María, y José, she says,
el olvido is a dangerous thing.

VOCABULARY SKILLS *(25 points; 5 points each)*

On the line provided, write the letter of the *best* answer to each question.

______ **1.** Death from *exposure* can result from an environment that is too —

A dark

B small

C cold

D damp

______ **2.** When we speak of the "*climate* of an era," we are talking about its —

F economy

G geography

H weather

J mood

______ **3.** If you do something with great *fervor*, you are *not* —

A courageous

B enthusiastic

C apathetic

D embarrassed

______ **4.** If you *disdain* something, you —

F have contempt for it

G yearn for it

H feel respect for it

J will save it

______ **5.** *Spurn* means to —

A accompany

B detest

C precede

D reject

COMPREHENSION *(25 points; 5 points each)*

On the line provided, write the *best* answer to each of the following items.

______ **6.** What does the term *el olvido* probably mean?

F danger

G forgetfulness

H mother

J birthplace

______ **7.** The speaker is warning against —

A wearing new clothes

B ignoring your heritage

C embarrassing your mother

D living in a cold, bare room

______ **8.** According to the speaker, it is dangerous to —

F kneel and pray

G wear traditional clothes

H scorn the religion of your childhood

J believe dreams and omens

______ **9.** In line 3, "to choke out" dead relatives' voices means to —

A ignore what they taught

B smother them with love

C forget their ways

D become angry with them

______ **10.** Which of the following adjectives *best* describes the speaker's tone?

F playful

G sarcastic

H optimistic

J solemn

READING SKILLS AND STRATEGIES: CONSTRUCTED RESPONSE *(20 points; 10 points each)*

Making Inferences

11. Whom do you think the speaker is addressing in this poem? What kind of person would abandon his or her traditions? Make an inference based on evidence from the poem.

______

______

______

______

______

______

12. What do you think the speaker means by "secret name"? Make an inference based on evidence from the poem.

LITERARY FOCUS: CONSTRUCTED RESPONSE *(30 points)*

13. Sometimes a poet expresses an **ironic** attitude toward a subject through the use of tone. On the lines provided, describe the speaker's attitude toward tradition. Then, describe the speaker's attitude toward the trappings of modern society—fashion, secularism, and the sparse, clean lines of minimalist interior decoration. Finally, explain how these attitudes contradict the tone that might be expected. Support your description with evidence from the poem.

NAME ______ CLASS ______ DATE ______ SCORE ______

COLLECTION 6 DIAGNOSTIC TEST

LITERATURE
INFORMATIONAL TEXT
VOCABULARY

Symbolism and Allegory

On the line provided, write the letter of the *best* answer to each of the following items. *(100 points; 10 points each)*

______ **1.** Which of the following elements would probably *not* be used as a **symbol**?

A Place
B Object
C Idea
D Person

______ **2.** Which statement about **symbols** is *false*?

F They appear in everyday life as well as in literature.
G They can be interpreted differently by readers.
H They may have multiple meanings.
J Their only purpose in a literary work is to stand for something else.

______ **3.** When readers interpret the meaning of a **symbol,** they *most* often —

A summarize a story
B analyze the author's writing style
C examine the context in which the symbol appears
D compare and contrast characters

______ **4.** A story's **theme** consists of —

F a central idea, or insight, about life
G the events of the plot and the order in which they occur
H the time and place of the action
J a subject, or topic

______ **5.** What is **imagery**?

A Language that appeals to the senses
B A type of poem
C The atmosphere of a literary work
D Words or phrases that an author uses repeatedly

_____ **6.** What would be the *best* way to understand an author's views about a subject?

F Examine other authors' opinions about the subject.

G Read a variety of articles by the author on the subject.

H Analyze the first work the author wrote about the subject.

J Learn about the author's personal life.

_____ **7.** An author's **purpose** is —

A the main idea of a work

B the structure of a text

C his or her attitude toward a subject

D his or her reasons for writing a work

_____ **8.** Which of the following strategies would be *most* useful if you were having trouble understanding a nonfiction text?

F Making predictions

G Visualizing

H Paraphrasing

J Comparing and contrasting

_____ **9.** A word's **connotations** are —

A the feelings associated with the word

B the contexts that the word is used in

C other related words

D the definitions of the word

_____ **10.** Which of the following words contains the same **root** as the word *reduction*?

F replace

G production

H emotion

J dull

NAME ______ CLASS ______ DATE ______ SCORE ______

SELECTION TEST **Student Edition page 343** **LITERARY RESPONSE AND ANALYSIS**

The Scarlet Ibis James Hurst

COMPREHENSION *(40 points; 4 points each)*
On the line provided, write the letter of the *best* answer to each of the following items.

______ **1.** The action of this story takes place —
- A in a green-draped parlor
- B at Old Woman Swamp
- C in a rural Southern town
- D in a French town

______ **2.** What does William Armstrong do to earn his nickname?
- F He doodles and sketches.
- G It takes him a long time to learn things.
- H The way he says his name makes it sound like "Doodle."
- J He crawls backwards like a doodlebug.

______ **3.** The narrator pulls Doodle in a cart because —
- A he's told to take Doodle wherever he goes
- B he feels sorry for Doodle
- C go-carts were popular in the South
- D he is teaching him to be independent

______ **4.** The central conflict in "The Scarlet Ibis" comes from the narrator's inability to accept his —
- F brother's limitations
- G parents' values
- H family responsibilities
- J own weaknesses

______ **5.** When the narrator teaches Doodle to walk, the narrator believes that —
- A it will free him from Doodle
- B he can teach Doodle to do other things, too
- C his parents will appreciate him more
- D Doodle will abandon him

______ **6.** During the story, Doodle —
- F learns to swim as well as his brother
- G refuses to learn to walk
- H nurses the fallen ibis back to health
- J begs his brother not to leave him alone

______ **7.** One example of the narrator's cruelty to his brother is when the narrator —

- **A** is ashamed of Doodle
- **B** makes Doodle bury the ibis
- **C** names Doodle after a bug
- **D** pretends he doesn't have a brother

______ **8.** Which of the following statements contains figurative language?

- **F** Doodle has a weak heart that is easily strained.
- **G** The flower garden is neat, and the house is perfectly white.
- **H** The smell of the graveyard flowers softly says names of the dead.
- **J** Doodle and the narrator want to live in the swamp when they are grown men.

______ **9.** From the way Doodle buries the ibis, you can infer that Doodle —

- **A** is just as cruel as his brother
- **B** is obedient but strong-willed
- **C** will do anything to get attention
- **D** is afraid of the natural world

______ **10.** When the two brothers race home to beat the storm, Doodle —

- **F** decides to take a different route
- **G** outruns his brother
- **H** tries to keep up but falls behind
- **J** pretends to be lost

LITERARY FOCUS *(20 points; 5 points each)*

On the line provided, write the letter of the *best* answer to each of the following items.

______ **11.** In fiction a **symbol** can be described as a(n) —

- **A** mood or emotion a story evokes
- **B** an object that stands for something other than itself
- **C** comparison between two unlike objects
- **D** story that can be understood on more than one level

______ **12.** Which of the following events *best* symbolizes Doodle's fate?

- **F** Doodle crawls backwards, not forwards.
- **G** The scarlet ibis falls from the tree and dies.
- **H** Doodle tells lies about people with wings.
- **J** Doodle hears the rain frog.

_____ **13.** The terrible storm could be a symbol for —

- **A** Doodle's disability
- **B** the scarlet ibis
- **C** Mama's anxiety
- **D** the narrator's inner conflict

_____ **14.** What *might* the war symbolize in "The Scarlet Ibis"?

- **F** The narrator's own struggle
- **G** Life in the rural South
- **H** The ibis's fight for survival
- **J** World War I

VOCABULARY DEVELOPMENT *(20 points; 4 points each)*
On the line before each sentence, write the word from the list that has a meaning similar to the italicized word or phrase in the sentence.

imminent **infallibility** **doggedness** **reiterated** **precariously**

_____________ **15.** The narrator's *stubbornness* contributes to Doodle's death.

_____________ **16.** When the storm arrives, the reader knows that disaster is *near*.

_____________ **17.** Doodle is perched *unsteadily* on the ladder leading to the barn loft.

_____________ **18.** Doodle *repeated* that he did not want to be left.

_____________ **19.** The narrator is so sure of his *inability to make a mistake* that he thinks he can teach Doodle anything.

CONSTRUCTED RESPONSE *(20 points)*

20. Choose a symbol from the story, and explain its meaning. Then, on a separate sheet of paper, tell how the symbol affects the way you as a reader respond to the characters and events in "The Scarlet Ibis."

NAME ______________________ CLASS ______________________ DATE ______________ SCORE ______________

SELECTION TEST **Student Edition page 359**

LITERARY RESPONSE AND ANALYSIS

The Grandfather Gary Soto

COMPREHENSION *(40 points; 4 points each)*
On the line provided, write the letter of the *best* answer to each of the following items.

______ **1.** This essay discusses events that take place over a period of —

A a few years
B five years
C ten years
D more than twenty years

______ **2.** Grandfather calls the narrator *hijo* because *hijo* is —

F the author's nickname
G a term of ridicule
H Spanish for "son"
J an expression of anger

______ **3.** The essay is about the growth of the avocado tree, but the selection is also about —

A working at the Sun Maid Raisin company
B new developments in gardening
C pollution in Fresno, California
D the people in the narrator's family

______ **4.** Which description *best* characterizes Grandfather?

F Able to tell a good joke in order to keep a family laughing
G A hard-working, devoted family man
H Strict only when it comes to following rules about his yard
J Believes that luck creates a healthy garden and a good family

______ **5.** The avocado tree was special to Grandfather for all of the following reasons *except* —

A it allowed him to retire early
B the avocados tasted delicious
C it allowed the family to save money
D he had grown it himself

______ **6.** What did Grandfather mean by his belief that a well-rooted tree was the color of money?

F A tree provides a family with food.
G You have to spend money to keep trees healthy.
H Trees must have strong roots.
J Money is the root of our problems.

______ **7.** What part did the avocado tree play in the boyhood of Gary Soto?

A He took care of the tree.

B He loved eating avocado meat.

C It was where daily life took place.

D It taught him to respect his elders.

______ **8.** According to Grandfather, why did the avocado tree rarely grow fruit in its early years?

F He had spent too much time working to take good care of the tree.

G His grandchildren had trampled on the tree and weakened it.

H Avocado trees only grow fruit in Mexico, not in California.

J Pollution and tall buildings prevented pollen from reaching his yard.

______ **9.** Gary Soto didn't climb the avocado tree when it grew tall enough for climbing because —

A he was afraid of heights and of his grandfather

B his brother wouldn't allow him to go near Grandfather's trees

C he preferred to hang out away from home with his brother

D he was afraid the neighbors would think he was a spy

______ **10.** How did the condition of the avocado tree compare to the condition of the family by the time Grandfather died?

F The tree was old and fruitless, but the family was large and healthy.

G Although the tree was big and healthy, the family had fallen apart.

H Just as the tree produced healthy fruit, the family produced healthy children.

J When Grandfather passed away, the tree withered and died.

LITERARY FOCUS *(20 points; 5 points each)*

On the line provided, write the letter of the *best* answer to each of the following items.

______ **11.** In this essay the avocado tree is used as a symbol to say that —

A avocados and people grow old at the same rate

B you cannot predict who or what will outlive you

C like a tree, a family takes time to root and prosper

D grandparents, like avocados, are wise

______ **12.** Which statement is *true* about how readers understand symbols?

F A symbol has only one universal meaning for readers.

G Readers may interpret symbols differently.

H Symbols help readers identify a main character.

J Symbols provide readers with clues about what will happen.

______ **13.** By its third year the avocado tree becomes very important to Gary Soto because it —
- **A** has become a safe place where he can think
- **B** provides him with physical challenges
- **C** helps him understand his grandfather
- **D** is a great source of income

______ **14.** Which statement is *true* about how literary characters relate to symbols?
- **F** A symbol has one meaning for all the characters in a story.
- **G** Older characters and younger characters interpret symbols differently.
- **H** Each character in a story may interpret a symbol differently.
- **J** If a symbol has more than one meaning for the characters, it is untrue.

VOCABULARY DEVELOPMENT *(20 points; 4 points each)*

Chose a Vocabulary word from the list to complete each sentence below. On the line provided, write each word. One Vocabulary word is used twice.

gurgle **hovered** **sulked** **meager**

15. The water might ______ as it runs over the pebbles in the garden.

16. A butterfly ______ over the flower and then decided to land on a bright red petal.

17. A bite of avocado might make for a ______ but nutritious snack.

18. When the young boy ______, he sat still with his head hanging down.

19. One young tree may seem like a ______ resource, but it can provide much for a family over time.

CONSTRUCTED RESPONSE *(20 points)*

20. On a separate sheet of paper, compare the phases of growth of the avocado tree with the changing life of the Soto family from the narrator's point of view. How does the symbol of the tree change as time passes? What does the tree represent for Gary Soto and his family? Include details from the essay to support your interpretation.

NAME ______ CLASS ______ DATE ______ SCORE ______

SELECTION TEST **Student Edition page 365**

LITERARY RESPONSE AND ANALYSIS

The Golden Kite, the Silver Wind Ray Bradbury

COMPREHENSION *(40 points; 4 points each)*

On the line provided, write the letter of the *best* answer to each of the following items.

_______ **1.** In the Mandarin's home, where this story takes place, the mood is —

A cheerful and optimistic

B suspicious and menacing

C indifferent and boring

D angry and violent

_______ **2.** Why does the Mandarin's daughter speak from behind a curtain?

F In this culture, girls are not supposed to show their cleverness.

G She is too shy for a face-to-face confrontation.

H The Mandarin wants to protect her from embarrassment.

J She wants to help the Mandarin gain confidence in his ability to rule.

_______ **3.** The *main* conflict between the two cities is that each city wants —

A to show it has the smartest citizens

B to attract people

C the other's land

D to be the most powerful

_______ **4.** Which statement *best* describes the attitude of the cities throughout the story?

F The spirit of the people is more important than the image the city projects.

G A city that acts on the advice of its female citizens is doomed to failure.

H The appearance of a city is more important than the spirit of its people.

J Only cities ruled by men can prosper and survive.

_______ **5.** As his city builds new walls, the Mandarin sleeps "like a happy fox every night." What does this image convey about the Mandarin?

A He is pleased with the clever actions he has taken.

B He is hiding like a fox in a hole.

C His dream is to be smarter than his enemy.

D He thinks he will outsmart his daughter.

_______ **6.** Why does the city plan to build its walls like a shining lake?

F The brightness of the lake will blind enemy soldiers.

G The water will put out the bonfire walls of Kwan-Si.

H In Chinese culture a shining lake stands for peace among neighbors.

J It is a gift for the Mandarin's daughter, who loves nature.

______ **7.** In attempting to compete, the people of the city become —

A smug from their continual success

B amused at their clever wall designs

C sickened by doing nothing but building walls

D educated about the process of building walls

______ **8.** Why does the Emperor of Kwan-Si come to visit the Mandarin?

F He wants to play a trick on the Mandarin's daughter.

G The Emperor of Kwan-Si wants to know what the Mandarin is up to.

H The daughter of the Mandarin wants the two rulers to talk.

J The Mandarin seeks advice from the Emperor.

______ **9.** Unlike the designs that the cities chose in the past, the golden kite and silver wind designs —

A complement rather than compete with one another

B remind the people of their past conflicts

C are much easier to build

D will most certainly lead to war

______ **10.** Which statement *best* expresses the theme of "The Golden Kite, the Silver Wind"?

F Love conquers all.

G Cooperation is better than competition.

H Good walls make good neighbors.

J Never give up without a fight.

LITERARY FOCUS *(20 points; 5 points each)*

On the line provided, write the letter of the *best* answer to each of the following items.

______ **11.** An **allegory** is a story that —

A is always set in the past

B generally has animal characters

C tries to persuade through use of imagery

D has both literal and symbolic meaning

______ **12.** The purpose of an **allegory** is to —

F show the lighter side of life

G present an interpretation of a story

H teach a lesson about life

J compare and contrast two stories

______ **13.** What does this story say about men and women?

A In most cases, women are smarter than men.

B Rarely is a woman as smart as the Mandarin's daughter.

C Ability is not related to a person's gender.

D In most cases, men are smarter than woman.

______ **14.** For which of the following people would "The Golden Kite, the Silver Wind" be the *most* helpful as an **allegory**?

F A government official who wants to get ahead

G An artist who designs murals

H Two businesses who are competing for business

J A competitive brother and sister

VOCABULARY DEVELOPMENT *(20 points; 4 points each)*

Match the definition on the left with the Vocabulary word on the right. On the line provided, write the letter of the Vocabulary word.

______ **15.** support

______ **16.** chaos

______ **17.** things or events believed to be signs of the future

______ **18.** strong and lasting

______ **19.** things that warn of events about to occur

a. portents

b. enduring

c. sustain

d. omens

e. pandemonium

CONSTRUCTED RESPONSE *(20 points)*

20. Think about a conflict that the story "The Golden Kite, the Silver Wind" might help to resolve. For instance, the conflict could involve two friends, schools, neighborhoods, or organizations. On a separate sheet of paper, describe the conflict briefly. Then, use the story to show how you think the conflict could be resolved.

NAME ______________________ CLASS ______________ DATE ____________ SCORE ________

SELECTION TEST **Student Edition pages 375, 376, 378, 379** INFORMATIONAL READING

Weapons of the Spirit Albert Einstein
Letter to President Roosevelt Albert Einstein
On the Abolition of the Threat of War Albert Einstein
The Arms Race Albert Einstein

COMPREHENSION *(50 points; 10 points each)*

On the line provided, write the letter of the *best* answer to each of the following items.

______ **1.** The interview, letters, and articles by Einstein all express the idea that —

A only the United States should possess weapons of mass destruction

B Gandhi was the greatest leader of the twentieth century

C people need to secure peace without turning to violence

D scientific research will result in weapons that will end all wars

______ **2.** What Einstein means by "their arms should be weapons of the spirit, not shrapnel and tanks" is that —

F people who put down their weapons are spirited

G the body is more important than the mind

H a person's spirit is like a weapon

J people should work out their differences by peaceful means

______ **3.** When Einstein wrote a letter to Roosevelt, the great scientist's purpose was to —

A warn him about what was going on in Germany

B urge the United States to sign a pact with Germany

C create the Manhattan Project

D urge the United States to stay out of Europe

______ **4.** Einstein considered Gandhi "the greatest political genius of our time" because Gandhi —

F stopped the development of nuclear weapons

G headed a nonviolent struggle for the liberation of India

H believed in achieving peace through any means available

J believed there was no peace without justice

______ **5.** According to Einstein, the cold war would end when —

A the Soviet Union ended the arms race

B there is cooperation and trust between people

C there is a military war

D Soviet citizens immigrated to the United States

VOCABULARY DEVELOPMENT *(50 points; 10 points each)*

Write the letter of the choice that is the *best* synonym for each italicized Vocabulary word.

______ **6.** *conceivable*

- **F** arrogant
- **G** imaginable
- **H** unbelievable
- **J** enormous

______ **7.** *invincible*

- **A** failed
- **B** unseen
- **C** quick
- **D** unbeatable

______ **8.** *radical*

- **F** extreme
- **G** circular
- **H** repetitive
- **J** branching

______ **9.** *eradicate*

- **A** seek
- **B** assist
- **C** eliminate
- **D** reply

______ **10.** *vanquished*

- **F** conquered
- **G** angered
- **H** enlarged
- **J** ignored

NAME CLASS DATE SCORE

Symbolism and Allegory

This test asks you to use the skills and strategies you have learned in this collection. Read this essay, "The Little Lizard's Sorrow," and then answer the questions that follow it.

The Little Lizard's Sorrow
by Mai Vo-Dinh

There is in Vietnam a certain species of small lizard only three inches long with webbed feet and a short, round head. They are often seen indoors, running swiftly upside down on the ceiling or along the walls, emitting little snapping cries that sound like "Tssst . . . tssst!" Suppose that you drop an egg on the kitchen floor; the kind of sound you would make then, with the tip of your tongue between your teeth, is like the cry of these harmless, funny little lizards. Sounds of mild sorrow, of genuine shock but somehow humorous regret that seem to say, "Oh, if only I had been . . . If only I had known . . . Oh, what a pity, what a pity . . . Tssst! Tssst!"

There was once a very rich man whose house was immense and filled with treasures. His land was so extensive that, as the Vietnamese say, "Cranes fly over it with outstretched wings," for cranes only do so over very long distances. Wealth breeding vanity, one of the rich man's greatest pleasures was beating other rich men at a game he himself had invented. One player would announce one of his rare possessions, the other would counter the challenge by saying that he, too—if he really did—owned such a treasure. "A stable of fifty buffalos," one man would say. The other would reply, "Yes, I also have fifty of them." It was then his turn to announce, "I sleep in an all-teak bed encrusted with mother-of-pearl." The first player would lose if he slept on cherry planks!

One day, a stranger came to the rich man's house. Judging from his appearance, the gatekeeper did not doubt that the visitor was a madman. He wanted, he said, to play the famous game with the mansion's master. Yet dressed in clothes that looked as if they had been mended hundreds of times, and wearing broken straw sandals, the stranger appeared to be anything but a wealthy man. Moreover, his face was gaunt and pale as if he had not had a good meal in days. But there was such proud, quiet dignity to the stranger that the servant did not dare shut the gates in his face. Instead, he meekly went to inform his master of the unlikely visitor's presence. Intrigued, the man ordered that the pauper be ushered in.

Trying to conceal his curiosity and surprise, the rich man offered his visitor the very best chair and served him hot, perfumed tea.

"Well, stranger, is it true that you have deigned to come here to play a game of riches with me?" he began inquiringly.

The visitor was apparently unimpressed by the rich surroundings, giving them only a passing, casual look. Perfectly at ease, sipping his tea from the rare porcelain cup, he answered in a quiet though self-assured voice, "Yes, sir, that is if you, too, so wish."

"Naturally, naturally," the rich man raised his hand in a sweeping motion. "But, may I ask, with your permission, where you reside and what is your honorable occupation?"

The stranger gave a little chortle, visibly amused. "Sir, would you gain any to know about these? I came here simply to play your game; only, I have two conditions, if you are so generous as to allow them."

"By all means! Pray, tell me what they are," the rich man readily inquired.

The visitor sat farther back on the brocaded chair, his voice soft and confidential. "Well, here they are. A game is no fun if the winner does not win anything and the loser does not lose anything. Therefore I would suggest that if I win I would take everything in your possession—your lands, your stables, your servants, your house and everything contained in it. But if you win—" Here the stranger paused, his eyes narrowed ever so slightly, full of humorous malice, "If you win, you would become the owner of everything that belongs to me." The stranger paused again. "And what belongs to me, sir, you will have no idea of. I am one of the most fortunate men alive, sir . . . . And besides that," he added with a knowing look, "I would remain in this house to serve you as a domestic the rest of my life."

For a long moment the rich man sat back in silence. Another long moment went by, then the rich man spoke: "That's agreed. But, please, tell me your other condition."

Eyes dreamy, the stranger looked out of the window. "My second condition, sir, is not so much a condition as a request. I hope you would not mind giving me, a visitor, an edge over you. May I be allowed to ask the first question?"

The rich man thought for a long second, then said, "That is also agreed. Let's begin."

"Do I really understand that you have agreed to both my conditions?" the stranger asked thoughtfully.

Something in this visitor's manner and voice hurt the rich man's pride. He was ready to stake out his very life on this game that he himself had created. There was no way out. "Yes," he said. "Yes, indeed I have. Now tell me, please, what do you have that I have not got?" The stranger smiled. Reaching to his feet, he took up his traveling bag, a coarse cotton square tied together by the four ends. Opening it up slowly, ceremoniously, he took out an object and handed it to his host without a word. It was an empty half of a coconut shell, old and chipped, the kind poor people use as a container to drink water from.

"A coconut-shell cup!" the rich man exclaimed. One could not know whether he was merely amused or completely shattered.

"Yes, sir, a coconut-shell cup. A *chipped* shell cup. I use it to drink from on my wanderings. I am a wanderer," the visitor said quietly.

Holding the shell between his thumb and his forefinger and looking as if he had never seen such an object before, the rich man interrupted, "But, but you don't mean that I do not have a thing like this?"

"No, sir, you have not. How could you?" the stranger replied.

Turning the residence upside down, the man and his servants discovered odds and ends of one thousand and one kinds, but they were unable to produce a drinking cup made from a coconut shell. In the servants' quarters, however, they found a few such utensils, but they were all brand new, not chipped. One could imagine that the servants of such a wealthy man would not deign to drink from a chipped cup. Even a beggar would throw it away . . . .

"You see, sir," the stranger said to the rich man once they were again seated across the tea table, "you see, I am a wanderer, as I have said. I am a free man. This cup here is several years old and my only possession besides these poor clothes I have on. If you do not think me too immodest, I would venture that I treasure it more than you do all your collections of fine china. But, from this day, I am the owner and lone master of all that belongs to you . . . ."

Having taken possession of the rich man's land, houses, herds and all other treasures, the stranger began to give them away to the poor and needy people. Then, one day, taking up his old cotton bag, he left the village and no one ever saw him again.

As for the dispossessed rich man, it is believed that he died of grief and regret and was transformed into this small lizard. Curiously, one sees him scurrying about only indoors. Running up and down the walls, crossing the ceiling, staring at people and furniture, he never stops his "Tssst, tssst." Vietnamese children, in particular, are very fond of him for he looks so harassed, so funny.

But, oh, such sorrow, such regret, such self-pity.

VOCABULARY SKILLS *(25 points; 5 points each)*
On the line provided, write the letter of the *best* answer to each of the following items.

______ **1.** Which word has connotations closest to those of *chortle*?

A sound
B whisper
C speech
D laugh

______ **2.** If an animal appears *gaunt*, its bones show through; a person who appears *gaunt* would be someone who is probably —

F hungry
G robust
H strong
J inhuman

______ **3.** Literally the word *deigned* means "thought of as beneath one's dignity." When someone has *deigned* to act a certain way, that person has —

A collapsed
B condescended
C cooperated
D contemplated

______ **4.** Suppose you are writing an essay about someone who acted with *malice.* You don't want to overuse the word, so you use another that has similar connotations, such as —

F sympathy

G interest

H spite

J kindness

______ **5.** The word *interrupted* contains the prefix *inter–* and the Latin root *–rupt–.* If you know that *inter–* means "between," then the word root *–rupt–* probably means —

A opinion

B rule

C break

D knowledge

COMPREHENSION *(30 points; 6 points each)*

On the line provided, write the letter of the *best* answer to each of the following items.

______ **6.** In this story the truth about the wanderer is that he —

F was a lizard that had been transformed into a rich man

G was a wise and clever man who was also generous

H was a crane that protected the lands of the rich man

J cannot win a game invented by the rich man

______ **7.** What is the relationship between the lizard and the rich man?

A The rich man laughs like a lizard whenever he wins a game.

B After his death the rich man becomes the lizard.

C The lizard turns into a rich man when it sips from a coconut-shell cup.

D By listening to the rich man, the lizard learns to say "Tssst, tssst."

______ **8.** The rich man *most* enjoys himself when he —

F wins at a game he invented

G feeds the hungry

H watches cranes fly

J surveys his vast land holdings

______ **9.** What challenge does the wanderer suggest to the rich man?

A Whoever loses the game gives up his most prized possession.

B The first one to find a chipped coconut-shell cup wins the game.

C The first one to ask a question loses the game.

D Whoever wins the game gives up all his possessions.

______ **10.** What is the outcome of the challenge between the wanderer and rich man?

F The rich man turns the wanderer into a lizard.

G The wanderer wins because of his cleverness.

H The wanderer loses because he is unlucky.

J The rich man cheats and then is found out.

READING SKILLS AND STRATEGIES: CONSTRUCTED RESPONSE *(15 points)*

Making Generalizations About an Allegory

11. This essay contains a traditional tale from Vietnam. What lesson do readers learn from the tale? In what way is this lesson universal?

______

______

______

______

______

______

LITERARY FOCUS: CONSTRUCTED RESPONSE *(30 points; 15 points each)*

12. In the first paragraph of this essay, the writer compares the lizard to people who think, "Oh, if only I had been . . . If only I had known . . . Oh, what a pity, what a pity . . . Tssst! Tssst!" What quality does the lizard in the story represent? Why do you think the character of the lizard is used to symbolize this quality?

______

______

______

______

13. The idea web below shows some **symbols** that appear in "The Little Lizard's Sorrow." In the spaces provided, write a meaning you associate with each symbol. Base your ideas on details in the story as well as your knowledge from prior experience.

Symbols and Their Meanings for "The Little Lizard's Sorrow"

cranes

____

____

lizard

____

____

chipped coconut-shell cup

____

____

Poetry

On the line provided, write the letter of the *best* answer to each of the following items. *(100 points; 10 points each)*

______ **1.** The **image** of icy winds appeals to our sense of —

A sight
B touch
C smell
D taste

______ **2.** What is the name for a word or phrase that describes one thing in terms of another and is not literally true?

F Description
G Figure of speech
H Allusion
J Inference

______ **3.** "My pillow is soft and fluffy like a cloud" is an example of a(n) —

A symbol
B simile
C metaphor
D extended metaphor

______ **4.** **Personification** occurs when —

F characters express the author's views
G reality contrasts with our expectations
H people are described as animals
J something not human is given human qualities

______ **5.** What is a **sonnet**?

A Two lines of poetry that rhyme
B A short humorous poem
C A fourteen-line poem that usually has a set pattern of rhythm and rhyme
D A poem that tells about a hero's actions

______ **6.** A **ballad** is a —

F serious poem written in memory of someone
G group of lines in a poem that form a single unit
H songlike poem that tells a story
J line that is repeated in a poem

______ **7.** Poetry that is written in **meter** —

A does not rhyme
B is also known as free verse
C has a regular pattern of stressed and unstressed syllables
D is normally very short

______ **8.** **Internal rhyme** occurs when —

F rhymes occur at the ends of lines
G words within a line of poetry rhyme
H the poet uses words that do not rhyme exactly
J only some parts of a poem contain rhyme

______ **9.** **Onomatopoeia** is the use of a word —

A that sounds like what it means
B from an older language
C in which a vowel sound is repeated
D that has shades of meaning

______ **10.** Which of the following phrases contains **alliteration**?

F pickled peppers
G loud shout
H long march
J eerie eels

NAME ______ CLASS ______ DATE ______ SCORE ______

SELECTION TEST **Student Edition page 405**

LITERARY RESPONSE AND ANALYSIS

A Blessing James Wright

COMPREHENSION *(60 points; 6 points each)*

On the line provided, write the letter of the *best* answer to each of the following items.

______ **1.** What real-life situation causes the poet to write "A Blessing"?

- A Discovering a pasture with many blossoms
- B Walking hand-in-hand with a girl he loves
- C Seeing two ponies in a pasture
- D Riding a pony through a pasture of blossoms

______ **2.** The speaker of this poem is *most* likely —

- F a girl in love
- G a pony
- H the poet's friend
- J the poet

______ **3.** "A Blessing" is set —

- A during an autumn sunrise
- B during a summer sunset
- C during a winter afternoon
- D during a spring sunset

______ **4.** When the speaker comes upon the ponies, the ponies are —

- F grazing in a pasture of grass
- G chasing one another in circles
- H looking for humans to ride on them
- J attempting to jump the barbed-wire fence

______ **5.** In response to finding the ponies, the speaker —

- A climbs over a barbed-wire fence and approaches them
- B asks his friend to ride the less shy pony through the pasture
- C feeds oats to the ponies that he has brought from Rochester, Minnesota
- D shoos away the ponies so that they do not scare his friend

______ **6.** In the poem the ponies are described in all of the following ways *except* —

- F break into blossom
- G welcome the speaker and his friend
- H nuzzle the speaker's hand
- J show darkened eyes

______ **7.** Throughout the events described in the poem, the ponies feel —

A afraid of the humans that have climbed into their pasture

B puzzled by the way the speaker bows and then tosses his dark hair

C pleased to be in the company of the speaker and his friend

D curious about the humans but too nervous to approach them

______ **8.** The mood that this poem stirs up in a reader is one of—

F fear and worry

G boredom and indifference

H affection and tenderness

J justice and courage

______ **9.** When the speaker says that he wants to "hold the slenderer one in my arms," he is referring to a —

A pony that has come up to him and nuzzled his hand

B pony that is too shy to approach the speaker or his friend

C girl with black hair who the poet has met in a pasture

D blade of swaying grass that reminds the speaker of his wife dancing

______ **10.** The blessing in the title of this poem refers to —

F the good fortune of living near Rochester, Minnesota, which is famous for its ponies

G the love a young woman with dark hair shows toward the speaker of the poem

H the speaker's good fortune at having been touched by nature, which brings out feelings of love in him

J the speaker's friend who has kindly traveled with the speaker all the way from Rochester, Minnesota

LITERARY FOCUS *(20 points; 5 points each)*

On the line provided, write the letter of the *best* answer to each of the following items.

______ **11.** An **image** in a poem —

A identifies the speaker's main concern

B describes the time and place of an event

C explains the real-life situation that the poem tells about

D creates a strong mental picture that uses one or more of the five senses

______ **12.** Which image helps the reader understand the special way in which the speaker sees the ponies and their relationship to each other?

F "Twilight bounds softly forth on the grass"

G "They bow shyly as wet swans"

H "And the light breeze moves me to caress her long ear"

J "if I stepped out of my body I would break / Into blossom"

______ **13.** All of the following quotations convey an image based on touch *except* —

A "They have come gladly out of the willows"

B "For she has walked over to me / And nuzzled my left hand"

C "I would like to hold the slenderer one in my arms"

D "And the light breeze moves me to caress her long ear"

______ **14.** To "bow shyly as wet swans" implies —

F anger and violence

G confusion and ignorance

H grace and beauty

J sincerity and respect

CONSTRUCTED RESPONSE *(20 points)*

15. In the last three lines of the poem, the poet says, "Suddenly I realize / That if I stepped out of my body I would break / Into blossom." Since a human cannot blossom like a plant or flower, what do you think the poet wants to convey with this image? On a separate sheet of paper, provide a brief explanation of how you see this image in your mind's eye. Then, explain what the poet communicates about himself through this image.

Woman Work Maya Angelou
Daily Naomi Shihab Nye

COMPREHENSION *(60 points; 6 points each)*
On the line provided, write the letter of the *best* answer to each of the following items.

______ **1.** "Woman Work" tells *mainly* about —
- A a woman who is tired from the work she must do
- B a woman who can no longer work because of bad storms
- C the speaker's experience in writing catalogs
- D a question a woman poses about how to get work

______ **2.** The attitude of the speaker in "Woman Work" is —
- F happy
- G indifferent
- H weary
- J violent

______ **3.** Of the following kinds of work, the speaker of "Woman Work" does *not* —
- A tend to the sick
- B take care of children
- C cut sugar cane
- D teach school

______ **4.** A shift takes place after the first stanza of "Woman Work," in which the speaker moves from —
- F telling about work inside to work she must perform outdoors
- G feeling bad about the work she does to feeling good about her work
- H telling about the work she does to asking nature for some help
- J feeling good about the future to feeling less hopeful about it

______ **5.** At the end of "Woman Work," the speaker would like —
- A to learn skills for another kind of job
- B nature to help her feel good again
- C to work with a more positive attitude
- D to continue her job, feeling as she does

______ **6.** The images in "Daily" are drawn from —
- F scientific discoveries
- G medical breakthroughs
- H everyday life
- J technological advances

______ **7.** In "Daily" the speaker's reaction to the images is —

A wonder

B boredom

C confusion

D exhaustion

______ **8.** Which of the following statements is the *best* description of what the speaker of "Daily" does every day?

F During the day she works outdoors, and at night she cooks or does laundry.

G She types and retypes her poems until they are good enough to publish.

H She makes flags for countries that otherwise would not have any.

J She performs household chores, gardens, and writes.

______ **9.** Of the activities listed below, the speaker of "Daily" does *not* —

A type a poem

B do laundry

C work in a factory

D work in a garden

______ **10.** The speaker in "Daily" finds everyday life to be —

F sacred

G absurd

H boring

J meaningless

LITERARY FOCUS *(20 points; 5 points each)*

On the line provided, write the letter of the *best* answer to each of the following items.

______ **11.** A **catalog poem** —

A tells about subjects related to daily life

B expresses feelings about a particular person

C lists titles of other poems

D lists images for the readers' attention

______ **12.** Both poems in this selection are catalogs that tell about —

- **F** the struggle of women to find better work
- **G** a catalog each speaker uses to list daily choices
- **H** the daily lives of the speakers
- **J** cures for common illnesses that affect women

______ **13.** The images in "Woman Work" tell about all of the following subjects *except* —

- **A** stormy weather
- **B** washing dishes
- **C** outdoor activities
- **D** light from the sun and the moon

______ **14.** Which of the following interpretations explains the image in the last two lines of "Daily"?

- **F** A person can make up a name for her hands the way a congregation makes a name for a church.
- **G** In churches, hands are used for prayer, but in houses, hands are used for h work.
- **H** In houses and churches, people can be found every day of the week.
- **J** A person's hands are like churches in that they help create wonder and go deeds every day of the week.

CONSTRUCTED RESPONSE *(20 points)*

15. "Woman Work" and "Daily" tell about women, and both present images of women's lives. The two poems are also catalog poems. With all of this in common, the poems are still very different. On a separate sheet of paper, discuss a way in which these two poems are different from each other. Use examples from the imagery in each poem to support your idea.

NAME ______ CLASS ______ DATE ______ SCORE ______

SELECTION TEST **Student Edition page 414** LITERARY RESPONSE AND ANALYSIS

in Just- E. E. Cummings

COMPREHENSION *(60 points; 6 points each)*

On the line provided, write the letter of the *best* answer to each of the following items.

______ **1.** "In Just-" tells *mainly* about —

A balloons

B creatures from myths

C two friends

D springtime

______ **2.** The word *mud-luscious* implies —

F mud puddles that are fun to play in

G the kind of mud the balloonman is made of

H a creature from ancient myths

J the friend a child invites to his house

______ **3.** The balloonman —

A plays marbles

B runs through spring fields

C whistles

D makes goat sounds

______ **4.** The number of children referred to in the word *eddieandbill* is —

F one

G two

H three

J four

______ **5.** Another word in the poem similar in structure to *eddieandbill* is —

A balloonman

B puddle-wonderful

C bettyandisbel

D goat-footed

______ **6.** The activities described in "in Just-" are *mostly* related to —

F sales

G made-up names

H play

J weather

______ **7.** The *piracies* the speaker refers to are —

A make-believe games

B stolen merchandise

C water sports

D costumes children wear

______ **8.** Which statement explains what is happening in this poem?

F Marbles is a better game for children than hopscotch.

G Children come out and play when they hear the balloonman each spring.

H Children must decide whether or not to buy balloons and jump-ropes.

J Children in a town are sad when springtime ends.

______ **9.** The mood of "in Just-" is —

A solemn

B joyous

C annoyed

D cynical

______ **10.** The phrase "far and wee" means —

F a great distance

G a place where a strange language is spoken

H rising in the air

J fading away

LITERARY FOCUS *(20 points; 5 points each)*

On the line provided, write the letter of the *best* answer to each of the following items.

______ **11.** E. E. Cummings creates fresh images by —

A using extra punctuation

B combining words

C formal word arrangement

D mentioning a Greek god

______ **12.** A cliché is —

F lively language

G another term for an extended image

H a new way of interpreting an idea

J a worn-out phrase

______ **13.** Of the following words from "in Just-," the one you would find in a dictionary is —

A mud-luscious

B puddle-wonderful

C eddieandbill

D hop-scotch

______ **14.** A characteristic the balloonman does *not* have in this poem is the ability to —

F whistle

G attract children

H play jump-rope

J walk goat-footed

CONSTRUCTED RESPONSE *(20 points)*

15. On the lines provided, explain how "in Just-" helps you see something in a fresh way. What do you see in your mind's eye? How is your new vision different from what you expect? Support your ideas with at least two details from the poem.

______

______

______

______

______

______

______

______

______

______

NAME ______ CLASS ______ DATE ______ SCORE ______

Haiku

Miura Chora, Chiyo, Matsuo Bashō, *and* Kobayashi Issa

COMPREHENSION *(60 points; 6 points each)*

On the line provided, write the letter of the *best* answer to each of the following items.

______ **1.** In the four haiku all the images come from —

A natural events

B the poet's own actions

C the wonders of city life

D water and mountains

______ **2.** The speaker of the haiku by Miura Chora attempts to —

F jump like a toad

G catch a toad

H plant crops

J harvest crops

______ **3.** What is surprising about the toad in the haiku by Miura Chora?

A It eats bamboo plants.

B This toad knows the farmer well.

C Toads aren't usually found along roads.

D It is being formally addressed by a human.

______ **4.** In the haiku by Chiyo, the speaker asks a neighbor for water because the —

F speaker is too lazy to fetch his own water with a bucket

G speaker's bucket is tangled in morning glories

H neighbor has planted morning glories in the speaker's bucket

J speaker's bucket is already full of water

______ **5.** The poem by Chiyo is *most* likely set in —

A an apartment house in a city

B the countryside

C an office in a skyscraper

D a desert with no rivers or lakes

______ **6.** The haiku by Matsuo Bashō takes place —

F on a pond
G in a kitchen
H in the forest
J in a farmer's field

______ **7.** What inner experience does the speaker describe in the haiku by Matsuo Bashō?

A Frogs are a man's best friend.
B Expect little from old things.
C Old things can seem new and lively.
D There's no reason to fear water.

______ **8.** In the haiku by Kobayashi Issa, in order to see distant hills, the speaker —

F travels beyond his farm fields
G gazes out of his window
H looks at a reflection on a full moon
J looks into the eyes of a dragonfly

______ **9.** The haiku by Kobayashi Issa is set —

A on a mountaintop, where the speaker follows a dragonfly's flight
B in a dark container in which the speaker has trapped a dragonfly
C outdoors in nature, where the speaker comes upon a dragonfly
D in a lake, where the speaker swims as a dragonfly flies overhead

______ **10.** In all of these haiku, the speakers learn —

F how animals and insects get in man's way
G something about nature as well as themselves
H how to better care for their land
J about their favorite pastimes

LITERARY FOCUS *(20 points; 5 points each)*

On the line provided, write the letter of the *best* answer to each of the following items.

______ **11.** A **haiku** allows the reader to —

A share a lifetime of experiences
B share a special moment
C focus on surface details
D understand Japanese history

______ **12.** A **haiku** is made up of —

- **F** five lines with five syllables in each of them
- **G** three lines with seven syllables, five syllables, and then seven syllables
- **H** seven words in three lines, each word having no more than five syllables
- **J** three lines of five syllables, seven syllables, and then five syllables

______ **13.** **Japanese haiku** does *not* —

- **A** present only extraordinary images
- **B** present a moment of discovery or enlightenment
- **C** usually contain a seasonal word or symbol
- **D** have seventeen syllables in three lines

______ **14.** In each of the haiku, the last line contains an image that —

- **F** explains where and when the poem is set
- **G** describes a symbol important in Japanese history
- **H** surprises the reader with something unexpected
- **J** repeats the event from the first line in a new and different way

CONSTRUCTED RESPONSE *(20 points)*

15. On a separate sheet of paper, explain the form of haiku and the purpose of images in this type of poem. Then, choose one of the haiku from the selection, and discuss it in terms of its form and imagery. In particular, discuss how the poet uses form in the haiku you choose to convey a mood and a theme.

NAME ______ CLASS ______ DATE ______ SCORE ______

SELECTION TEST **Student Edition pages 423, 425** LITERARY RESPONSE AND ANALYSIS

Once by the Pacific Robert Frost
Country Scene by Hồ Xuân Hư'ơng, *translated by* John Balaban

COMPREHENSION *(60 points; 6 points each)*
On the line provided, write the letter of the *best* answer to each of the following items.

______ **1.** The atmosphere of "Once by the Pacific" is —

A joyous
B threatening
C tragic
D hilarious

______ **2.** The first four lines of "Once by the Pacific" describe —

F clouds in the sky
G darkness falling over the earth
H waves in the ocean
J daylight breaking on shore

______ **3.** What do lines 5 and 6 of "Once by the Pacific" help you infer about what is happening in the poem?

A The ocean will turn as dark as hairy clouds and then disappear forever.
B When clouds cover the ocean, people should grow their hair for warmth.
C Hairy clouds may be cut and trimmed like the shapes of people's haircuts.
D A new age may bring darkness and change to life on earth.

______ **4.** Lines 7–9 in "Once by the Pacific" describe how landforms support one another as ocean waves advance. How does this description relate to the speaker's caution, stated in lines 10 and 11?

F Without cliffs and continents, the earth becomes a less interesting place to live; then people prefer darkness in order to sleep.
G People must prevent an age of darkness and rage just as cliffs and continents must support the earth against advancing ocean waves.
H People love the ocean in the daylight, but they do not like the ocean as well at night.
J There is nothing on earth that can stop a wave, not even the cover of darkness or the rage of humans.

______ **5.** The poet compares the ocean to God's word because the ocean is —

A powerful
B unpredictable
C salty
D influenced by the moon

______ **6.** The mood of this poem is —

F humorous and joking

G thoughtful and sad

H fearful and suspect

J helpless and meek

______ **7.** The element in nature that is the main focus of "Country Scene" is —

A land

B fire

C air

D water

______ **8.** Which of the following items does *not* appear in the scene described in "Country Scene"?

F The waterfall produces mist.

G A fisherman stands under a waterfall.

H A shepherd's horn is heard.

J Fishnets are spread to dry.

______ **9.** In "Country Scene" the idea of love is compared to —

A water plunging over a steep cliff

B an emerald shadow cast over a valley

C the sound of a bell that disappears after it is rung

D a poem that is written about a country scene

______ **10.** Which question does the speaker of the poem answer?

F What human activity lasts like a country scene?

G Who can describe the area around the waterfall?

H How do people fall in love?

J Why is nature so interesting to humans?

LITERARY FOCUS *(20 points; 5 points each)*

On the line provided, write the letter of the *best* answer to each of the following items.

______ **11.** Which characteristic is *not* true of **sonnets**?

A They tell about love and friendship.

B They contain fourteen lines.

C They are written with a pattern of rhyme.

D Each line usually has five stressed syllables.

NAME ____________________ CLASS ____________ DATE ________ SCORE ________

______ **12.** The lines in an **Italian sonnet** are organized so that —

F every other line ends with the same word, and all the lines rhyme

G the first six lines present a problem, and the next four present one solution

H the first eight present a problem, and the last six lines present a solution

J the first eight lines describe love, and the last six lines describe nature

______ **13.** An **English sonnet** takes the form of —

A two stanzas, each with seven lines

B free verse that presents a moment of discovery

C an eight-line stanza followed by a six-line stanza

D three stanzas of four lines each followed by a two-line stanza

______ **14.** Which is the definition of a **lyric poem**?

F It presents a speaker's problem but not a solution.

G It is a brief expression of a speaker's thoughts and feelings.

H The speaker presents a brief solution to someone else's problem.

J The speaker briefly expresses the secret thoughts of readers.

CONSTRUCTED RESPONSE *(20 points)*

15. On a separate sheet of paper, explain how the form of the sonnet or lyric poem helps the speaker express his feelings in either "Once by the Pacific" or "Country Scene." Cite details from the poem you select to support your answer.

Tiburón Martín Espada

COMPREHENSION *(60 points; 6 points each)*
On the line provided, write the letter of the *best* answer to each of the following items.

______ **1.** The title of the poem is the Spanish word for —
- **A** car
- **B** red
- **C** radio
- **D** shark

______ **2.** Which statement describes the scene of this poem?
- **F** A fisherman catches a long red shark while a radio plays.
- **G** A red car has stalled and sits on 116th Street.
- **H** A shark grows to the length of a long red car.
- **J** The speaker thinks about a car as he observes a red shark.

______ **3.** The *first* thing that the speaker mentions is the —
- **A** car
- **B** shark
- **C** radio
- **D** street

______ **4.** The long red car in this poem is —
- **F** the car the speaker of the poem would like to own
- **G** a powerful car that moves as fast as a shark moves in water
- **H** an old, not very reliable car that does not function properly
- **J** a new car used by the speaker to show off

______ **5.** The line "mouth yanked open" refers to —
- **A** a car's open hood
- **B** the fisherman as he screams in excitement
- **C** the speaker when he sees a red shark
- **D** the singer whose voice is heard on the radio

______ **6.** In this poem the phrase "roaring salsa" means —
- **F** loud Hispanic music
- **G** engines revving
- **H** onlookers cheering
- **J** sharks circling

______ **7.** The speaker uses the phrase "prize shark" because the —

A car is painted to look like a shark
B car is as long as a shark
C speaker feels that the car is a prize
D fisherman struggles to catch the shark

______ **8.** What is the relationship between the radio and the shark?

F The speaker imagines a shark enjoying the music from a car radio.
G The speaker imagines a car radio playing after it has been swallowed by a shark.
H The speaker would like to install a radio that plays sharklike music in the car.
J A fisherman uses a radio to successfully lure a shark and catch it.

______ **9.** What is the relationship between the fisherman and the shark?

A The fisherman wants to catch the shark, which is a car.
B The fisherman is the speaker looking for a shark that has swallowed a radio.
C The fisherman would prefer a long, red car over a shark.
D A shark has swallowed the fisherman's radio.

______ **10.** The tone of this poem is mainly —

F disturbed
G solemn
H playful
J sarcastic

LITERARY FOCUS *(20 points; 5 points each)*

On the line provided, write the letter of the *best* answer to each of the following items.

______ **11.** All of the following elements are figures of speech *except* —

A simile
B metaphor
C stanza
D personification

______ **12.** In this poem the connective word that is a clue to a **figure of speech** is —

F like
G car
H shark
J to

______ **13.** The two things being compared in "Tiburón" are —

A 116th Street and roaring salsa

B a car and a shark

C a shark and a radio

D a car and a fisherman

______ **14.** What do a **simile** and a **metaphor** have in common?

F Both need footnotes for readers to understand them.

G Both make comparisons between two forms of poetry.

H Both are imaginative ways to restate a poem's title.

J Both make comparisons between dissimilar things.

CONSTRUCTED RESPONSE *(20 points)*

15. Explain how the use of figurative language gives "Tiburón" tone and meaning. In your response, include an example of a figure of speech from the poem.

NAME ______________ CLASS ______________ DATE ______________ SCORE ______________

SELECTION TEST **Student Edition pages 433, 434** LITERARY RESPONSE AND ANALYSIS

Folding Won Tons In Abraham Chang
On "Folding Won Tons In" Abraham Chang

COMPREHENSION *(60 points; 6 points each)*

On the line provided, write the letter of the *best* answer to each of the following items.

______ **1.** A *won ton* is —

A hunger for Chinese food
B a Chinese-style dumpling
C a son's memories of his mother
D the use of words to describe cooking

______ **2.** In the essay, what situation do you learn about that led Abraham Chang to write this poem?

F He promised to make the recipe his mother gave him.
G Abraham Chang invented a recipe for pork won tons.
H As a young man, he was learning how to live on his own.
J He was frustrated because he couldn't buy won tons at a store.

______ **3.** From the essay you learn that "Folding Won Tons In" takes place —

A in the old apartment of the poet's grandparents
B at the graduate school the poet attends
C in a kitchen of a new apartment the poet will move to someday
D at a Chinese food store where the poet does his shopping

______ **4.** The phrase "the color of the fat sun in October" at the end of the poem's second stanza refers to —

F the speaker's memories from childhood
G the color of the pork filling
H the color of the cooking surface
J his cheeks, flushed from hard work

______ **5.** In the third stanza of the poem, the speaker uses the phrase "misshapen flower" to refer to —

A the pork he has seasoned incorrectly
B the store where he bought "sheets of doughy skin"
C the won tons he has just made
D a memory from childhood he cannot forget

______ **6.** The speaker talks about "newborns" in the fourth stanza of the poem. The phrase in that stanza that has a similar meaning is —

F "hands powderdusted"

G "new blossom"

H "waiting to be fed"

J "distant fathers"

______ **7.** In the fourth stanza, the "newborns huddled" are —

A eaten for dinner

B thrown away

C saved from one more day

D placed in boiling soup

______ **8.** How does the speaker feel in the last stanza?

F He looks forward to eating the won-ton soup he has made.

G The newborns do not survive, which saddens him.

H Disappointed, he gives up on his recipe.

J He feels defeated and drowns his sorrows.

______ **9.** The speaker's attitude at the end of the poem might be *best* described as —

A fearing that he will have too little food for the future

B worrying that his mother will not be proud of his cooking skills

C feeling indifferent about his family and its Chinese traditions

D savoring and prolonging his successful attempt to cook for himself

______ **10.** An alternative title that fits the theme of the poem is —

F "Surviving on Traditions"

G "Forget the Past"

H "The Future Is a New Day"

J "Hurry Up and Catch Up"

LITERARY FOCUS *(20 points; 5 points each)*

On the line provided, write the letter of the *best* answer to each of the following items.

______ **11.** A **simile** —

A is a comparison between two similar things

B uses a connective word to compare two unlike things

C is a comparison of two unlike things

D is the personification of objects

NAME ______ CLASS ______ DATE ______ SCORE ______

______ **12.** In a **metaphor** —

F two unlike things are compared

G more than two things act like living beings

H two things are compared with the words *like* or *as*

J memories are made to seem like current events

______ **13.** The simile in "Folding Won Tons In" compares —

A the sun and the color pink

B flowers and blossoms

C fresh won tons and newborns

D cooked won tons and memories

______ **14.** Why is a metaphor a stronger statement than a simile?

F Metaphors are more imaginative than similes.

G Metaphors make a more direct comparison.

H Metaphors tell the truth while similes don't.

J Similes compare more than two things.

CONSTRUCTED RESPONSE *(20 points)*

15. Explain how "Folding Won Tons In" uses figurative language to express meaning. Cite details from the poem to support your answer.

______

______

______

______

______

______

______

______

NAME ______ CLASS ______ DATE ______ SCORE ______

"Hope" is the thing with feathers Emily Dickinson
Internment Juliet S. Kono

COMPREHENSION *(60 points; 6 points each)*

On the line provided, write the letter of the *best* answer to each of the following items.

______ **1.** In Dickinson's poem, "Hope" is in —

A the soul
B the sea
C a crumb
D a song

______ **2.** In the Dickinson poem the dashes stand for a —

F mistake
G connection between ideas
H pause
J missing word

______ **3.** The speaker of Dickinson's poem believes hope will flourish even though —

A the bird's song is wordy
B storms might threaten
C the bird is not fed
D the bird cannot fly

______ **4.** In Dickinson's poem the denotations of *storm* and *gale* refer to —

F downed power lines, slashing rain, and danger
G a disturbance in the atmosphere and a strong wind
H a caged bird singing in the rain
J a soaring eagle in the morning sky

______ **5.** According to the poem's last line, Dickinson feels that hope —

A is selfish for not sharing its crumbs with her
B is a bird that eats crumbs when it's hungry
C is like crumbs—small and unimportant
D gives and asks for nothing in return

______ **6.** The speaker's tone at the beginning of "Internment" is —

F indifferent
G bitter
H objective
J accepting

______ **7.** What is the situation described in the first stanza of "Internment"?

- **A** Santa Rosa is not a good town for people to live in.
- **B** A young girl falls asleep during a train ride.
- **C** People are sent far from home and then imprisoned.
- **D** DDT is a chemical used to kill insects, including lice.

______ **8.** The pasture described in the second stanza of "Internment" has become —

- **F** a prison
- **G** a train station
- **H** a corral
- **J** Crystal City, Texas

______ **9.** Which statement *best* describes what happens to the "she" in "Internment"?

- **A** She falls asleep on a train, but then awakens in a new place.
- **B** She forgets all her troubles and finds joy in the beauty of nature.
- **C** She learns to see beauty in nature despite her suffering.
- **D** She learns to treat people like branded cattle by delousing them.

______ **10.** The connotation for the word *impaled* at the end of "Internment" is —

- **F** stuck through
- **G** wounded
- **H** lost color
- **J** shone

LITERARY FOCUS *(20 points; 5 points each)*

On the line provided, write the letter of the *best* answer to each of the following items.

______ **11.** An **extended metaphor** —

- **A** develops a metaphor for several lines or for an entire poem
- **B** compares two unlike things using the word *like* or *as*
- **C** exaggerates how people and things act
- **D** uses two or more connotations for the same word in a poem

______ **12.** Dickinson's extended metaphor for hope is a(n) —

- **F** eagle floating on unseen currents
- **G** destructive gale and storm
- **H** small bird perched in the soul
- **J** ostrich burying its head in the sand

______ **13.** In the second stanza, how does Dickinson extend her metaphor of "'Hope' is the thing with feathers"?

- **A** A storm is heard, which relates to a bird that sings in the first stanza.
- **B** At the end of the stanza, Dickinson warms up the bird so it can fly.
- **C** The bird from stanza one becomes lost in a storm in stanza two.
- **D** She explains that the bird representing hope remains even during bad weather.

______ **14.** By creating an extended metaphor in "'Hope' is the thing with feathers," Dickinson does all of the following things *except* —

- **F** explore feelings she has about hope
- **G** creatively communicate a complicated idea
- **H** create an original pattern of repetitive rhymes
- **J** develop an image through an entire poem

CONSTRUCTED RESPONSE *(20 points)*

15. Identify the things that Dickinson compares in the extended metaphor of her poem. Then, think about Dickinson's choices for her comparison. Explain why you think she made the choice she did. Do you agree with her comparison? Why or why not? Use details from the poem and what you know from life experience and prior reading to support your response.

NAME ______ CLASS ______ DATE ______ SCORE ______

SELECTION TEST **Student Edition pages 440, 441**

LITERARY RESPONSE AND ANALYSIS

Fog Carl Sandburg
Fire and Ice Robert Frost

COMPREHENSION *(60 points; 6 points each)*
On the line provided, write the letter of the *best* answer to each of the following items.

______ **1.** According to the poem "Fog," fog —

A moves by appearing suddenly and by surprise
B falls over an area quickly and then stays in place
C moves slowly into and then out of an area
D is not real but is something imagined

______ **2.** Fog in a harbor or city reminds Sandburg of a —

F cat that sits
G bird that flies
H cat that pounces
J dog that barks

______ **3.** In "Fog" a cat acts in all of the following ways *except* —

A mews
B sits
C creeps
D stares

______ **4.** What is the *main* action of the first stanza of "Fog"?

F Cats are silent.
G Fog arrives.
H Fog lifts.
J Cats sit and stare.

______ **5.** What is the *main* action of the second stanza of "Fog"?

A Cats live in harbors.
B Some animals are nocturnal.
C More fog arrives.
D Fog sits then leaves.

______ **6.** In "Fire and Ice" the speaker expresses views on the —

F destructive force of ideas
G destructive force of emotions
H healing power of words
J healing power of natural phenomena

______ **7.** In "Fire and Ice," fire is a metaphor for —

A suffering

B friendship

C desire

D hate

______ **8.** Ice in "Fire and Ice" is a metaphor for —

F desire

G poets

H hate

J destruction

______ **9.** Which of the following statements is *not* a possible interpretation of Frost's main idea in "Fire and Ice"?

A Hate and desire are equally destructive emotions.

B Human beings will cause the end of the world.

C Human emotions are as destructive as natural forces.

D Human beings should eliminate emotions from their lives.

______ **10.** In "Fire and Ice" the attitude of the speaker toward the main idea is one of —

F distance and wisdom

G confusion and suspicion

H fury and rage

J indifference and boredom

LITERARY FOCUS *(20 points; 5 points each)*

On the line provided, write the letter of the *best* answer to each of the following items.

______ **11.** An **implied metaphor** —

A compares more than two things at one time

B suggests comparisons rather than state them directly

C includes words from more than one language in a figure of speech

D states a comparison directly over several lines or an entire poem

______ **12.** Which line of poetry is an example of implied metaphor?

F My heart chugs like a train down the track of love.

G My heart chugs down the track of love.

H My heart is a train, chugging down love's track.

J My heart is not a train but the track a train chugs along.

______ **13.** Sandburg uses a metaphor in "Fog" to describe —

A the movements of a cat

B the way day becomes night in foggy weather

C how fog clings to everything in its path

D soft fog descending on a city

______ **14.** The implied metaphor in Frost's poem compares —

F desire to fire, and hate to ice

G imagination to fire, and fear to ice

H youth to fire, and old age to ice

J summer to fire, and winter to ice

CONSTRUCTED RESPONSE *(20 points)*

15. In "Fire and Ice" the implied metaphor also states the main idea of the poem. In your own words, briefly explain the main idea of Frost's poem. Then, use details from the poem, including details about the implied metaphor, to defend your decision about the poem's main idea. Use at least one example or direct quotation from the poem to support your idea.

______

______

______

______

______

______

______

______

______

______

NAME ______ CLASS ______ DATE ______ SCORE ______

SELECTION TEST **Student Edition page 444**

LITERARY RESPONSE AND ANALYSIS

The Seven Ages of Man

William Shakespeare

COMPREHENSION *(60 points; 6 points each)*

On the line provided, write the letter of the *best* answer to each of the following items.

______ **1.** Jaques compares all men and women with players in a —

A game of polo
B card game
C theatrical production
D child's game

______ **2.** "The Seven Ages of Man" describes —

F stories that start in the middle and then go back in time
G acts in a play, ending with a conclusion
H a popular, old English team sport related to soccer
J human life from infancy to old age

______ **3.** According to the poem, the second stage in a man's life is the —

A schoolboy
B lover
C soldier
D justice

______ **4.** The stage in a man's life that follows the lover is the —

F infant
G schoolboy
H soldier
J old man

______ **5.** The man who is "full of wise saws" is the —

A soldier
B justice
C shrinking man
D old man

______ **6.** A man is "sudden and quick in quarrel" during the —

F third stage of life
G fourth stage of life
H fifth stage of life
J sixth stage of life

NAME ________________ CLASS ________________ DATE ________________ SCORE ________________

______ **7.** What is characteristic of man in the third stage of life?

A He sings ballads to a mistress.

B He takes strange oaths.

C He carries a satchel.

D He wears pantaloons.

______ **8.** Why in one stage of life does man experience "a world too wide / For his shrunk shank"?

F After a war, a hungry soldier does not fit into the clothes he wore before battle.

G A lover feels smaller and smaller because the power of love is so large.

H When man begins to get old, he also begins to shrink in size.

J The judge understands that he makes decisions about a big, complicated world.

______ **9.** Jaques makes old age seem —

A carefree

B funny

C dignified

D pathetic

______ **10.** According to the speaker, the "players" in these seven acts of life —

F can choose whether or not to be in one of the acts

G must wear spectacles and stockings

H enter as infants and exit as aged people

J enter as adults and exit as school children

LITERARY FOCUS *(20 points; 5 points each)*

On the line provided, write the letter of the *best* answer to each of the following items.

______ **11.** An **extended metaphor** is a(n) —

A metaphor that has a larger, more philosophical meaning

B comparison developed over several lines or throughout an entire poem

C analogy that is used in the first and third stanzas of a poem

D metaphor that compares two unlike things in a single image

______ **12.** The extended metaphor in "The Seven Ages of Man" compares a —

F schoolboy and a snail

G sighing lover and a furnace

H person's life and a play

J soldier and a leopard

______ **13.** The part of "The Seven Ages of Man" that makes up the extended metaphor is —

A the first few lines, which identify the two items being compared

B lines 5–10, which describe the early stages of man

C lines 5–25, which present all the stages of man

D all the lines of the poem

______ **14.** What kind of figure of speech is the famous first line, "All the world's a stage"?

F Metaphor

G Implied metaphor

H Extended metaphor

J Personification

CONSTRUCTED RESPONSE *(20 points)*

15. Explain why the extended metaphor in "The Seven Ages of Man" is an appropriate comparison. Support your ideas with at least two details from the poem.

Women Alice Walker

COMPREHENSION *(60 points; 6 points each)*

On the line provided, write the letter of the *best* answer to each of the following items.

______ **1.** The speaker talks about women of —

A the present

B the future

C the past

D ancient times

______ **2.** The women in this poem come from —

F foreign countries

G the speaker's dreams

H the speaker's life experience

J a story the speaker has read

______ **3.** Which characteristic does the speaker use to describe the women in this poem?

A Stepping softly through a room

B Speaking with husky voices

C Quietly opening doors

D Speaking in whispers

______ **4.** The women in the poem are —

F determined

G meek

H insincere

J cruel

______ **5.** The women in Walker's poem struggle on behalf of their —

A employers

B friends

C teachers

D children

______ **6.** The women "Step / With fists as well as / Hands" because they —

F do not know the difference between anger and calm

G fight for what they want in life at their jobs

H are confused about how to do their jobs properly

J enjoy playing jokes on their employers and families

______ **7.** Walker uses an implied metaphor to compare the women in the poem to —

A fists and hands

B army generals

C teachers at desks

D husky voices

______ **8.** Based on the implied metaphor, you can infer that these women —

F act only on command of their employers

G are trained to prepare traps

H are a powerful force

J cause fights in their families

______ **9.** The women in this poem work toward the goal of —

A educating their children

B getting a raise

C not ironing

D supporting an army

______ **10.** What does Walker tell you about the women in the last three lines of the poem?

F The women succeed in reaching their goal.

G None of the women know that a poem has been written about them.

H The speaker does not appreciate the effort of the women.

J The women are not educated and cannot read.

LITERARY FOCUS *(20 points; 5 points each)*

On the line provided, write the letter of the *best* answer to each of the following items.

______ **11.** The **tone** of a poem communicates the —

A speaker's attitude toward a poem's subject

B main idea of a poem without the use of figurative language

C poet's relationship to the speaker of a poem

D reason for the chosen rhythm or rhyme in a poem

______ **12.** **Diction** has to do with the poet's choice of —

F poetic form

G rhythm and rhyme pattern

H words

J punctuation

NAME ______ CLASS ______ DATE ______ SCORE ______

______ **13.** The tone of "Women" is —

A frightened and nervous

B amused and relaxed

C admiring and proud

D shy and questioning

______ **14.** The "battered down / Doors" in the poem represent all of the following ideas *except* —

F racism

G poverty

H segregation

J opportunity

CONSTRUCTED RESPONSE *(20 points)*

15. In your own words, describe the tone of "Women." Identify the origins of the tone based on what you can infer about the life experience of the speaker. How does the speaker communicate her attitude through her words? Use at least one example or quotation from the poem to support your response.

Boy at the Window Richard Wilbur

COMPREHENSION *(60 points; 6 points each)*
On the line provided, write the letter of the *best* answer to each of the following items.

______ **1.** The setting of this poem is a(n) —

A bright and cold winter morning
B nighttime in spring with a full moon
C afternoon on a brisk autumn day
D winter day as the sun is about to set

______ **2.** Why is the boy weeping in the first stanza?

F The snowman's bitumen eyes frighten him.
G He is sorry for the snowman outside at dusk, cold and alone.
H He is alone in a house with no one to play with.
J The curtains have been drawn and he can't see outside.

______ **3.** What do you infer about the boy, based on the details in this poem?

A He cannot always distinguish living from nonliving things.
B As the saying goes, "He is too wise for his years."
C He is knowledgeable about weather and physical science.
D His ability to make snowmen is unsurpassed.

______ **4.** The boy's mood in the first stanza is —

F gleeful
G upset
H sinister
J happy

______ **5.** The first stanza focuses on the attitude of —

A the speaker of the poem
B the snowman
C the boy
D Adam

______ **6.** The speaker compares Adam to the snowman because —

F Adam is cast out from Paradise, and the snowman is outcast from the house
G the boy decided to name the snowman Adam
H Adam and the snowman both have strange stares that the boy observes
J the boy wants the snowman to live in a winter paradise

______ **7.** The second stanza focuses on the attitude of —

A the speaker of the poem
B the snowman
C the boy
D Adam

______ **8.** Why is the snowman content?

F The boy has been kind to him.
G He has a new friend—Adam.
H He is fine being outside.
J He is fine being indoors.

______ **9.** What event causes the snowman to cry?

A Snow around his eye socket melts.
B Adam sprays water on the snowman's face.
C His tear ducts swell with tears.
D The boy acts like a crying snowman.

______ **10.** The last line draws the conclusion that —

F snowmen may be both fun and hazardous for children to play with
G children experience many intense emotions, sometimes all at once
H poets make fantastic situations seem real through images
J readers who live in cold, snowy places can share this boy's experience

LITERARY FOCUS *(20 points; 5 points each)*

On the line provided, write the letter of the *best* answer to each of the following items.

______ **11.** "Boy at the Window" is a lyric poem because it —

A has no pattern of rhymes or rhythm
B honors a person who lived in the past
C expresses the speaker's thoughts and feelings
D presents a problem for the reader to solve

______ **12.** **Personification** is a kind of figurative language in which —

F nonliving things have human qualities
G two like things are compared
H the actions of someone are exaggerated to make a point
J the writer focuses on the five senses

_____ **13.** Which detail from the first stanza is an example of personification?

A The boy weeps as he looks out the window.

B The night moans.

C A snowman has bitumen eyes.

D Adam is an outcast from Paradise.

_____ **14.** Which detail from the second stanza is *not* an example of personification?

F The snowman stands outside.

G The snowman feels content.

H The snowman is moved by the boy's tears.

J A tear falls from the snowman's eye.

CONSTRUCTED RESPONSE *(20 points)*

15. How does Richard Wilbur use personification in the poem to express his feelings about sympathy? Use at least two details from the poem to support your ideas.

NAME ______ CLASS ______ DATE ______ SCORE ______

SELECTION TEST **Student Edition pages 457, 459** LITERARY RESPONSE AND ANALYSIS

I Wandered Lonely as a Cloud William Wordsworth
I Never Saw Daffodils So Beautiful Dorothy Wordsworth

COMPREHENSION *(60 points; 6 points each)*

On the line provided, write the letter of the *best* answer to each of the following items.

______ **1.** Why does the speaker compare himself to a cloud at the beginning of the poem?

A That's how he feels as he looks down at a lake from higher up.

B He believes that poets have thoughts that rise as high as the clouds.

C He is outdoors performing a scientific experiment.

D He spills ink in the shape of a cloud on a page of his journal.

______ **2.** When the speaker first sees the daffodils, he is —

F indifferent

G weeping

H joyful

J angry

______ **3.** How do the words *fluttering* and *dancing*, at the end of the first stanza, influence what the speaker wants you to feel about daffodils?

A The words add a positive energy to the image of the daffodils.

B The speaker thinks of dancing daffodils as a silly joke.

C The words make the daffodils seem lonely and depressed.

D The speaker believes that fluttering daffodils bring bad luck.

______ **4.** In the second stanza the stars in the Milky Way are compared to —

F the clouds overhead

G the speaker's sister, who silently walks beside him

H the towns that the speaker has already wandered past

J the many daffodils growing in a line

______ **5.** Besides daffodils, what else dances in the poem?

A Waves

B Clouds

C Stars

D The speaker

______ **6.** The daffodils bring "wealth" to the speaker because they —

F give him something to write about

G increase the value of his lakeside property

H serve as a gift for his sister

J provide him with rich memories

______ **7.** The last stanza of the poem is set —

A on the banks of the lake the speaker has wandered to

B in the Milky Way, above the clouds

C at a later time, on a couch in the speaker's home

D at another lake where daffodils do not grow as well

______ **8.** When memories of the daffodils appear to the speaker's "inward eye," he feels —

F deprived

G pleasure

H depressed

J blissful

______ **9.** Dorothy Wordsworth claims that on April 15, 1802, she and her brother saw —

A a stormy sky with a line of clouds shaped like daffodils

B the town of Water Millock without any people in it

C a new highway constructed alongside a beautiful bay

D a long belt of beautiful daffodils growing along a shore

______ **10.** Like the speaker of "I Wandered Lonely as a Cloud," Dorothy Wordsworth also —

F imagines that the daffodils are dancing

G believes that people feel lonely in nature

H thinks that the Milky Way extends farther than scientists know

J believes that wealth is the key to their success

LITERARY FOCUS *(20 points; 5 points each)*

On the line provided, write the letter of the *best* answer to each of the following items.

______ **11.** When you **scan** a poem, you discover its —

A pattern of rhymes

B central image

C pattern of rhythm

D tone and theme

______ **12.** The **rhythm** of a poem —

F is its main idea

G are its words that have the same end sounds

H are its repeated initial consonant sounds within lines

J is its pattern of sound repetitions

______ **13.** In "I Wandered Lonely as a Cloud," the pattern of rhyme is —

A *ababcc*

B *abacbb*

C *aabbcc*

D *abcabc*

______ **14.** The number of stressed syllables in the line "And dances with the daffodils" is —

F two

G three

H four

J five

CONSTRUCTED RESPONSE *(20 points)*

15. Read "I Wandered Lonely as a Cloud," concentrating on the rhythm. Do you hear a pattern? How does the sound pattern help to create a tone in the poem? Identify the poem's tone. Then, use two examples of rhythm from the poem to support your idea.

The Courage That My Mother Had

Edna St. Vincent Millay

COMPREHENSION *(60 points; 6 points each)*

On the line provided, write the letter of the *best* answer to each of the following items.

______ **1.** The *main* idea of this poem is that —
- **A** daughters must choose which gift to inherit from their mothers
- **B** New England is the best place to bury a loved one
- **C** the speaker would like to have inherited her mother's courage
- **D** rocks can tell the story of a person's life

______ **2.** The mother in this poem has —
- **F** moved to New England
- **G** opened a rock quarry
- **H** passed away
- **J** given the speaker a gift

______ **3.** The rock "from New England quarried" is used —
- **A** for the headstone of the grave of the speaker's mother
- **B** as a way to describe how the mother of the speaker looked
- **C** as a stand for the brooch the speaker received as a gift
- **D** to build a house for the speaker and her mother

______ **4.** Why does the speaker treasure the brooch?
- **F** It is the most beautiful brooch she has ever seen.
- **G** It once belonged to her mother.
- **H** Whenever the speaker wears it, her personality changes.
- **J** She can sell it for a lot of money.

______ **5.** What contradiction does the speaker present in the second stanza?
- **A** First she says the brooch is granite, and then she says it's made of gold.
- **B** She loves New England, but she will not miss it when she moves.
- **C** She loves the brooch, but she doesn't need to keep it.
- **D** Even though her mother loved the brooch, her mother gave it away.

______ **6.** From the second stanza, you can infer that the relationship between the speaker and her mother is —
- **F** difficult and strange
- **G** strong and loving
- **H** sarcastic but acceptable
- **J** friendly but indifferent

______ **7.** What does the speaker's mother take to the grave?

A Granite from a granite hill

B A golden brooch

C Something the speaker can spare

D Her courage

______ **8.** In the third stanza the two end punctuation marks ("!—") serve a special purpose: They —

F show the poet's confusion with standard English

G are meant to confuse the reader so that the next line will surprise him or her

H show the speaker's strong emotion, after which she pauses before going on

J are part of the speaker's experiment to use punctuation in a totally new way

______ **9.** The two things compared in the simile in the third stanza are —

A a rock and courage

B granite and gold

C the mother and a New England hill

D the speaker and a granite quarry

______ **10.** What conclusion does the speaker come to at the end of the third stanza?

F When people die, they leave many gifts from which their heirs must pick and choose.

G The speaker's mother has no more need for courage because she is dead, but the speaker has need for it.

H It was unfair for the mother not to leave a rock from a New England quarry as part of the speaker's inheritance.

J The speaker feels courageous enough to exchange her mother's brooch for a rock.

LITERARY FOCUS *(20 points; 5 points each)*

On the line provided, write the letter of the *best* answer to each of the following items.

______ **11.** The element in a word that creates a rhyme is its —

A consonant sounds

B silent letters

C digraphs

D vowel sounds

______ **12.** A **rhyme scheme** is —

F the pattern of end rhymes in lines of a poem

G the pattern of consonant sounds in a line

H the pattern of rhymes within a line of a poem

J all words in a poem that contain the same sound

______ **13.** The word from the first stanza that partially rhymes with *had* is —

A mother

B England

C quarried

D hill

______ **14.** The rhyme scheme of "The Courage That My Mother Had" is

F *aabb, ccdd, acbd*

G *abba, cddc, effe*

H *abab, cdcd, eeff*

J *abab, cdcd, efef*

CONSTRUCTED RESPONSE *(20 points)*

15. Read "The Courage That My Mother Had," concentrating on the rhymes. How does the sound pattern help to create a tone in the poem? Identify the tone of the poem. Then, use two examples of rhyme from the poem to support your idea.

NAME ______ CLASS ______ DATE ______ SCORE ______

SELECTION TEST **Student Edition page 464** LITERARY RESPONSE AND ANALYSIS

Ballad of Birmingham Dudley Randall

COMPREHENSION *(60 points; 6 points each)*
On the line provided, write the letter of the *best* answer to each of the following items.

______ **1.** The dialogue in the poem is spoken by —
- A the speaker and his mother
- B a mother and daughter
- C the narrator and the reader
- D a baby and her sister

______ **2.** The *main* subject of the dialogue is —
- F what a child can do that a mother approves of
- G how to avoid trouble during a freedom march
- H reasons to sing in a children's choir
- J popular places to visit in Birmingham, Alabama

______ **3.** The second stanza might be *best* summarized by saying that a —
- A girl argues with her sister about dogs
- B mother explains the dangers a child might face
- C young girl decides to play at home
- D mother marches for freedom in Birmingham

______ **4.** According to the third stanza, children will march in the streets of Birmingham for —
- F fun
- G their church
- H freedom
- J money

______ **5.** In the first through fourth stanzas, the outcome of the dialogue is that the —
- A child runs away to a freedom march downtown
- B mother tells the child to go downtown in her place
- C child stays home and helps the mother dress for church
- D mother tells the child to sing in the church choir

______ **6.** Between the fourth and fifth stanzas —
- F the main subject of the poem changes
- G some time passes before the narrator speaks
- H a bomb explodes, and then the mother speaks
- J the child runs away, upsetting the narrator

______ **7.** The fifth stanza describes the act of —

- **A** marching
- **B** talking
- **C** dressing
- **D** playing

______ **8.** In the sixth stanza the child —

- **F** plays dress-up
- **G** goes downtown
- **H** has gone to the church
- **J** goes to church with her mother

______ **9.** The last two stanzas tell about a —

- **A** bomb that goes off in the mother's house
- **B** freedom march downtown that is as loud as a bomb exploding
- **C** bomb that goes off in a church where the child has gone to sing
- **D** baby who is found in the ruins of a church explosion

______ **10.** What is the story this ballad tells?

- **F** Innocent children died in the bombing of the church in Birmingham.
- **G** Mothers cannot be trusted to tell stories about historical events.
- **H** Downtown Birmingham is now a safe place for children to play.
- **J** Only a mother understands why a mother and daughter disagree.

LITERARY FOCUS *(20 points; 5 points each)*

On the line provided, write the letter of the *best* answer to each of the following items.

______ **11.** A **ballad** is a —

- **A** series of images
- **B** poem with sound patterns
- **C** song that tells a story
- **D** poem about feelings

______ **12.** Many **ballads** are told in the form of —

- **F** a mystery that needs to be solved
- **G** dialogue among story characters
- **H** a riddle in which readers need to find clues to the solution
- **J** a newspaper or magazine article

______ **13.** How would you describe the rhymes in this ballad?

A In every stanza the second and fourth lines rhyme.

B The lines in every stanza rhyme.

C In every stanza the first and fourth lines rhyme.

D In every stanza every other line rhymes.

______ **14.** How would you describe the rhythm of this ballad?

F Every line in the poem has the same iambic pentameter pattern of rhythm.

G The stanzas with dialogue are more like free verse, but the stanzas spoken by a narrator are in iambic pentameter.

H The poem is written in free verse, but repeated refrains create a pattern of rhythm from time to time.

J The poem does not follow a strict pattern of rhythm, but most lines contain three or four feet of meter.

CONSTRUCTED RESPONSE *(20 points)*

15. On a separate sheet of paper, briefly compare and contrast how the real-life story in "Ballad of Birmingham" affects the reader as a poem and how a newspaper account of the same events would affect the reader. Include one example of rhythm or rhyme from the poem and one example related to the characteristics of literary ballads to support your response.

The Gift Li-Young Lee

COMPREHENSION *(60 points; 6 points each)*
On the line provided, write the letter of the *best* answer to each of the following items.

______ **1.** What causes the speaker to write this poem?

- **A** As he removes a splinter from his wife's hand, he is reminded of a time his father did the same thing for him.
- **B** Someone enters a room while he is removing a splinter from his wife's hand and surprises the speaker.
- **C** The speaker's father comes to visit him now that the speaker is an adult with a wife of his own.
- **D** As the father removes a splinter from the speaker's hand, the speaker remembers when he first met his wife.

______ **2.** This poem is based on the speaker's —

- **F** dream
- **G** research
- **H** wife
- **J** memories

______ **3.** The poem is set in —

- **A** the past with predictions about the future
- **B** the present with memories from the past
- **C** ancient China
- **D** the future

______ **4.** The literal event that the speaker focuses on throughout the poem is —

- **F** his marriage
- **G** the removal of a splinter
- **H** the death of his father
- **J** an assassination attempt with a silver spike

______ **5.** When remembering his father, the speaker thinks *mostly* about —

- **A** his father's manner
- **B** the story his father told him
- **C** the size of the sliver
- **D** the pain of the sliver

______ **6.** The father of the speaker is —

F strict

G humorous

H caring

J harmful

______ **7.** The third stanza is addressed to "you." This pronoun stands for the —

A father

B splinter

C wife

D reader

______ **8.** The speaker guesses that a viewer might think the father had planted a "silver tear" or a "tiny flame" in a boy's hand because —

F tiny flames actually rise up from the boy's palm

G the wife, who is looking on, misunderstands what is taking place

H the father uses a blade to remove the splinter from the boy's hand

J the boy's hand has liquid dripping from it

______ **9.** After the sliver is removed, the speaker does not worry because he —

A has already had an imaginary conversation with an assassin

B predicts that his father will protect him from evil spirits

C is more focused on thanking his father than feeling the pain

D is too young to understand what he feels

______ **10.** What is the gift that the title of this poem refers to?

F The speaker will know how to remove any kind of splinter for the rest of his life.

G Because the speaker has received love as a child, he now knows how to give it.

H The speaker can turn his focus to something positive and never feel physical pain.

J The speaker enjoys things made of silver that his father gave him as a boy.

LITERARY FOCUS *(20 points; 5 points each)*

On the line provided, write the letter of the *best* answer to each of the following items.

______ **11.** A **free-verse** poem —

A is written in iambic pentameter

B has no punctuation marks

C should be read using natural rhythm

D has forced end rhymes

______ **12.** The tone of "The Gift" is —

F insincere

G perplexed

H arrogant

J affectionate

______ **13.** When you read "The Gift" aloud, you should pause —

A only at the end of every line

B only between stanzas

C according to punctuation

D only after end-rhyme words

______ **14.** The stanzas in the poem are organized according to —

F ideas and subjects

G the beat and meter of lines

H patterns of rhyming words

J stressed syllables

CONSTRUCTED RESPONSE *(20 points)*

15. Read "The Gift" once again and study the way Li-Young Lee breaks lines in the poem. On a separate sheet of paper, describe how the line-break choices affect the way the poem sounds as it is read aloud. How do the line breaks affect the tone of the poem? Use an example from the poem to support your ideas.

NAME ______ CLASS ______ DATE ______ SCORE ______

SELECTION TEST **Student Edition page 473** LITERARY RESPONSE AND ANALYSIS

Legal Alien / Extranjera legal Pat Mora

COMPREHENSION *(60 points; 6 points each)*

On the line provided, write the letter of the *best* answer to each of the following items.

______ **1.** Why does this poem appear in two versions?

A Because the subject is someone who is Mexican American, the poem appears in the main language from each culture.

B The first poem poses a problem in English, and the second poem presents a solution in Spanish.

C The first version is written in a humorous tone, and the second is written in a serious tone.

D Both versions are the same, except that the second version is written in an older version of English.

______ **2.** Who is "able to slip" in the second line of the poem?

F Someone who falls in an accident

G A poet whose dreams vanish

H Someone who speaks both English and Spanish

J Someone who orders food in a Mexican restaurant

______ **3.** The term "American but hyphenated" means someone who —

A is unfamiliar with all punctuation marks

B identifies the state as well as the nation that he or she is from

C is waiting to become an American citizen

D has two cultural backgrounds, one of them American

______ **4.** The speaker in the poem uses Spanish to —

F write memos in an office

G order food in a restaurant

H avoid judging others

J write letters

______ **5.** According to the speaker, Mexican Americans are viewed by other Americans —

A as exotic

B as strange

C as inferior

D in different ways

______ **6.** Why do the lines "(their eyes say, 'You may speak / Spanish but you're not like me')" appear in parentheses?

F It is a sentence written in English, without Spanish words.

G They express someone's thoughts but not spoken words.

H It is an exotic and unusual idea that is unrelated to the rest of the poem.

J The line is written by someone other than the speaker.

______ **7.** In the experience of the speaker, both Mexicans and Americans —

A are extremely patriotic

B treat her as one of their own

C treat her as an outsider

D enjoy Mexican food

______ **8.** Of the following words used in lines 16–18, which one does not express the idea that Mexican Americans are not completely part of an American or Mexican world?

F handy

G token

H sliding

J fringes

______ **9.** To be "pre-judged / Bi-laterally" means to be judged —

A by two people who know you well

B with two standards before anyone knows you

C half now, half later by a justice in a courtroom

D as someone passes by or stops to speak with you

______ **10.** What is the speaker's opinion of people who are legal aliens in America?

F Life as a legal alien is difficult and confusing.

G Life is double the pleasure when you have two cultural traditions and languages.

H Legal aliens should chose just one language to use all of the time.

J If legal aliens learn a third language, they will have fewer problems.

LITERARY FOCUS *(20 points; 5 points each)*

On the line provided, write the letter of the *best* answer to each of the following items.

______ **11.** The **speaker** of a poem may have any of the following voices *except* that of —

A the poet

B the reader

C an animal or object

D a person who is not the poet

______ **12.** Regarding the speaker's relationship to the subject of "Legal Alien," you can conclude that the speaker —

F has eaten in a Mexican restaurant

G can write business documents

H speaks only one language

J is Mexican American

______ **13.** The tone of this poem is *mostly* —

A bored and indifferent

B frustrated and confused

C sarcastic and uncaring

D timid and reluctant

______ **14.** The Spanish phrase affects the poem's tone because the phrase —

F shows off the speaker's well-rounded education

G emphasizes the confusion of living in two cultures

H allows the speaker to come across as arrogant

J shows the speaker's lack of understanding of poetic forms

CONSTRUCTED RESPONSE *(20 points)*

15. Who do you think is the speaker of "Legal Alien / Extranjera legal"? On a separate sheet of paper, describe the characteristics of the speaker that show up in the poem. How do those characteristics connect to the poem's meaning and tone? Use two examples from the poem to support your ideas.

The Base Stealer Robert Francis
American Hero Essex Hemphill

COMPREHENSION *(60 points; 6 points each)*
On the line provided, write the letter of the *best* answer to each of the following items.

______ **1.** What situation is described in "The Base Stealer"?

A A fan runs onto a baseball field and steals a base.
B The speaker describes his past career as a baseball player.
C A baseball player is on base and about to steal the next base.
D A pitcher decides how to pitch a baseball.

______ **2.** The line "Fingertips pointing the opposites" in "The Base Stealer" refers to —

F two people standing on a baseball field
G baseball fans raising fingertips in the air
H the two bases a base stealer chooses between
J a base stealer who laughs at the other team

______ **3.** How does the speaker feel toward the player he describes in "The Base Stealer"?

A unappreciative
B admiring
C annoyed
D amused

______ **4.** Which line from "The Base Stealer" implies how the base stealer acts toward the players on the other team?

F "Poised between going on and back, pulled"
G "Fingertips pointing the opposites"
H "Running a scattering of steps sidewise"
J "Taunts them, hovers like an ecstatic bird"

______ **5.** At the end of "The Base Stealer," the —

A baseball player runs to the next base on a steal
B speaker makes a judgment about the base stealer
C fans yell in frustration at the still base stealer
D baseball stealer is compared to a bird

______ **6.** What does the speaker of "American Hero" mean when he begins the poem with the line "I have nothing to lose tonight"?

F He has already been robbed of all of his worldly possessions.

G The basketball game is over, and the speaker's team has won.

H Because he is conceited, the speaker believes he will win every contest in life.

J He feels he can never lose when he plays basketball, regardless of the score.

______ **7.** What action is *not* described in "American Hero"?

A Someone spins a basketball on his finger.

B Players sweat hard as they play basketball.

C A player jumps up and dunks the ball through the net.

D A player is called out of the game to the bench.

______ **8.** During a game, the crowd's reaction to the speaker of "American Hero" is to —

F boo him when he fails to score

G boo him when he does score

H cheer him when he scores

J ignore him when he scores

______ **9.** The speaker of "American Hero" suggests that some people in the crowd admire him only for —

A who his father is

B what he can do

C where he was born

D how he can write

______ **10.** What is the theme of "American Hero"?

F If you are an athlete, people will always treat you with respect.

G Being a sports hero doesn't stop people's prejudice against you.

H If you are a famous athlete, people will try to take advantage of you.

J Basketball is the greatest of all American team sports.

LITERARY FOCUS *(20 points; 5 points each)*

On the line provided, write the letter of the *best* answer to each of the following items.

______ **11.** Which line from "The Base Stealer" is *not* an example of **alliteration**?

A "Delicate, delicate, delicate, delicate—now!"

B "Taunts them, hovers like an ecstatic bird"

C "How he teeters, skitters, tingles, teases"

D "Running a scattering of steps sidewise"

_______ **12.** Which line is *not* an example of **simile** in "The Base Stealer"?

F "Both ways taut like a tightrope-walker"

G "Now bouncing tiptoe like a dropped ball"

H "He's only flirting, crowd him, crowd him"

J "Taunts them, hovers like an ecstatic bird"

_______ **13.** The **tone** of the speaker in "American Hero" is —

A conceited and foolish

B victorious but realistic

C stubborn but loving

D defeated and miserable

_______ **14.** In "American Hero" an example of **onomatopoeia** is the word —

F ball

G slap

H choke

J wild

CONSTRUCTED RESPONSE *(20 points)*

15. Choose one of the poems in this lesson, and study its tone. On a separate sheet of paper, describe how the speaker feels about the subject of the poem. How do the words in the poem affect the tone, especially those words used in alliteration or as onomatopoeia? How does figurative language, especially simile, also help to set the tone? Cite one example related to a sound device and one example related to figurative language to support your ideas.

NAME ____________ CLASS ____________ DATE ____________ SCORE ____________

COLLECTION 7 SUMMATIVE TEST

Poetry

This test asks you to use the skills and strategies you have learned in this collection. Read the poem "The Secret Heart," and then answer the questions that follow it.

The Secret Heart
by Robert P. Tristram Coffin

Across the years he could recall
His father one way best of all.

In the stillest hour of night
The boy awakened to a light.

Half in dreams, he saw his sire[1]
With his great hands full of fire.

The man had struck a match to see
If his son slept peacefully.

He held his palms each side the spark
His love had kindled in the dark.

His two hands were curved apart
In the semblance[2] of a heart.

He wore, it seemed to his small son,
A bare heart on his hidden one,

A heart that gave out such a glow
No son awake could bear to know.

It showed a look upon a face
Too tender for the day to trace.

One instant, it lit all about,
And then the secret heart went out.

But it shone long enough for one
To know that hands held up the sun.

1. **sire:** father.
2. **semblance:** form.

VOCABULARY SKILLS *(25 points, 5 points each)*

______ **1.** Suppose a poet wrote, "The tender horse nuzzled the boy." In this context the word *tender* means —

A gentle
B offer for someone to take
C young
D care of something

______ **2.** The word *wore* might be described by all of the following words or phrases *except* —

F fight between two or more parties
G damaged
H carried on the body
J made by the friction of rubbing or scraping

______ **3.** One meaning for the word *match* is "a stick whose tip catches fire when rubbed on a certain surface." Which line below uses this meaning of *match*?

A "The brightness of the fire was a match for his courage."
B "Could she match her wit to his intelligence?"
C "He could match fire with notions of fear but not warmth."
D "He held the match before her dark face and beheld a smile."

______ **4.** Suppose the refrain of a poem was: "The palms of their hands and the soles of their feet." In this context the word *palms* means —

F tall slender trees that grow in warm climates
G to get something sold
H parts of human anatomy
J to use trickery

______ **5.** One meaning for the word *sire* is "father." This meaning may be applied to either a man or an animal. Which line of poetry below does *not* use this meaning of *sire*?

A "The sire snapped at his scampering pups."
B "The boy saw a sire sleekly run through the field and toss its mane."
C "Simple love for his sire the boy did show daily with a hug."
D "The sire of the kingdom waved to the people as he rode past."

COMPREHENSION *(25 points; 5 points each)*

On the line provided, write the letter of the *best* answer to each of the following items.

______ **6.** The secret heart of this poem is created by —

- **F** a lit match a father holds over a sleeping son
- **G** a dream in which a sick boy gets well again
- **H** the speaker's fondness for the poem's diction
- **J** an experiment involving an artificial heart

______ **7.** The setting of the poem is a —

- **A** classroom during a science demonstration
- **B** campfire far from houses and towns
- **C** boy's room in a house at night
- **D** dreamscape the speaker has imagined

______ **8.** The tone of the poem is —

- **F** adventurous
- **G** loving
- **H** fearful
- **J** unreliable

______ **9.** What is the relationship between the boy and father?

- **A** The boy is afraid of his father, and the father ignores his son.
- **B** The boy is afraid of his father, and the father is afraid of the son.
- **C** The boy does not know how he feels about his father.
- **D** They love each other.

______ **10.** Which statement expresses the conclusion of "The Secret Heart" as it is stated in the last stanza of the poem?

- **F** The boy is safe in the father's protective and loving hands.
- **G** If young children awaken in the night, they might think that it is already day.
- **H** Love of a parent is a fading memory that slips away in the dark of night.
- **J** The boy will grow up and conduct scientific experiments involving the sun.

READING SKILLS AND STRATEGIES: CONSTRUCTED RESPONSE *(30 points; 10 points each)*

Describing Poetic Form

11. On a separate sheet of paper, describe the rhythm and any rhythmic pattern you find in "The Secret Heart."

Summarizing a Character

12. Part of the purpose of this poem is to create a memorable description of the father. What words would you use to describe this man and what he means to the boy?

___

___

Analyzing Form

13. In what ways does the pattern of stanzas and rhyme in this poem appropriately describe the father and what he means to his son?

___

___

___

___

___

LITERARY FOCUS: CONSTRUCTED RESPONSE *(20 points; 10 points each)*

14. An **extended metaphor** in "The Secret Heart" becomes clear in the lines "He wore, it seemed to his small son, / A bare heart on his hidden one." On a separate sheet of paper, briefly explain what two things are being compared in this metaphor. Then, point out another detail in the poem in which this extended metaphor is repeated or implied.

NAME ______ CLASS ______ DATE ______ SCORE ______

15. The left-hand column on the chart below shows elements of poetry that help to create a poem's tone. For each of the listed elements, the right-hand column is left blank for you to complete with examples from "The Secret Heart." In the last row of the chart, entitled "Tone," write a few words to describe the tone of "The Secret Heart."

Elements of Tone	Examples from the Poem
Diction/word choice	
Form	
Rhythm/rhyme	
Figurative language	
Voice of speaker	
Tone	

COLLECTION 8 DIAGNOSTIC TEST

LITERATURE
INFORMATIONAL TEXT
VOCABULARY

Evaluating Style

On the line provided, write the letter of the *best* answer to each of the following items. *(100 points; 10 points each)*

______ **1.** A writer's **style** includes all of the following elements *except* —

A sentence structure

B subject matter

C figures of speech

D word choice

______ **2.** In what way does the sentence *The celebration will commence at 7:00 P.M.* differ from *The party will begin at 7:00 P.M.*?

F The language in the first sentence is more formal than that of the second sentence.

G The first sentence uses technical language, but the second sentence uses slang.

H The structure of the first sentence is more poetic than that of the second sentence.

J The second sentence appeals to the reader's emotions, but the first sentence does not.

______ **3.** Describing a puppy as *playful* rather than *disobedient* suggests a **tone** that is —

A affectionate

B angry

C critical

D respectful

______ **4.** The **mood** of a literary work is —

F its hidden message

G the feeling it evokes

H the main event in the work

J its theme

______ **5.** The **image** of an empty house set in the woods creates a feeling of —

A power

B hope

C loneliness

D enthusiasm

______ **6.** What is **dialect?**

F A type of figure of speech

G A form of poetry

H The changes that occur in a character

J The way of speaking characteristic of a particular region

______ **7.** Which of the following items is *not* a type of **evidence**?

A Statistics

B Main idea

C Facts

D Expert testimony

______ **8.** What is **false cause and effect**?

F An inaccurate example that does not support an opinion

G The assumption that event A caused event B because A happened first

H A guess that is based on predictions, not facts

J An author's attempt to deceive the reader by withholding information

______ **9.** **Etymology** refers to a word's —

A spelling

B meaning

C sound

D origin

______ **10.** Which of the following synonyms has the *most* negative **connotations**?

F group

G crowd

H assembly

J mob

NAME ______ CLASS ______ DATE ______ SCORE ______

SELECTION TEST **Student Edition pages 499, 511**

A Sound of Thunder Ray Bradbury
from Jurassic Park Michael Crichton

COMPREHENSION *(40 points; 4 points each)*

On the line provided, write the letter of the *best* answer to each of the following items.

______ **1.** Eckels travels with Time Safari because he wants to —
- **A** be young again
- **B** correct past mistakes
- **C** hunt dinosaurs
- **D** learn how the time machine works

______ **2.** At the beginning of the story, what event has just occurred?
- **F** Time travel has been outlawed.
- **G** Deutscher has been elected president.
- **H** Eckels has been offered a new job.
- **J** Keith has been elected president.

______ **3.** The men who travel back in time are told they must —
- **A** stay on the safari path
- **B** not shoot animals with red paint on them
- **C** promise not to tell anyone of their adventure
- **D** maintain a strict diet a week before departure

______ **4.** When Eckels sees the tyrannosaurus, he —
- **F** immediately opens fire
- **G** runs away in a blind panic
- **H** attacks the other hunters
- **J** changes his mind about the safari

______ **5.** Travis is angry with Eckels because —
- **A** he thinks Eckels is an arrogant fool
- **B** Eckels stepped off the path
- **C** he and Eckels are old rivals
- **D** Eckels has attacked other hunters

______ **6.** In this story the future is altered because —
- **F** Travis left Eckels behind
- **G** the dinosaur was killed
- **H** the wrong man won the presidency
- **J** Eckels didn't follow instructions

______ **7.** The climax of the story occurs when —

- **A** Travis orders Eckels out of the time machine
- **B** Eckels kills a butterfly
- **C** the tree falls on the dinosaur
- **D** we learn the results of Eckels' actions

______ **8.** The words *anti-human* and *anti-intellectual* both contain the prefix *anti–*, which means —

- **F** against
- **G** all
- **H** before
- **J** never

______ **9.** What do "A Sound of Thunder" and the passage from *Jurassic Park* have in common?

- **A** Both stories feature modern people among prehistoric dinosaurs.
- **B** Both stories are written by Ray Bradbury.
- **C** In each story modern people travel through time.
- **D** In each story prehistoric dinosaurs come to life.

______ **10.** In *Jurassic Park,* what causes the situation Tim and Lex find themselves in?

- **F** They can't remember the command that stops dinosaurs in their tracks.
- **G** They don't know how to return to the present from the ancient past.
- **H** Dinosaurs that have broken free attack the car that Tim and Lex are in.
- **J** By accident the car strays inside the dinosaur-park fence.

LITERARY FOCUS *(20 points; 5 points each)*

On the line provided, write the letter of the *best* answer to each of the following items.

______ **11. Diction** is the —

- **A** main conflict in a story
- **B** choice of words in a piece of writing
- **C** mood that a story evokes
- **D** time and place a story is set

______ **12.** A story's **mood** refers to —

- **F** the events that a story's characters experience
- **G** the sentence structure the author uses
- **H** the feeling or atmosphere the story evokes
- **J** the story's genre, or the kind of literature it is

______ **13.** The mood of "A Sound of Thunder" can be described as —

A tense and frightening

B past and present

C somber and serious

D science-fiction and adventure

______ **14.** Which sentence from "A Sound of Thunder" uses diction to set the mood?

F "Thank God Keith won."

G "The jungle was wide and full of twitterings, rustlings, murmurs, and sighs."

H "They put on their oxygen helmets and tested the intercoms."

J "The guns fired."

VOCABULARY DEVELOPMENT *(20 points; 4 points each)*

Match the definition on the left with the Vocabulary word on the right. On the line provided, write the letter of the Vocablualry word.

______ **15.** destroy; wipe out

______ **16.** worth sacrificing to gain an objective

______ **17.** elastic

______ **18.** something that has or seems to have contradictory qualities

______ **19.** cancel; withdraw

a. expendable

b. paradox

c. resilient

d. revoke

e. annihilate

CONSTRUCTED RESPONSE *(20 points)*

20. How does Ray Bradbury's use of diction and figurative language add to the mood of the story? How does his style affect your understanding of the message? To support your answer, include at least two story details related to diction or figurative language.

____

____

____

____

____

____

NAME ______ CLASS ______ DATE ______ SCORE ______

SELECTION TEST **Student Edition pages 518, 521**

INFORMATIONAL READING

Rising Tides Bob Herbert
An Arctic Floe of Climate Questions Robert Cooke

COMPREHENSION *(50 points; 10 points each)*
On the line provided, write the letter of the *best* answer to each of the following items.

______ **1.** "Rising Tides" and "An Arctic Floe of Climate Questions" focus mostly on the effects of —

A the North Pole
B polynyas
C global warming
D ice shelves

______ **2.** Which statement *best* reflects the main argument in "Rising Tides"?

F As long as it's cold in New York in February, the earth is not in danger of global warming.
G People must not ignore the effects of global warming.
H Sea levels change when temperatures change.
J The United States should help developing countries that are affected by global warming.

______ **3.** All of the following details from "Rising Tides" are reasons or evidence that support Bob Herbert's main argument *except* —

A we have convinced ourselves that global warming is someone else's problem
B part of the Larsen Ice Shelf has collapsed and disappeared
C areas of permafrost have thawed
D a report states that "effects of climate change are expected to be greatest in developing countries in terms of loss of life and relative effects on investment and the economy"

______ **4.** Which statement reflects the *main* argument in "An Arctic Floe of Climate Questions"?

F Scientists state that polynyas may close when ice sheets move.
G Temperatures have risen about 3 degrees Fahrenheit in the last 150 years.
H Wind as well as temperature may affect the amount of sea ice.
J Scientists are not sure if recent weather patterns are normal or abnormal.

______ **5.** Which piece of evidence in "An Arctic Floe of Climate Questions" seems to contradict theories of global warming?

- **A** Temperatures have risen steadily in the last 150 years.
- **B** Winters are now shorter because ice on rivers and lakes freeze later and thaw sooner.
- **C** There is more ice on the pole now than there was in the 1940s and 1950s.
- **D** There is significantly less sea ice now than in 1972 when satellite observations began.

VOCABULARY DEVELOPMENT *(50 points; 10 points each)*
Write the letter of the choice that gives the *best* synonym for the Vocabulary word.

______ **6.** indiscriminate

- **F** disappointed
- **G** careless
- **H** chosen
- **J** decisive

______ **7.** ominous

- **A** threatening
- **B** hungry
- **C** capable
- **D** wild

______ **8.** catastrophic

- **F** fortunate
- **G** motionless
- **H** incomplete
- **J** disastrous

______ **9.** implications

- **A** conclusions
- **B** accomplices
- **C** rewards
- **D** absences

______ **10.** equitable

- **F** experienced
- **G** likable
- **H** fair
- **J** wrong

To Da-duh, in Memoriam

Paule Marshall

COMPREHENSION *(40 points; 4 points each)*

On the line provided, write the letter of the *best* answer to each of the following items.

______ **1.** The title of this story suggests that the author is writing about —

- **A** her grandmother's memories
- **B** someone who has died
- **C** her childhood experiences
- **D** life in the Caribbean

______ **2.** This story is set *mostly* —

- **F** on the island of Barbados in the 1930s
- **G** in New York City in the 1930s
- **H** on a farm in New York in the present
- **J** in a studio in downtown New York City

______ **3.** In addition to Da-duh, the other main character in this story is —

- **A** Da-duh's youngest daughter
- **B** the narrator's mother
- **C** Da-duh's mother
- **D** the narrator

______ **4.** The grandchildren visit Da-duh in order to —

- **F** experience life in New York City
- **G** find out who will inherit her land
- **H** meet her for the first time
- **J** learn about Caribbean culture

______ **5.** To *best* describe the narrator's first impression of Da-duh, you might say that Da-duh is a —

- **A** large woman who moves in a graceful and quick manner
- **B** middle-aged woman who speaks a strange language
- **C** thin, old woman who looks weak but serious
- **D** middle-aged woman whose eyes are dim and lifeless

______ **6.** Da-duh's first impression of the narrator is that the girl —

- **F** looks more like her father than her mother
- **G** reminds Da-duh of herself as a girl
- **H** is as tall as a royal palm tree
- **J** has a strong personality

______ **7.** On the grounds and in the gully, Da-duh and the narrator *mostly* —

A compare life in Barbados to life in New York

B have fun singing Caribbean and Tin Pan Alley songs

C talk about how they will one day grow sugar cane

D try to learn the names of the trees and plants they find

______ **8.** The narrator promises to send Da-duh a postcard of the Empire State Building because she wants —

F to assure her that the family arrived back home safely

G to give Da-duh a souvenir of her stay in New York

H to prove that the building is taller than Bissex Hill

J Da-duh to paint a picture of the Empire State Building in a cane field

______ **9.** When the British fly planes over Barbados as a show of force, Da-duh —

A asks her remaining family to move to Brooklyn

B hides in the gully until they leave

C writes the narrator a letter about the event

D watches them from her chair and then dies

______ **10.** Which statement *best* expresses the theme of "To Da-duh, in Memoriam"?

F Travel sparks creativity.

G Your family greatly influences your life.

H Heredity is destiny.

J Never give up without a fight.

LITERARY FOCUS *(20 points; 5 points each)*

On the line provided, write the letter of the *best* answer to each of the following items.

______ **11.** **Connotations** refer to a word's —

A part of speech

B shades of meaning

C dialect

D traditions

______ **12.** The story says, "The dim little limestone shops and offices along the way marched with us, at the same mournful pace, toward the same grave ceremony." Which three words in the story sentence convey the narrator's attitude?

F toward, same, along

G dim, mournful, grave

H shops, offices, ceremony

J little limestone shops

______ **13.** Which passage from the story includes a figure of speech?

A "Those eyes betrayed a child's curiosity about the world."

B "I longed then for the familiar: for the street in Brooklyn where I lived."

C "'This here is a breadfruit,' she said."

D "The name sounded like thunder fading softly in the distance."

______ **14.** Which passage from the story contains dialect?

F "It was as stark and fleshless as a death mask, that face."

G "'Yes, God is good,' Da-duh said with a nod that was like a tic."

H "You would think New York is the only place in the world to hear wunna."

J "Da-duh sat on a trunk in our midst, a monarch amid her court."

VOCABULARY DEVELOPMENT *(20 points; 4 points each)*
On the line before each sentence, write the Vocabulary word from the list that has a meaning *similar* to the italicized word or phrase in the sentence.

unrelenting **truculent** **austere** **formidable** **admonished**

______________ **15.** Walking through the tall, dense sugar cane was an *impressive, almost fearful* experience for the narrator.

______________ **16.** Da-duh *mildly scolded* her daughter for suggesting that she make bush tea.

______________ **17.** The narrator was *not letting up* about all the modern conveniences available in Brooklyn.

______________ **18.** Life in Barbados, in general, was more *plain* than life in New York.

______________ **19.** The narrator was *ready to fight* even though she was skinny and small.

CONSTRUCTED RESPONSE *(20 points)*

20. Describe Paule Marshall's writing style in terms of figurative language and diction. Use one or two examples from the story to show the effectiveness of Marshall's writing style.

NAME ______ CLASS ______ DATE ______ SCORE ______

SELECTION TEST **Student Edition pages 543, 545**

How to Eat a Guava *from* When I Was Puerto Rican Esmeralda Santiago
The Tropics in New York Claude McKay

COMPREHENSION *(60 points; 6 points each)*

On the line provided, write the letter of the *best* answer to each of the following items.

______ **1.** Why does the author write about a guava in "How to Eat a Guava"?

- **A** She is particularly fond of colorful foods.
- **B** Guavas remind her of her mother.
- **C** She wants to tell us that there will soon be no guavas left.
- **D** It is a fruit from Puerto Rico, where she grew up.

______ **2.** How do you know when a guava is ripe and ready to be eaten?

- **F** The skin turns yellow or yellow with a slight pink tint.
- **G** It falls to the ground and breaks open.
- **H** The skin turns dark green and the flesh feels hard.
- **J** It turns a bright red color.

______ **3.** The part of the guava that you are supposed to eat is the —

- **A** pink heart with seeds
- **B** flesh under the skin
- **C** thick skin and flesh
- **D** entire fruit

______ **4.** In order to eat a guava, you —

- **F** cut it in half with a knife and then dig out the seeds with a spoon
- **G** use your teeth to grip the skin and bite without touching the seeds
- **H** bite off the top of the fruit and then suck out the juices
- **J** lick the skin like a lollipop or an ice-cream cone

______ **5.** According to the author of "How to Eat a Guava," when rain falls and nights are cool, guavas —

- **A** turn dark green
- **B** fade from red to yellow
- **C** contain fewer seeds
- **D** have more seeds than usual

______ **6.** According to the author of "How to Eat a Guava," a guava that is not quite ripe will —

- **F** have a sweet taste
- **G** burst open with one small bite
- **H** contain tiny seeds that are poisonous
- **J** have a sour taste

______ **7.** Why doesn't the author of "How to Eat a Guava" buy guavas in New York City?

A They cost much too much.

B She believes that guavas are good for children, not adults.

C Guava is the fruit of her childhood, not her life as an adult.

D She prefers to buy fruit that is grown locally.

______ **8.** The first stanza of "The Tropics in New York" describes —

F fruits and other foods sold at fairs in the tropics

G the scene the speaker sees outside of a window in New York

H the speaker's childhood in the tropics

J feelings the speaker has about life in New York

______ **9.** In the second and third stanzas of "The Tropics in New York," the speaker is —

A in the tropics

B having a dream

C looking through a window

D in a store

______ **10.** From the last line of "The Tropics in New York," you learn that the speaker —

F eats well no matter where he lives

G misses his old life in the tropics

H dreams about places he might visit

J does not see as well as he once did

LITERARY FOCUS *(20 points; 5 points each)*

On the line provided, write the letter of the *best* answer to each of the following items.

______ **11.** In "How to Eat a Guava," the author says, "You hear the skin, meat, and seeds crunching inside your head, while the inside of your mouth explodes in little spurts of sour." This image appeals to the senses of —

A smell and touch

B hearing and taste

C sight and hearing

D touch and smell

______ **12.** Which word does *not* describe the tone of "How to Eat a Guava"?

F loving

G mournful

H nostalgic

J delighted

_____ **13.** Which word describes the tone of "The Tropics in New York"?

A frivolous

B lighthearted

C loving

D heartbroken

_____ **14.** The images and sensory details in "The Tropics in New York" *mostly* relate to the sense of —

F sight

G hearing

H touch

J taste

CONSTRUCTED RESPONSE *(20 points)*

15. Choose either "How to Eat a Guava" or "The Tropics in New York" and identify its theme. How do the tone and mood of the piece relate to the theme? How does the writer use figurative language to emphasize this theme? Use at least two details from the piece you selected to support your answer.

NAME CLASS DATE SCORE

COLLECTION 8 SUMMATIVE TEST

Evaluating Style

This test asks you to use the skills and strategies you have learned in this collection. Read the story "The Black Cat" by Liam O'Flaherty, and then answer the questions that follow it.

The Black Cat

by Liam O'Flaherty

Heaslip and his wife rented an old house for the summer months in the Glendara district. The house stood alone, halfway down the slope of a cone-shaped mountain. There were trees, planted close together on the north; to the south, in a gap made by a road passing through two hills, the rim of the sea could be seen at a distance. The gorse was in bloom all over the mountain side. And the cone of the mountain quite near it seemed, was caressed by sunrays that danced on the brown stones, making them sparkle like jewels. Or perhaps at dawn, just as the sun began to rise, a pale mist could be seen, like a Tudor ruff, around the neck of the cone, with its stone head already shining in the sun: a saint's halo or a king's crown.

It was very beautiful. The house was old and dilapidated, but it seemed that a house in that quarter in summer was merely a human eccentricity that one had to endure in order to abide by the conventions. The Heaslips would be delighted to live in a cowshed, in this mountain solitude, after the winter spent in the city, where everything had been stuffy, artificial and hurried. So many human beings running to and fro, quarreling, jabbering and gesticulating, in a small space where there was not room enough for one-tenth of their number to breathe.

In the city, among the multitude of human beings, there had been no repose, no dignity. Here everything had a majestic character. The mountains were kingly individuals, sprawling imperially on their primeval thrones of stone and soil. The birds were free, beautiful creatures that delighted the eye and aroused wonder in the mind; the ponderous flight of the shy heron, flying with slowly flapping heavy wings at dusk over the deep glens, where silent brutes fed in peace; the tiny saucy robins, standing on the tips of thorns, daintily heaving their chests, like manikins showing off their gorgeous array of plumage and their shapely busts. And the extraordinary volume of song that poured from their chests, through beaks that hardly seemed to open.

It seemed to the Heaslips that there was peace and beauty among this life of nature and of animals, a peace that was altogether lacking in the life of human beings. One could see the rabbits, safe from sportsmen, lying on their sides in the sun, or chasing one another around bushes. For a whole week they reveled in this peace of nature, and although they had been married three years and had quarreled almost every day in the city, here they seemed to have begun another courtship. There seemed to be nothing else to do but walk arm in arm, kiss and say sweet things to one another.

Then they became aware that the house was full of mice.

The house had been unoccupied for some time. The walls were old. The flooring was decayed. The mice had bored holes into everything, walls, floors and fireplaces. They had regular lines of approach and departure, and such was the daring developed in them by their numbers that these naturally timid animals looked curiously at a human being before running away. The servant, a raw country girl, found mice in her bed and threatened to leave if something were not done. The cheese was nibbled away. Every sort of food bore traces of their tiny feet; and although Mrs. Heaslip pointed out to the servant and to her husband that they were field mice and not in any way dangerous, both Mr. Heaslip and the servant insisted on their extermination.

"They're a damn nuisance," said Heaslip. "I don't believe in this sort of sentimentality."

"But the tiny creatures are so beautiful," said Mrs. Heaslip.

In the sitting room, which they also used as a dining room, there was a particular mouse which used that room as its own particular haunting ground. After lunch, when the Heaslips were wont to sit by the window and read, the mouse appeared every day, just about two o'clock. Twitching its little snout, it roamed about the room, making little short rushes, smelling the carpet and nibbling at everything.

"Oh, look at the little mouse," Mrs. Heaslip would say, with a delighted smile. "There's our tiny little mouseen. Oh, dear! What a pretty little weeny thing!"

"Horrible!" grunted Mr. Heaslip. "Wait, I'll get the poker!"

"No. Please don't," said Mrs. Heaslip. "I love him. It's doing no harm."

And the little mouse, rushing back to its hole at every sound, pottered about the room, picking up crumbs.

The most extraordinary thing was that, although the Heaslips had a cat, the cat never interfered with the mice. Seeing one, it shrugged itself and then watched the little animal with bored interest. It had been reared in the city, pampered and civilized by constant petting and good treatment.

Being <u>inured</u> to receiving its food regularly since the day it was born, waited upon, brushed and kept warm, it had lost all its primitive instincts. The struggle for existence meant nothing to it. It was as <u>innocuous</u> as an old maiden lady with a fixed income.

At last, however, even Mrs. Heaslip had to consent to the destruction of the mice. It was impossible to live in the house with them. She had a choice of two courses of action. Either to evacuate the house or cause the mice to evacuate it. They thought of traps.

"No," said Mr. Heaslip. "I don't like traps. They're cruel. A good cat is what we need. A cat kills a mouse without any pain. At least as painlessly as possible. It's its natural way of earning a living."

"Very well," said Mrs. Heaslip.

They got a black cat from an old lady who lived near.

"Do please be kind to it," said the old lady. "I saved it from a horrible boy that was going to drown it. I'd keep it myself but I have already seven cats and nine dogs."

They promised to be kind to the animal and brought it home in a basket. On the way home, when Mrs. Heaslip looked into the basket to pet the new cat, she saw two flaring eyes and heard a savage hiss, then the sound of spitting.

"Ah!" said Mr. Heaslip. "I believe we have the right animal at last."

VOCABULARY SKILLS *(25 points; 5 points each)*

On the line provided, write the letter of the *best* answer to each of the following items.

______ **1.** Which word has a connotation closest to that of *dilapidated*?

A dignified
B collapsed
C elevated
D shrunk

______ **2.** The word *primeval* means "of the first or earliest ages." In this word the Latin root meaning "first" is —

F *–pri–*
G *–rim–*
H *–imev–*
J *–eval–*

______ **3.** The prefix *in–* means "not." The word *innocuous* means —

A full of harm
B repeated harm
C endless harm
D without harm

______ **4.** If you are *inured* to something, you are —

F hardened to it
G familiar with it
H interested in it
J friendly to it

______ **5.** When someone has *reveled* in something, that person has had an experience that he or she has —

A refused
B enjoyed
C ignored
D denied

COMPREHENSION *(25 points; 5 points each)*

On the line provided, write the letter of the *best* answer to each of the following items.

______ **6.** Compared with the city, the Heaslips see the countryside as —

F boring and dull

G peaceful and spacious

H built up and congested

J demanding and unappealing

______ **7.** The move to Glendora affects the relationship between Mr. and Mrs. Heaslip by making them —

A more loving and compatible with each other

B more willing to share their opinions with each other

C colder and less friendly with each other

D less interested in the same activities

______ **8.** Which of the following situations most affects the Heaslips' summer in the old house?

F Their neighbor owns too many pets.

G They find a black cat in a basket.

H Mice live in the house.

J A cat catches a mouse in the sitting room.

______ **9.** To resolve their problem, the Heaslips —

A search for a new residence in Glendora

B adopt a cat from an old lady that lives nearby

C train their cat to hunt for its own food

D pack their bags and move back to the city

______ **10.** Why does Mr. Heaslip say at the end of this selection, "I believe we have the right animal at last"?

F Mrs. Heaslip falls in love with the new kitten immediately.

G The Heaslip's pet cat chases the small kitten for sport.

H The new cat is wild, so it will kill for food and survival.

J The kitten seems to be happy as long as the Heaslips are together.

Reading Skills and Strategies: Constructed Response *(10 points)*

Comparing and Contrasting

11. As O'Flaherty makes quite clear, life in the city is very different from life in the country. Briefly list some of the qualities that distinguish the two environments.

City	Country
______________________	______________________
______________________	______________________
______________________	______________________
______________________	______________________

Literary Focus: Constructed Response *(40 points; 10 points each)*

12. Choose one figure of speech from the beginning and one from the end of "The Black Cat." How does each figure of speech affect the mood, or emotional atmosphere, the author evokes in the story? How does the mood change from the beginning to the end of "The Black Cat"?

____

____

____

____

____

____

____

____

NAME ______ CLASS ______ DATE ______ SCORE ______

13. On a separate sheet of paper, describe the writing **style** of the author of "The Black Cat." Support your idea with at least two examples related to the diction or sentence structure of the story.

14. If tone is the writer's attitude, what **tone** does Liam O'Flaherty express through his characters and subject? How does the tone connect to the plot or theme of the story? Use a separate sheet of paper to answer this question.

15. Fill in the chart for each element of style that appears in the first column. Describe how the author treats each element and, if possible, supply an example from the story.

Elements of Style	Description / Example
Diction	
Sentence structure	
Tone	
Mood	

NAME ______ CLASS ______ DATE ______ SCORE ______

COLLECTION 9 DIAGNOSTIC TEST

LITERATURE
INFORMATIONAL TEXT
VOCABULARY

Biographical and Historical Approach

On the line provided, write the letter of the *best* answer to each of the following items. *(100 points; 10 points each)*

______ **1.** Writers would be *least* likely to draw on their own lives when —

A choosing the setting of a story

B creating characters

C determining the theme of a story

D selecting an appropriate length for a work

______ **2.** If you were a writer who traveled to Oregon in a covered wagon during the 1800s, your writing would *most* likely include —

F fewer symbols than similes

G language related to computer technology

H the attitude of people who settled the American West

J an opinion about the American Revolution

______ **3.** Which of the following sentences would *most* likely express the **theme** of a story based on events during World War II?

A War can change the lives of both soldiers and citizens.

B Airplanes have become much more sophisticated since World War II.

C Many people who lived during World War II are no longer alive.

D No one knows when another war will occur.

______ **4.** Which of the following statements about the **title** of a story is *false*?

F A title may sometimes reflect the theme of a work.

G A writer's choice of a title may be influenced by the setting of a story.

H A title may reveal something about a character in a story.

J Titles of stories have only literal meanings.

______ **5.** What is **conflict**?

A A battle of wills with no resolution

B A struggle or clash between opposing characters or forces

C The moment of greatest suspense in a plot

D A method of characterization

______ **6.** Which of the following texts is a **primary source**?

- **F** Diary
- **G** Reference book
- **H** History book
- **J** Encyclopedia article

______ **7.** One way to verify that the **facts** in a source are accurate is to —

- **A** compile a bibliography
- **B** check other sources
- **C** decide whether the author's tone suits the subject
- **D** determine the main idea of the work

______ **8.** An **opinion** is a —

- **F** story based on personal experience
- **G** quotation used as evidence
- **H** belief or idea that cannot be proved to be true or false
- **J** prediction based on facts

______ **9.** Which of the following items is *not* a relationship typically found in a **word analogy**?

- **A** Time and place
- **B** Synonyms
- **C** Cause and effect
- **D** Part to whole

______ **10.** What is **technical vocabulary**?

- **F** Common word roots
- **G** Specialized words used in certain professions
- **H** Frequently used words
- **J** Words that relate to the study of languages

NAME ______ CLASS ______ DATE ______ SCORE ______

SELECTION TEST **Student Edition pages 565, 573** LITERARY RESPONSE AND ANALYSIS

American History Judith Ortiz Cofer

Volar Judith Ortiz Cofer

COMPREHENSION *(40 points; 4 points each)*

On the line provided, write the letter of the *best* answer to each of the following items.

______ **1** "American History" is a story about a girl who —

- **A** is trying to make friends with everyone in her neighborhood
- **B** enrolls in a history class and discovers her life's calling
- **C** learns about barriers to friendship that are beyond her control
- **D** is totally devastated by the death of President John F. Kennedy

______ **2.** Elena felt she knew Eugene before she actually met him because she —

- **F** had been reading *Gone with the Wind*, which takes place in Georgia
- **G** had watched his house from her fire escape during the summer
- **H** knew the people who had previously lived in Eugene's house
- **J** asked her classmates about him

______ **3.** Elena experiences prejudice firsthand when —

- **A** the girls on the playground tell her to turn the rope harder and faster
- **B** Mr. DePalma tells the class about President Kennedy's assassination
- **C** Eugene's mother tells her that Eugene cannot study with her
- **D** she introduces herself to Eugene

______ **4.** Which of the following statements about Eugene's mother is *true*?

- **F** She pretends that she is not prejudiced against the people in El Building.
- **G** She has taught her son not to be embarrassed by his Georgia accent.
- **H** Her plan is to stay in Paterson forever because she does not miss Georgia.
- **J** The death of the president does not make her feel distraught.

______ **5.** Which of the following statements about Elena's mother is *true*?

- **A** She wants to retire to a house in California.
- **B** She predicts what happens between Elena and Eugene's mother.
- **C** She always trusts Elena to choose the right path.
- **D** Her warning keeps Elena from being hurt by Eugene's mother.

______ **6.** On the day President John F. Kennedy is assassinated, Elena's parents stay up late discussing —

- **F** their hopes and dreams for a better future
- **G** the sorrow of the president's family
- **H** how to cheer up Elena after Eugene's mother rejects her
- **J** how to explain the children's friendship to Eugene's mother

______ **7.** Mr. DePalma handles the unruly students by —

A giving all of them one month of detention

B explaining to them what happened

C asking other teachers for help in disciplining them

D yelling at them and telling them that they are losers

______ **8.** Which of the following statements *best* expresses one possible theme of this story?

F Where we live is not always a true representation of who we are.

G Be kind to strangers because they might do you a good turn one day.

H Enjoy today because tomorrow may never come.

J Prejudice often occurs when people are upset about political events.

______ **9.** The information presented in "Volar" is —

A fictional

B biographical

C autobiographical

D historical

______ **10.** The narrator of "Volar" admires —

F her mother

G Supergirl

H her father

J rich people

LITERARY FOCUS *(20 points; 5 points each)*

On the line provided, write the letter of the *best* answer to each of the following items.

______ **11.** All of the following details are historical references in "American History" *except* —

A popular fashions of the early 1960s

B the assassination of President John F. Kennedy

C the situation of Puerto Rican immigrants in Paterson, New Jersey

D Eugene's mother works at St. Joseph's Hospital

______ **12.** All of the following details in "American History" are based on details similar to those in "Volar" *except* —

F living in El Building in Paterson, New Jersey

G being Puerto Rican

H having a father who works hard

J having a mother who warns her to behave properly

______ **13.** What is a difference between Elena and the narrator of "Volar"?

A Elena is older than the narrator of "Volar."

B Elena gets good grades; the narrator of "Volar" doesn't.

C The narrator of "Volar" is more serious than Elena.

D The narrator of "Volar" has a boyfriend, but Elena doesn't.

______ **14.** The mother in "Volar" —

F is unhappy living in America

G doesn't understand her husband

H has the same dream as her daughter

J likes to read *Supergirl* comic books

VOCABULARY DEVELOPMENT *(20 points; 4 points each)*
On the line before each sentence, write the Vocabulary word that has a meaning *similar* to the italicized word or phrase in the sentence.

literally **infatuated** **vigilant** **enthralled** **solace**

______ **15.** From her perch on the fire escape of El Building, Elena is *fascinated* by what happens in Eugene's kitchen.

______ **16.** The other girls tease Elena with their refrain until she *actually* cannot coordinate the jump-rope with Gail.

______ **17.** Elena returns home to an empty apartment, where there is no one to give her *comfort.*

______ **18.** Elena is *foolishly in love with* Eugene and can't wait until the next time she sees him.

______ **19.** Mr. DePalma is put in charge of all the troublemakers because he is a *watchful* coach.

NAME CLASS DATE SCORE

CONSTRUCTED RESPONSE *(20 points)*

20. Through the author's use of details and imagery, El Building seems like a character in the story. A similar building also appears in "Volar." Explain the significance of El Building in "American History," and relate El Building to what you learn about the author in "Volar."

NAME ______ CLASS ______ DATE ______ SCORE ______

SELECTION TEST **Student Edition pages 580, 584, 586** **INFORMATIONAL READING**

A Warm, Clear Day in Dallas *from* John F. Kennedy Marta Randall

Address to Congress, November 27, 1963

Lyndon B. Johnson

Students React to President Kennedy's Death

from Children and the Death of a President

COMPREHENSION *(50 points; 10 points each)*

On the line provided, write the letter of the *best* answer to each of the following items.

______ **1.** The author's purpose in writing "A Warm, Clear Day in Dallas" is to —

A inform readers about the assassination of President Kennedy in 1963

B persuade readers that Lee Harvey Oswald acted alone

C inform readers that the assassination of President Kennedy was a conspiracy

D entertain readers with the tragic death of President Kennedy

______ **2.** The words spoken by Jimmy Carter in "A Warm, Clear Day in Dallas"—

F are a monologue

G serve as a primary source

H serve as a secondary source

J were created by a writer of a history textbook

______ **3.** What is the main idea of Johnson's address to Congress?

A President Johnson was saddened by the death of President Kennedy.

B The people listening to President Johnson's speech were all the members of Congress.

C President Johnson wanted the ideas of President Kennedy to continue.

D As of 1963, passage of a civil rights bill was already one hundred years too late.

______ **4.** Which is the *best* evaluation of "Students React to President Kennedy's Death"?

F The fact that a sixth-grade math class had its math test discontinued shows that teachers were more upset than students by the assassination of President Kennedy.

G Opinions of students about the assassination of President Kennedy help readers understand what it was like to experience November 23, 1963.

H Not everyone was saddened by the news of President Kennedy's death, and some people wrote about the event less sympathetically than others.

J Even though some students did not correct errors in their writing in the 1960s, their feelings are still understood by readers today.

______ **5.** Of the pieces of literature in this selection, information from a secondary source appears in —

A "A Warm, Clear Day in Dallas"

B "Address to Congress, November, 1963" and "Students React to President Kennedy's Death"

C "Address to Congress, November, 1963"

D all of the selections

VOCABULARY DEVELOPMENT *(50 points; 10 points each)*

Write the letter of the choice that *best* explains a difference between the two words.

______ **6.** The difference between *denouncing* and *announcing* is that *denouncing* —

F condemns while *announcing* tells

G forgives while *announcing* blames

H tells while *announcing* repeats

J is said at a lower volume than *announcing*

______ **7.** The difference between *controversial* and *contradict* is that *controversial* —

A is something that has been removed while *contradict* is the action of disagreeing

B represents a change of mind while *contradict* represents a bad feeling

C is the announcement of an opinion while *contradict* is the announcement of a fact

D is a topic that people disagree about while *contradict* means "oppose"

______ **8.** The difference between *conspiracy* and *idea* is that a *conspiracy* —

F is a secret plan while an *idea* is a good plan

G makes people disagree while an *idea* makes people agree

H blames people while an *idea* supports people

J is a secret plan while an *idea* is a thought

______ **9.** The difference between *resolve* and *wish* is that *resolve* —

A removes something while a *wish* adds something

B expresses something sad while *wish* expresses something happy

C expresses determination while *wish* expresses desire

D is the act of forgetting while a *wish* is a thought you remember

______ **10.** The difference between *defiant* and *cooperative* is that *defiant* —

F is to boldly resist while *cooperative* is a willingness to work together

G expresses agreement while *cooperative* expresses disagreement

H reveals a secret while *cooperative* tells of open communications

J is something governments do while *cooperative* is something individuals do

Beware of the Dog Roald Dahl
Wounded and Trapped Ernie Pyle

COMPREHENSION *(40 points; 4 points each)*
On the line provided, write the letter of the *best* answer to each of the following items.

______ **1.** The circumstance that creates the main conflict in "Beware of the Dog" centers on a pilot who —

A is unsure of his location as he awakens over the English Channel
B is joking with his squadron members about his wounded leg
C speaks English in a place where most people speak French
D parachutes from his plane after being shot down by enemy gunfire

______ **2.** The pilot's reaction to his situation during the story goes from —

F indifference to frustration
G upset to anger
H calm to nervousness
J nervousness to calm

______ **3.** When the pilot describes a world that turns "from white to black, then back to white again," he is referring to —

A facing the clouds, which are all white, and then facing the dark English Channel
B a world full of good people and evil people
C being awake and aware of himself and then losing consciousness
D the difference between the English and French languages

______ **4.** According to the pilot, he awakens —

F in a field in an unknown country, with his leg blown off
G to the company of his squadron members
H as his parachute opens and he floats through the white clouds to safety
J in a hospital in Brighton, England, with his leg amputated

______ **5.** What bothers the pilot about the sound of a Junkers 88 is that —

A it reminds him of his own plane, which he crash-landed
B it is like that of the plane the Germans use to bomb England
C two engines are heard even though the plane usually uses just one engine
D it is like that of the most common plane in the U.S. Air Force

______ **6.** Suspense in the story builds rapidly up to the point when the pilot —
- **F** can no longer find the fly on the ceiling that he has been following for days
- **G** reads a sign in French and realizes he has landed behind enemy lines
- **H** decides to get out of bed and walk to the window on only one leg
- **J** hears the Junkers 88 but learns from his nurse that no bombs are being dropped

______ **7.** Which of the following events is *not* a clue to the true situation the pilot is in?
- **A** The water is so hard that soap will not lather.
- **B** The pilot recognizes the kind of plane flying overhead as enemy aircraft.
- **C** A sign in front of a farmhouse reads, "*Garde au chien.*"
- **D** The nurse offers to bring him another egg for breakfast if he rings the bell.

______ **8.** By the end of the story, the pilot realizes that he —
- **F** wants to rejoin his squadron
- **G** can joke about his serious injuries
- **H** appreciates the nurses' efforts to help him
- **J** has become a prisoner of war

______ **9.** The pilot in "Beware of the Dog" is worried that —
- **A** his injuries affected his mind as well as his body
- **B** his parachute will tangle and not open
- **C** the British have invaded France
- **D** the nurse will not change his bed sheets

______ **10.** What shocks the Americans *most* about the British pilot in "Wounded and Trapped" is the pilot's —
- **F** terrible injuries
- **G** lack of complaint
- **H** destroyed airplane
- **J** happiness

NAME ______________________ CLASS ______________________ DATE ______________ SCORE ______________

LITERARY FOCUS *(20 points; 5 points each)*

On the line provided, write the letter of the *best* answer to each of the following items.

______ **11.** The setting of "Beware of the Dog" is —

- **A** Brighton, England, shortly after World War II ends on September 2, 1945
- **B** an unknown country at some time during the twentieth century
- **C** somewhere in France during the Battle of Britain
- **D** within the cockpit of an airplane as it flies over the English Channel

______ **12.** Both "Wounded and Trapped" and "Beware of the Dog" focus on —

- **F** British pilots shot down during World War II battles
- **G** fields in France where battles of World War II were fought
- **H** British soldiers who worked with Americans during World War II
- **J** people who use humor to deal with tragedy

______ **13.** In "Wounded and Trapped" and "Beware of the Dog," you learn that during World War II Britain and America were —

- **A** enemies
- **B** allies
- **C** hero worshipers
- **D** the only countries with pilots

______ **14.** In "Beware of the Dog," what do you learn about the relationship between the British and the French during World War II?

- **F** Britain didn't like France, but the French cared for wounded British soldiers.
- **G** They were enemies while Germany occupied France.
- **H** They were allies who fought against Germany and Russia.
- **J** The British liked the French, but the French didn't like the British as much.

NAME ______________________ CLASS ______________________ DATE ______________ SCORE ______________

VOCABULARY DEVELOPMENT *(20 points; 4 points each)*
Match each definition on the left with a Vocabulary word on the right. On the line provided, write the letter of the Vocabulary word.

______ **15.** pulled up; lifted	**a.** undulating
______ **16.** without aim	**b.** giddy
______ **17.** moving in waves	**c.** idly
______ **18.** dizzy	**d.** delirious
______ **19.** temporarily confused and seeing imaginary things	**e.** hoisted

CONSTRUCTED RESPONSE *(20 points)*

20. Describe how a British pilot would *most* likely feel about Americans, the French, and Germans during World War II. Use the information you learn directly from "Beware of the Dog" and "Wounded and Trapped," or make inferences. Cite at least two details from the story or war report to support your ideas.

____

____

____

____

____

____

____

____

____

____

NAME ____________ CLASS ____________ DATE ____________ SCORE ____________

COLLECTION 9 SUMMATIVE TEST

Biographical and Historical Approach

This test asks you to use the skills and strategies you have learned in this collection. Read this excerpt from the television play *Thunder on Sycamore Street* by Reginald Rose, and then answer the questions that follow it.

FROM Thunder on Sycamore Street
by Reginald Rose

Frank (*to* CLARICE). Where's that sitter?
Clarice. It's not time yet. Take it easy, Frank.

[FRANK *gets up from the table, goes over to a box of cigars on top of the TV set, and lights one.* CLARICE *and* ROGER *watch him silently.*]

Clarice. Aren't you going to have some dessert, Frank? There's some cherry pie left.
Frank. I'll have it later.

[*He puffs on the cigar.*]

Roger (*low*). I'm sorry, Dad.
Frank (*turning*). Well, it's about time you learned some respect, d'you hear me? If I want you to know something, I'll tell it to you.
Roger (*softly*). OK . . .
Clarice (quickly). Have some pie, honey. I heated it special.

[FRANK *goes to the table and sits down. He puts the cigar down, and* CLARICE *begins to cut him some pie.*]

Clarice. How late do you think we'll be, Frank?
Frank. I don't know.
Clarice. Do you think I ought to pack a thermos of hot coffee? It's going to be chilly.
Frank. Might not be a bad idea.

[FRANK *now begins to show the first signs of being excited about the evening. He speaks, almost to himself.*]

Frank. Boy, I can't wait till I see his face. The nerve of him. The absolute nerve. (*Grinning*) What d'you think he'll do when we all—
Clarice (*looking at* ROGER). Frank . . .
Frank (*as* ROGER *stares*). Oh, yeah, go ahead, Rog. You can turn on your program.
Roger. Gee thanks, Dad.

[*He jumps up, goes to the TV set and turns it on.* FRANK *and* CLARICE *watch him get settled in front of TV set. We hear dialogue from set faintly.* ROGER *watches in background, enraptured.*]

Frank (*quietly*). What are they saying on the block?
Clarice. I didn't speak to anyone. I was ironing all day.
Frank. Charlie Denton called me at the office. I was right in the middle of taking an order from Martin Brothers for three A-81 tractors.

Clarice. Three! Frank, that's *wonderful*!
Frank. Not bad. Anyway, I made Mr. Martin wait while I spoke to Charlie. Charlie says it's gonna be one hundred percent. Every family on the block. He just called to tell me that.
Clarice. Well, that's good. Everyone should be in on this.
Frank (*eating*). Clarry, I'm telling you this is going to be a job well done. It's how you have to do these things. Everybody getting together first . . . and boom, it's over. I can't wait till it's started. It's been long enough.
Clarice. I saw her out the window today, hanging clothes in her yard like nothing was wrong. She didn't even look this way.
Frank. What time is it?
Clarice. Now you just asked me two minutes ago. It's about three minutes to seven. What's the matter with you? You'll be getting yourself an ulcer over this thing. Relax, Frank. Here, have some more pie.
Frank. No, no more.

[*He gets up and walks around nervously, slapping his fist into his palm.* ROGER *is looking at him now. He is tense, excited, completely caught up in the impending event.*]

Frank. This is something big, you know that, Clarry? We're getting action without pussy-footing for once. That's it. That's the big part. There's too much pussyfooting going on all the time. Can't hurt anyone's feelings. Every time you turn around you're hurting some idiot's feelings. Well that's tough, I say. . . .
Clarice (*indicating* ROGER). Frank . . .
Frank. He can hear! He's old enough. You want something bad, you gotta go out and get it! That's how this world is. Boy, I like this, Clarry. You know what it makes me feel like? It makes me feel like a man!

[*He stalks up and down the room for a few moments as they watch him. Then he goes to the window and stands there looking out.*]

Clarice (*quietly*). I think I'll just stack the dishes.

[*She starts to do it. The doorbell rings.* ROGER *jumps up.*]

Roger. I'll get it.

[*He goes to the door and opens it.* ARTHUR HAYES *stands there a bit apologetically. He wears no overcoat, having just come from next door. He looks extremely upset.*]

Arthur. Rog, is your dad in?
Roger. Sure. Come on in, Mr. Hayes.

[ARTHUR *walks in slowly.* FRANK *turns around, still excited. He goes over to* ARTHUR.]

Frank (*loud*). Hey, Artie. Come on in.
Arthur. Hello, Frank . . .
Frank (*laughing*). What can I do for you? (ARTHUR *looks hesitatingly at* ROGER.) Oh, sure. Rog, go help your mother.

Roger (*annoyed*). Okay . . .

[*He walks off to dining table.*]

Frank (*chuckling*). That's some kid, isn't he, Artie? How old is yours now?
Arthur. Twenty-one months.
Frank. Yeah. Well that's still nothing but a crying machine. Wait a couple of years. He'll kill you.
Arthur. I guess so.
Frank. And how! Sit down for a minute, Artie. What's on your mind?
Arthur (*sitting. Hesitantly*). Well, I don't know. . . . I just . . . well . . . I just wanted . . . to talk.
Frank. No kidding. Say, y'know you look a little green around the gills? What's the matter?

[ARTHUR *takes off his eyeglasses and begins to polish them, a nervous habit in which he indulges when upset.*]

Arthur. Nothing. I've had an upset stomach for a couple of days. Maybe that's it.
Frank (*nodding*). Yeah, that'll get you down all right. Probably a virus.

[ARTHUR *nods and they look at each other awkwardly for a moment.*]

Frank. Well, what did you want to talk about?

[ARTHUR *looks at the floor, trying to frame his answer carefully, afraid to offend. Finally he blurts it out.*]

Arthur. What do you think about this thing tonight?
Frank (*surprised*). What do you mean what do I think about it?
Arthur. Well, I've been kind of going over it all day, Frank. I talked with Phyllis before.
Frank (*a little hard*). And . . .
Arthur. Well, it was just talk. We were just talking it over to get clear on it, you know.
Frank. Go ahead.
Arthur. And . . . well, look, Frank, it's a pretty hard thing. Supposing it were you?
Frank. It's not.
Arthur. Well, I know that, but supposing it were?

[FRANK *stands up and goes over to* ARTHUR.]

Frank. Your glasses are clean. You wear 'em out, you have to buy a new pair. (ARTHUR *looks down at his glasses, then puts them on nervously.*) Now what about it, Artie? What if I was the guy?
Arthur. Well, you know . . . how would you feel?
Frank. How would I feel, huh? Now that's a good question, Artie. I'll answer it for you. It doesn't make any difference how I'd feel. Now let me ask you a question. Is he a lifelong buddy of yours?
Arthur. Well, now, you know he's not, Frank.
Frank. Do you know him to say hello to?
Arthur. That's not the idea. He's—
Frank. Artie . . . you don't even know the guy. What are you getting yourself all hot and bothered about? We all agreed, didn't we?

Arthur. Yes . . . everybody agreed.
Frank. You. Me. The Dentons. The McAllisters. The Fredericks. The Schofields. Every family on Sycamore Street for that matter. We all agreed. That's how it is. The majority. Right?
Arthur. Well . . . I think we all ought to talk it over, maybe. Let it wait a few days.

[*He takes off his glasses again and begins to wipe them.*]

Frank. Artie . . . we talked it over. (FRANK *takes the handkerchief out of* ARTHUR'S *hand and tucks it into his pocket.*) In about ten minutes we're starting. We expect to have a solid front, you know what I mean? Everybody. You included. You're my next-door neighbor, boy. I don't want to hear people saying Artie Hayes wasn't there.
Arthur (*hesitantly*). Well, I don't know, Frank. I thought —

[*The phone rings.* FRANK *goes toward it.*]

Frank. Go home. Artie. Don't worry about it. I'll see you in a few minutes. (FRANK *goes to the phone and picks it up.* ARTHUR *stares at him.*) Hello . . . (ARTHUR *turns away and walks slowly to door.*) Speaking.

[ARTHUR *goes out, dazed and frightened.* CLARICE *comes into living room and stands waiting as* FRANK *listens to phone.*]

Frank (*angry*). What do you mean you can't get here? (*Pause*) Well, this is a great time to call! (*Pause*) I know. Yeah. (*He slams the phone down. To* CLARICE.) Our sitter can't get here. How d'you like that?
Clarice. What's wrong with her?
Frank. I don't know. She's got a cold, or something. Nice dependable girl you pick.
Clarice (*snapping*). Well, I didn't exactly arrange for her to get a cold, you know.
Frank. Look, Clarry, we're going to this thing no matter what.
Clarice. Well, I'm not leaving Chris with Roger. They'll claw each other to pieces.
Frank. Then we'll take them with us.
Clarice. You wouldn't . . .
Frank. Who wouldn't? We're doing it for them as much as anyone else, aren't we? Well, they might as well see it.
Clarice. Maybe I'd better stay home with them.
Frank. No, sir. You've been in on this from the beginning. You're going. Come on, get Chris dressed. We haven't got much time.
Clarice. Well . . . whatever you think, Frank . . .
Frank. I'm telling you it's all right. Won't hurt 'em a bit. (To ROGER) What d'you say, son? Want to come along?
Roger (*eagerly*). Oh, boy! Really? (FRANK *nods and grins.* ROGER *leaps happily.*) Gee, Dad, you're the greatest guy in all the whole world.

[*He runs over and hugs* FRANK.]

VOCABULARY SKILLS *(30 points; 6 points each]*

On the line provided, write the letter of the *best* answer to each of the following items.

______ **1.** An impending event is one that is —

- **A** unpleasant
- **B** frightful
- **C** about to happen
- **D** from the past

______ **2.** When Frank stalks, we know he is feeling —

- **F** hungry
- **G** happy
- **H** depressed
- **J** impatient

______ **3.** When Arthur speaks hesitantly, we can tell he is —

- **A** ill
- **B** uncertain
- **C** friendly
- **D** tired

______ **4.** Having a solid front means the neighbors —

- **F** are working in agreement
- **G** all live on the same street
- **H** will all walk together
- **J** all know one another

______ **5.** When Frank sarcastically calls the sitter dependable, we know he thinks she is not —

- **A** healthy
- **B** qualified
- **C** reliable
- **D** immature

COMPREHENSION *(30 points; 6 points each)*

On the line provided, write the letter of the *best* answer to each of the following items.

______ **6.** Clarice tries to soothe Frank by —

- **F** getting him to talk about work
- **G** convincing him to watch TV
- **H** serving him some cherry pie
- **J** talking about the other family

______ **7.** We *first* sense that something out of the ordinary is going on when —

- **A** Frank asks what other people are saying
- **B** Roger is allowed to turn on the TV
- **C** Frank announces that he sold three tractors
- **D** Arthur comes over to talk

______ **8.** Frank is tense and excited because —

- **F** he made a big sale at work that day
- **G** a big event is about to happen
- **H** Arthur is trying to stand up to him
- **J** the sitter calls to cancel

______ **9.** The main antagonist to the other characters within this excerpt is —

- **A** Frank
- **B** Arthur
- **C** Clarice
- **D** the other family

______ **10.** In this excerpt the chief conflict occurs between —

- **F** Roger and Frank
- **G** Frank and the other family
- **H** Frank and Clarice
- **J** Frank and Arthur

READING SKILLS AND STRATEGIES: CONSTRUCTED RESPONSE *(10 points)*

Using Prior Knowledge

11. Reginald Rose wrote this play to appeal to a wide audience. To accomplish this goal, he included many details that most people could identify with. In addition, he used the informal language of a family to help create a familiar atmosphere. Briefly identify some of these common, everyday details about life in the twentieth century.

Food: ______________________________

Technology: ______________________________

Activities: ______________________________

Language: ______________________________

Other: ______________________________

LITERARY FOCUS: CONSTRUCTED RESPONSE *(30 points; 10 points each)*

12. The **historical approach** considers how the events and attitudes of the time in which a play is written affect the characters and events as well as the play's message or theme. *Thunder on Sycamore Street* was written as a television play in 1956. At the time one of the most serious problems facing the United States was racism and discrimination. (The civil rights laws that President John F. Kennedy first proposed when he came to office in 1963 would not be passed until 1965, when Lyndon B. Johnson was president.)

Now, think about the conflict in this excerpt from *Thunder on Sycamore Street,* and relate it to the events of the historical period of 1956 in the United States. Choose what you believe is the *strongest* statement of the conflict. On the lines below, write the letter of the answer you choose, and briefly defend your choice. Use at least one example from the selection to support your ideas.

A Frank wants Arthur to become a calmer, more agreeable neighbor.

B Frank and Clarice may not be able to attend a big event because of a sick baby sitter.

C Arthur has second thoughts about a neighborhood event and expresses those thoughts to Frank.

D The neighborhood families want everyone in the area to join together in a big event.

13. When Reginald Rose presented his play to CBS in 1956, the television network decided to put the play on the air but requested a change. At first, Rose based the conflict of *Thunder on Sycamore Street* on a newspaper story about a Chicago suburb. The report stated that people of this white suburb organized in order to force from their neighborhood an African American family that had recently moved in. The television network had Rose remove any clue to the ethnic or racial identity of the family. Rose, instead, identified the family as one headed by an ex-convict who had turned his life around.

Now, use the **biographical approach** to think about how an author's biography might influence ideas within a play. How does the writer's attitude affect the way a conflict is presented in a play? How might this excerpt from *Thunder on Sycamore Street* have been different if it had been written by someone strongly against the principles of civil rights and integration in 1956 (nine years before civil rights laws were passed in the United States)? Use at least one detail from the excerpt to support your idea.

NAME ______ CLASS ______ DATE ______ SCORE ______

14. Now you have some understanding of the **historical** and **biographical influences** of *Thunder on Sycamore Street* by Reginald Rose. What do you think the theme of the play is? At the center of the theme web, write a sentence that identifies the theme. Then, complete the web with details from the play that relate to its theme and historical and biographical influences.

Theme

______
______
______
______

Biographical Influence

______
______
______
______

Historical Influence

______
______
______
______

NAME ______ CLASS ______ DATE ______ SCORE ______

COLLECTION 10 DIAGNOSTIC TEST

Epic and Myth

LITERATURE
INFORMATIONAL TEXT
VOCABULARY

On the line provided, write the letter of the *best* answer to each of the following items. *(100 points; 10 points each)*

______ **1.** An **epic** is —

A an account of a person's life written by another person

B a long narrative poem that tells about the adventures of a hero

C a novel that describes several generations of a family

D a literary work set in a particular historical period and based on true events

______ **2.** What are **myths**?

F Traditional stories, rooted in a particular culture, that explain something about the world

G Stories in which the characters are animals who represent human beings

H Short comic stories that are told for entertainment

J Stories that teach a lesson by showing why characters succeed or fail

______ **3.** Characters who face **external conflicts** —

A help others resolve their difficulties

B have only minor problems

C remain unaffected by the central problem in a story

D struggle against other characters or outside forces

______ **4.** What characters say and do —

F creates the setting of a story

G reveals their personalities

H does not contribute to a story's plot

J determines who is telling the story

______ **5.** A figure of speech that compares two dissimilar things using a word such as *like* or *as* is —

A a simile

B a metaphor

C personification

D a symbol

______ **6.** An author might **foreshadow** events by —

F vividly describing them

G having characters summarize them

H explaining their significance

J hinting at what will happen later in a story

______ **7.** Why would writers use **anecdotes** and **loaded words** in arguments?

A To appeal to the reader's emotions

B To structure their arguments using comparison and contrast

C To use logic to support their ideas

D To prove their points using reliable sources

______ **8.** The **tone** of an argument in which a writer is trying to persuade readers to take action would *most* likely be —

F playful

G inspirational

H patient

J mocking

______ **9.** **Context clues** help you to —

A pronounce a word

B spell a word

C determine a word's meaning

D learn a word's root

______ **10.** If your brother tells you to bite your tongue, he is using —

F an analogy

G onomatopoeia

H an idiom

J a pun

NAME ______ CLASS ______ DATE ______ SCORE ______

SELECTION TEST **Student Edition page 652** LITERARY RESPONSE AND ANALYSIS

from the Odyssey, Part One: The Wanderings

Homer *translated by* Robert Fitzgerald

COMPREHENSION *(40 points; 4 points each)*

On the line provided, write the letter of the *best* answer to each of the following items.

______ **1.** Calypso allows Odysseus to leave her island because —

A she understands his grief and cannot bear to see him suffer

B Hermes has told her that Zeus has ordered it

C Hermes thinks that Odysseus has spent enough time in exile

D Penelope is growing old and needs his assistance

______ **2.** Odysseus tells Calypso that he wishes to return to Penelope because —

F he no longer finds Calypso attractive

G he is a sailor and sailors love the sea

H he longs to see his home again

J Penelope is the only woman who interests him

______ **3.** Odysseus's encounter with the Cicones after the Greeks leave Troy indicates that the Greeks —

A seem to be victims everywhere they go

B obey every command Odysseus gives them

C love to drink and make merry

D are violent warriors and plunderers

______ **4.** After Odysseus's men eat the lotus plant, they —

F fall ill and die

G are captured by the Lotus Eaters

H are thrown into the sea

J forget their homeland

______ **5.** Why does Odysseus blind Polyphemus rather than kill him?

A Teiresias and Circe have advised him to do so.

B Odysseus takes pity on the Cyclops.

C Only Polyphemus can move the boulder blocking the cave's entrance.

D Odysseus knows that killing Polyphemus will anger Poseidon.

_____ **6.** From what we discover about Circe, we can assume that her tame wolves and mountains lions are —

F constantly drugged into a stupor

G men transformed into animals

H trained to attack on command

J gods in animal disguise

_____ **7.** What does the shade of Teiresias require in order to provide Odysseus with a prophecy?

A Light

B Payment

C A taste of blood

D Permission

_____ **8.** Odysseus saves his crew from the Sirens' song by —

F plugging his men's ears with beeswax

G tying his men to their rowing stations

H sailing away from the coast

J shouting to distract the Sirens

_____ **9.** Odysseus does not warn his crew about Scylla because he thinks they would —

A not believe what he says

B panic and endanger the entire ship

C insist on sailing closer to Charybdis

D accuse him of being a coward

_____ **10.** What prophecy of Teiresias and Circe does Odysseus withhold from his men?

F Odysseus and his crew will return triumphant to Ithaca.

G The sailors' adventure will last another ten years.

H Only Odysseus will survive and return home.

J Poseidon will capsize their ship near Charybdis.

LITERARY FOCUS *(20 points; 5 point each)*

On the line provided, write the letter of the *best* answer to each of the following items.

_____ **11.** Which of the following formulas is *not* used by Homer to describe Odysseus?

A "master of landways and seaways"

B "raider of cities"

C "son of Laertes and the gods of old"

D "blue girdler of the islands"

______ **12.** In epic poetry, the poet often begins by asking for assistance in telling the story. This convention is known as the —

- **F** Homeric simile
- **G** quest structure
- **H** exposition
- **J** invocation

______ **13.** One of the things that the Greeks regarded as *most* offensive to the gods was to —

- **A** enslave women
- **B** mistreat guests
- **C** sack and burn cities
- **D** wear sandals indoors

______ **14.** To Homer and his listeners, the stories that we call myths *primarily* expressed —

- **F** sound morals that everyone agreed with
- **G** the fundamental values of Greek society
- **H** the ways that gods disguised themselves on earth
- **J** how men are influenced by the spiritual realm

VOCABULARY DEVELOPMENT *(20 points; 2 points each)*
Match each definition on the right with a Vocabulary word on the left. On the line provided, write the letter of the definition.

______ **15.** formidable	**a.** abundance
______ **16.** adversary	**b.** very unpleasantly
______ **17.** restitution	**c.** destroy violently
______ **18.** ardor	**d.** bitter hatred
______ **19.** abominably	**e.** passion
______ **20.** profusion	**f.** hardship
______ **21.** ravage	**g.** awe-inspiring
______ **22.** adversity	**h.** enemy
______ **23.** tumult	**i.** commotion
______ **24.** rancor	**j.** repayment

CONSTRUCTED RESPONSE *(20 points)*

25. Odysseus does not tell his crew everything Teiresias and Circe predict will happen to them as they get closer to home. Do you think Odysseus's decision to withhold this information is a good one? On a separate sheet of paper, explain your opinion. Support your ideas with at least two details from the selection.

NAME ______ CLASS ______ DATE ______ SCORE ______

SELECTION TEST **Student Edition page 690** LITERARY RESPONSE AND ANALYSIS

from the Odyssey, Part Two: Coming Home

Homer *translated by* Robert Fitzgerald

COMPREHENSION *(40 points; 4 points each)*

On the line provided, write the letter of the *best* answer to each of the following items.

______ **1.** When Odysseus returns home, Athena advises him to disguise himself as a —

A swineherd

B soothsayer

C beggar

D soldier

______ **2.** Which of the following events is an example of dramatic irony?

F Athena provides Odysseus with new clothes and a younger appearance.

G Telemachus returns to Ithaca unharmed.

H Eumaeus is sent to tell Penelope about Telemachus's safe return.

J Telemachus does not recognize that the stranger is his father.

______ **3.** When Odysseus reveals himself to Telemachus, his son —

A confuses him with the swineherd

B thinks only a god could make such a transformation

C accuses him of abandoning his mother

D asks for proof that Odysseus is his father

______ **4.** The old hound Argos knows that Odysseus has returned because the dog —

F recognizes Odysseus's face

G picks up the scent of his master

H recognizes Odysseus's voice

J dies just as Odysseus appears

______ **5.** Penelope proposes that her suitors perform a difficult task. They have to —

A kill Polyphemus

B string Odysseus's bow

C pull Odysseus's sword from a stone

D build a new palace for her

______ **6.** To enlist the aid of the swineherd and cowherd in his battle with the suitors, Odysseus —

F explains that Athena has willed their participation

G offers them wives, cattle, and houses

H tells them that it is their duty to help him

J plays on their affection for Penelope

______ **7.** Who joins Odysseus in the fight against the suitors?

A The swineherd, the shepherd, and the cowherd

B Telemachus, Penelope, and Argos

C Penelope, her maids, and Eurycleia

D Telemachus, the swineherd, and the cowherd

______ **8.** Telemachus executes the maids because they have —

F associated with the suitors

G neglected the dog Argos

H revealed Odysseus's identity

J ridiculed Penelope

______ **9.** To stop Odysseus from killing all the suitors, Eurymachus does everything *but* —

A blame everything on Antinous

B offer to repay Odysseus

C ask for a fair fight with Odysseus

D admit that Odysseus's anger is just

______ **10.** Odysseus proves his identity to Penelope by —

F summoning Argos with a secret name

G showing her the secret passage under their bed

H telling her how he built their bed

J telling her how the two of them met

LITERARY FOCUS *(20 points; 5 point each)*

On the line provided, write the letter of the best answer to each of the following items.

______ **11.** When Eumaeus calls Telemachus "light of my days," he is using a(n) —

A Homeric epithet

B character trait

C invocation

D exposition

______ **12.** In Part Two of the *Odyssey*, Odysseus exhibits the traits of an epic hero by —

F stringing the bow
G having the swineherd executed
H sparing Antinous's life
J asking Penelope to prove her identity

______ **13.** The *Odyssey* includes all of the following themes *except* —

A loyalty to family and friends
B the importance of truth
C overcoming obstacles
D the relationship between humans and gods

______ **14.** Penelope's test of Odysseus in Book 23 of the *Odyssey* —

F prolongs the story's resolution
G shows how Odysseus has changed
H shows Penelope's resentment of Odysseus
J results from the violence at the palace

VOCABULARY DEVELOPMENT *(20 points; 2 points each)*

Match each definition on the right with a Vocabulary word on the left. On the line provided, write the letter of the definition.

______ **15.** aloof
______ **16.** candor
______ **17.** tremulous
______ **18.** lavished
______ **19.** pliant
______ **20.** disdainful
______ **21.** revelry
______ **22.** adorn
______ **23.** glowered
______ **24.** avails

a. gave generously
b. honesty
c. helps
d. flexible
e. glared
f. add beauty to
g. merrymaking
h. unfriendly
i. trembling
j. scornful

NAME ____________ CLASS ____________ DATE ____________ SCORE ____________

CONSTRUCTED RESPONSE *(20 points)*

25. Which character (other than Odysseus) in Part Two of the *Odyssey* do you think is the *most* heroic? On a separate sheet of paper, explain the reasons for your choice. Support your ideas with at least two details from the selection.

NAME ______ CLASS ______ DATE ______ SCORE ______

SELECTION TEST **Student Edition pages 719, 721** INFORMATIONAL READING

Where I Find My Heroes Oliver Stone
Heroes with Solid Feet Kirk Douglas

COMPREHENSION *(50 points; 10 points each)*
On the line provided, write the letter of the *best* answer to each of the following items.

______ **1.** The authors of both articles would probably agree that —
- A Odysseus represents the ideal hero
- B heroes are usually born and not made
- C heroes often go unrecognized
- D heroes need a war to really shine

______ **2.** For Oliver Stone, what is essential to the nature of heroism?
- F The rigors of war
- G Physical impairment
- H Early training
- J Growth as a human being

______ **3.** Central to Kirk Douglas's thoughts on his visit to Berlin is the fact that he —
- A has become somewhat cynical about lifetime achievement awards
- B wonders if it is appropriate for a Jew to be in Berlin
- C wants to appear heroic to the Germans but doubts this will happen
- D wants to explain that heroes often have clay feet

______ **4.** Who among the following people is *not* cited by Oliver Stone as heroic?
- F The inner-city kid who works at McDonald's instead of selling drugs
- G Scientists who spend years of their lives trying to find cures for diseases
- H A kind and loving parent
- J A rich businessman who gives money to others

______ **5.** What important lesson does Kirk Douglas learn in Berlin?
- A The Germans, like everyone else, admire true heroes.
- B The Germans are not afraid to face up to their history.
- C Everyone, including Germans, can become a hero.
- D If you can speak German, Berliners will approve of you.

Vocabulary Development *(50 points; 10 points each)*
On the lines provided, write the Vocabulary word that *best* completes each sentence.

advocate **defers** **emaciated** **annihilate** **emulate**

6. A student who ______________ his final exams may find that makeup tests are harder.

7. The actor wore pale makeup to look delicate, but under the stage lights she merely looked______________.

8. When you ______________ a hero, you live up to his or her example.

9. The object of the bombing campaign was to ______________ the storage facility.

10. Is "______________ for endangered rodents" the title you want to be known by?

NAME ______ CLASS ______ DATE ______ SCORE ______

SELECTION TEST **Student Edition page 728** LITERARY RESPONSE AND ANALYSIS

The Fenris Wolf *retold by* Olivia Coolidge

COMPREHENSION *(60 points; 6 points each)*

On the line provided, write the letter of the *best* answer to each of the following items.

______ **1.** The gods feel that they can't do without Loki, the fire god, because —

- **A** he is handsome and ready-witted
- **B** although he seems evil, he is good inside
- **C** he helps them avoid most misfortunes
- **D** he gets them out of difficulties

______ **2.** The children of Loki include —

- **F** the world serpent, Odin, and the Fenris Wolf
- **G** the world serpent, Hel, and the Fenris Wolf
- **H** Hel, the Fenris Wolf, and Odin
- **J** Hel and the Fenris Wolf

______ **3.** The early attitude of the gods of Asgard toward the Fenris Wolf could be described as one of —

- **A** considerable interest
- **B** hatred and fear
- **C** amusement and fun
- **D** nervous avoidance

______ **4.** Why do the gods decide to put chains on the Fenris Wolf?

- **F** He keeps wandering off.
- **G** He is becoming a threat to their lives.
- **H** He is becoming a threat to humans.
- **J** They need to assert their power.

______ **5.** What do the ingredients of the dwarfs' silken string have in common?

- **A** All have been taken from fierce creatures.
- **B** Each represents a corner of the world.
- **C** All are impossibilities.
- **D** Each once belonged to Loki.

______ **6.** The Fenris Wolf shows that he is the son of a god in all these ways *except* that he is —

- **F** able to break any chains that the gods can make
- **G** relaxed and self-assured with the gods
- **H** proud and does not give in to anyone
- **J** unable to break the last rope

______ **7.** Why is it appropriate that Tyr offers to sacrifice his hand for the gods?

A He was born to make sacrifices for others.

B He knows that the Fates have decided it.

C Like all the gods, he can grow another hand.

D He has taken responsibility for the Fenris Wolf.

______ **8.** Who, or what, overrules even the gods?

F Mother Nature

G The Fates

H Time

J Good and evil

______ **9.** According to this myth, Odin will eventually —

A be eaten by the Fenris Wolf

B be defeated by the demons of ice and fire

C become the sun and the moon

D be drowned

______ **10.** Why is Tyr the only admirable character in the myth?

F He is the opposite of Loki.

G He is the character who shows heroism.

H Everyone else avoids responsibility.

J He is smarter than everyone but the dwarfs.

LITERARY FOCUS *(20 points; 5 point each)*

On the line provided, write the letter of the *best* answer to each of the following items.

______ **11.** The myth "The Fenris Wolf" provides an explanation of why —

A we live and die

B there is evil in the world

C people make up stories

D the seasons change

______ **12.** "The Fenris Wolf" contains all of the following archetypes *except* —

F a sacrificial hero

G a heroic quest

H powerful animals

J clever dwarfs

______ **13.** Norse myths such as the "The Fenris Wolf" differ from myths of other cultures in which of the following ways?

A Dogs are represented as evil.

B The gods live in a special place.

C Good triumphs over evil.

D Evil triumphs in the end.

______ **14.** In the final days of time, the gods of Asgard will be attacked by —

F demons of ice and fire

G Loki

H dwarfs from underground

D Thor

CONSTRUCTED RESPONSE *(20 points)*

15. What does the gods' toleration of the god Loki suggest about the views of pre-Christian Scandinavians? Give two examples from the myth to support your view.

______

______

______

______

______

______

______

______

COLLECTION 10 SUMMATIVE TEST

Epic and Myth

This test asks you to use the skills and strategies you have learned in this collection. Here is an excerpt from the *Odyssey* that you have not read before. Read it and then answer the questions that follow the passage.

FROM THE **Odyssey**
by Homer
translated by Robert Fitzgerald

Two nights, two days, in the solid deep-sea swell
he drifted, many times awaiting death,
until with shining ringlets in the East
the dawn confirmed a third day, breaking clear
5 over a high and windless sea; and mounting
a rolling wave he caught a glimpse of land.
What a dear welcome thing life seems to children
whose father, in the extremity, recovers
after some weakening and malignant illness:
10 his pangs are gone, the gods have delivered him.
So dear and welcome to Odysseus
the sight of land, of woodland, on that morning.
It made him swim again, to get a foothold
on solid ground. But when he came in earshot
15 he heard the trampling roar of sea on rock,
where combers, rising shoreward, thudded down
on the sticking ebb—all sheeted with salt foam.
Here were no coves or harborage or shelter,
only steep headlands, rockfallen reefs and crags.
20 Odysseus' knees grew slack, his heart faint,
a heaviness came over him, and he said:
"A cruel turn, this. Never had I thought
to see this land, but Zeus has let me see it—
and let me, too, traverse the Western Ocean—
25 only to find no exit from these breakers.
Here are sharp rocks off shore, and the sea a smother
rushing around them; rock face rising sheer
from deep water, nowhere could I stand up
on my two feet and fight free of the welter.
30 No matter how I try it, the surf may throw me
against the cliffside; no good fighting there.
If I swim down the coast, outside the breakers,
I may find shelving shore and quiet water—
but what if another gale comes on to blow?
35 Then I go cursing out to sea once more.
Or then again, some shark of Amphitritê's
may hunt me, sent by the genius of the deep.

I know how he who makes earth tremble hates me."
During this meditation a heavy surge
40 was taking him, in fact, straight on the rocks.
He had been flayed there, and his bones broken,
had not gray-eyed Athena instructed him:
he gripped a rock-ledge with both hands in passing
and held on, groaning, as the surge went by,
45 to keep clear of its breaking. Then the backwash
hit him, ripping him under and far out.
An octopus, when you drag one from his chamber,
comes up with suckers full of tiny stones:
Odysseus left the skin of his great hands
50 torn on that rock-ledge as the wave submerged him.
And now at last Odysseus would have perished,
battered inhumanly, but he had the gift
of self-possession from gray-eyed Athena.
So, when the backwash spewed him up again,
55 he swam out and along, and scanned the coast
for some landspit that made a breakwater.
Lo and behold, the mouth of a calm river
at length came into view, with level shores
unbroken, free from rock, shielded from wind—
60 by far the best place he had found.
But as he felt the current flowing seaward
he prayed in his heart:
"O hear me, lord of the stream:
how sorely I depend upon your mercy!
65 derelict[1] as I am by the sea's anger.
Is he not sacred, even to the gods,
the wandering man who comes, as I have come,
in weariness before your knees, your waters?
Here is your servant; lord, have mercy on me."

1. derelict: here, abandoned.

NAME ______ CLASS ______ DATE ______ SCORE ______

VOCABULARY SKILLS *(30 points; 6 points each)*

Each of the underlined words below has also been underlined in the selection. Re-read those passages in which the underlined words appear, and then use your knowledge of literal and figurative language as well as Greek mythology to help you select an answer. On the line provided, write the letter of the word or words that *best* complete each sentence.

______ **1.** When he finally spots land, Odysseus feels weak, as though he has recovered from a malignant illness.

A mild
B deadly
C brief
D lingering

______ **2.** To reach home, Odysseus must traverse several seas.

F swim
G go around
H cross
J discover

______ **3.** The breakers threaten to tear Odysseus to pieces.

A foaming waves near land
B raging gods
C starving sea monsters
D fierce winds

______ **4.** Distracted by his meditation, Odysseus nearly drowns.

F high hopes
G deep thought
H brief illness
J silent prayers

______ **5.** At one point the waves completely submerge Odysseus.

A join
B conquer
C drench
D cover

NAME ______ CLASS ______ DATE ______ SCORE ______

COMPREHENSION *(30 points; 6 points each)*

______ **6.** Before he sees land, Odysseus is adrift in the ocean for —

- **F** two weeks and two days
- **G** one month
- **H** two nights and two days
- **J** one week

______ **7.** The *best* place Odysseus finds to come ashore is the —

- **A** edge of a beach
- **B** mouth of a river
- **C** entrance to a harbor
- **D** side of a cliff

______ **8.** At one point, Odysseus swims away from the shore because he wants to —

- **F** return to Troy
- **G** find Poseidon
- **H** find his raft
- **J** search for a safer place to land

______ **9.** Odysseus would have died if he had not possessed —

- **A** self-control
- **B** self-pity
- **C** self-esteem
- **D** self-doubt

______ **10.** Odysseus bases his appeal to the lord of the stream on the rights of —

- **F** soldiers
- **G** sailors
- **H** guests
- **J** heroes

READING SKILLS AND STRATEGIES: CONSTRUCTED RESPONSE *(10 points)*

Monitoring Your Comprehension

11. What alternatives does Odysseus consider when he views the cliffside from the water? What choice does he make? Does he pursue it?

______

______

______

Literary Focus: Constructed Response *(30 points; 10 points each)*

12. There are many examples of **poetic imagery** in the selection. Review the excerpt, and quote specific passages that create vivid images of the items listed in the chart below. Then, tell to which senses the image appeals.

	Direct Quotations	Appeal to Sense
Sunrise		
Sea		
Land		

13. What are some of the characteristics of an **epic**? Describe the characters, what the main character tends to do, and the language and/or tone that is used. Use examples from this excerpt to support your ideas.

Relating Setting to Historical Concerns

14. Much of the *Odyssey* is set on or near the ocean. Explain how this **setting** relates to **historical issues**—the everyday concerns of Homer's audience at their time in history. How would Homer's audience have reacted to a recitation of this excerpt? Could they have identified with Odysseus's plight?

NAME ______ CLASS ______ DATE ______ SCORE ______

COLLECTION 11 DIAGNOSTIC TEST

LITERATURE
INFORMATIONAL TEXT
VOCABULARY

Drama

On the line provided, write the letter of the *best* answer to each of the following items. *(100 points; 10 points each)*

______ **1.** A conversation between two or more characters is called —

A dialect

B dialogue

C narration

D exposition

______ **2.** Actors learn how to move onstage and say their lines with the help of a play's —

F lighting

G audience

H stage directions

J props

______ **3.** What is the **climax** of a play?

A The moment of greatest emotional intensity or suspense

B The resolution of the conflict

C A series of obstacles that a character must overcome

D The point in the play when the main character learns a lesson

______ **4.** In a play, **dramatic irony** occurs when —

F a struggle is repeated in the course of the plot

G a character grows or changes as events unfold

H the audience knows something that a character onstage does not know

J a suspenseful plot keeps the audience guessing about future events

______ **5.** In a line of poetry written in **iambic pentameter,** —

A each unstressed syllable is followed by a stressed syllable

B the poet uses internal rhyme

C there is no regular meter

D the poet uses only five words

______ **6.** What is a **couplet**?

F Two lines of poetry that are the same length

G Two consecutive lines of poetry that rhyme

H An image formed by two words

J Two words that share vowel sounds

______ **7.** When you **compare** sources that discuss the same issue, you —

A elaborate on the authors' ideas

B make generalizations

C look for similarities

D find support for the authors' points

______ **8.** When you **paraphrase** a text, you—

F make an outline

G critique the main points

H connect the main idea to your life

J restate the ideas in your own words

______ **9.** Which of the following statements about the English language is *false*?

A The meanings of some words have changed over time.

B Many words that are now part of the English language have come from other languages.

C Some older English words are no longer used today.

D The roots of some words have changed over the years.

______ **10.** If a word has strong **connotations,** it —

F evokes associations that go beyond its literal meaning

G has a very positive meaning

H provokes a negative reaction

J has the same meaning as a number of other words

NAME ______________________ CLASS ______________________ DATE ______________ SCORE ______________

Visitor from Forest Hills *from* Plaza Suite Neil Simon

COMPREHENSION *(40 points; 4 points each)*

On the line provided, write the letter of the *best* answer to each of the following items.

______ **1.** What is the basic problem in this play?

A The mother and father of the groom leave their son's wedding.

B The mother and father of a bride have an argument.

C A bride locks herself in a bathroom before her wedding.

D A groom becomes embarrassed by what he tells his bride-to-be.

______ **2.** The play is set —

F in the Green Room of the Plaza Hotel

G in a bedroom suite of the Plaza Hotel

H throughout New York City

J at the Eisler home and in the Plaza Hotel

______ **3.** The relationship between Mimsey and Borden is one of —

A brother and sister

B bride and groom

C mother and father

D husband and wife

______ **4.** Why is the telephone an important prop in this play?

F There are no other props and little scenery on the stage.

G Roy uses the telephone to break down a door.

H Mimsey uses the phone to communicate with her parents.

J Important information in the plot is communicated in phone conversations.

______ **5.** Roy Hubley has a temperament that could be described as —

A peaceful

B explosive

C tranquil

D indifferent

______ **6.** At first, Roy seems most concerned about —

F the cost of the wedding that might not take place

G the future happiness of his daughter

H his wife's fear of having suffered a heart attack

J a hotel door that cannot be broken down

_____ **7.** Which is an example of a silly reaction Norma has to the situation?

A She calls her husband in the Green Room.

B She talks with Mimsey through the door.

C She asks for money to buy a new pair of stockings.

D Her worry that Mimsey is too afraid to get married.

_____ **8.** Roy does all of the following things *except* —

F try to break down a bathroom door with his arm

G give up and leave New York City for Forest Hills

H attempt to climb out onto a seventh-story ledge

J ask Mimsey to knock one time for "no" and two times for "yes" to questions he asks her

_____ **9.** What Mimsey finally tells her parents is that she —

A is afraid of becoming like them when she is married

B does not love Borden anymore

C cannot get married in the dress she is wearing

D prefers to elope than go through a wedding in the Plaza Hotel

_____ **10.** What resolves the conflict near the end of the play?

F Roy climbs onto a window ledge and forces his way into the bathroom to speak with Mimsey.

G Borden comes to the room, says something to Mimsey through the bathroom door, and then goes downstairs to wait for her.

H Norma telephones the Eisler family, calls off the wedding, and then returns to Forest Hills embarrassed.

J Mimsey allows her parents into the bathroom one at a time and tells them her fears for the future.

LITERARY FOCUS *(20 points; 5 points each)*

On the line provided, write the letter of the *best* answer to each of the following items.

_____ **11.** Which is the main characteristic of a **comedy**?

A It points out silly, untruthful aspects of life.

B It has a happy ending.

C Every scene makes people laugh.

D The flaws of a character create his or her downfall.

_____ **12.** A **farce** focuses on —

- **F** physical comedy and ridiculous situations
- **G** truthful insights into human behavior
- **H** funny situations that turn sad or tragic
- **J** a plot without conflict, climax, or resolution

_____ **13.** Which is an example of farce in *Visitor from Forest Hills*?

- **A** Mimsey feels fearful.
- **B** Roy yells loudly.
- **C** Roy's jacket tears down the back.
- **D** Norma talks on the telephone.

_____ **14.** Which form of opposites does Neil Simon use in *Visitor from Forest Hills* to create comedy?

- **F** A clever person and a fool argue with each other.
- **G** A rich person and a poor person decide to get married.
- **H** A hotel clerk and a woman have endless phone conversations.
- **J** The opposite sexes battle each other.

VOCABULARY DEVELOPMENT *(20 points; 4 points each)*

On the line before each sentence, write the Vocabulary word that has a meaning similar to the italicized word or phrase in the sentence.

volatile **incredulously** **despondently** **torrent** **interminable**

_______________ **15.** Mimsey was silent for what seemed like an *endless* hour.

_______________ **16.** A *flood* of feelings caused Roy to act.

_______________ **17.** Mimsey acted *sadly* rather than happily just before her wedding.

_______________ **18.** Norma was afraid of Roy's *hot-tempered* personality.

_______________ **19.** Hoping against hope that the bathroom door would open, Norma, *unable to believe*, turned the doorknob.

CONSTRUCTED RESPONSE *(20 points)*

20. Choose either Roy or Norma Hubley. On a separate sheet of paper, briefly describe the character, and then explain how the character's personality helps to create the comedy in this play. In particular, include at least two of your character's actions as evidence of his or her comedic or farcical quality.

The Tragedy of Romeo and Juliet, the Prologue, Act I William Shakespeare

COMPREHENSION *(60 points; 6 points each)*
On the line provided, write the letter of the *best* answer to each of the following items.

______ **1.** Shakespeare uses a prologue to inform the audience that —
- **A** Juliet is a widow
- **B** Romeo is a fugitive
- **C** the lovers from the feuding families will die
- **D** Romeo is a Montague and Juliet is a Capulet

______ **2.** The fight in Scene 1 starts when —
- **F** Capulet and Montague servants quarrel over petty insults
- **G** Tybalt loses his temper
- **H** Benvolio insults Tybalt
- **J** the officer stirs up the two sides

______ **3.** Adjectives that describe the character of Tybalt are —
- **A** clever and witty
- **B** saucy and hotheaded
- **C** lovesick and moody
- **D** intelligent and obedient

______ **4.** When Benvolio talks with Romeo, he finds his cousin —
- **F** happy-go-lucky and ready for fun
- **G** prepared to fight anyone that insults a Montague
- **H** interested in everyone else's situation but his own
- **J** focused on love and temperamental

______ **5.** Lord and Lady Capulet plan for their daughter to —
- **A** marry Paris in two years
- **B** marry whomever she falls in love with
- **C** marry Tybalt in two years
- **D** not to attend a dance if they are not present

______ **6.** Adjectives that describe the character of Juliet are —
- **F** shy and frightened
- **G** rebellious and angry
- **H** intelligent and obedient
- **J** sarcastic and angry

______ **7.** What is unusual about the Montague clan at the Capulets' party?

A They draw swords against Tybalt.

B Each of the Montagues makes a joke about Lord Capulet.

C They wear masks.

D Each of the clan dances with Juliet.

______ **8.** Juliet first meets Romeo —

F on a walk in the woods

G at the Capulets' party

H through her cousin Tybalt

J through Romeo's friend Mercutio

______ **9.** What is the subject of the conversation between the Nurse and Juliet at the end of Act I?

A Juliet wants the Nurse to identify Romeo.

B Juliet refuses to fall in love with anyone.

C The Nurse reminds Juliet of when Juliet was a baby.

D The Nurse encourages Juliet to marry Romeo.

______ **10.** All of the following words are archaic *except* —

F coz

G God-den

H halt

J ope

LITERARY FOCUS *(20 points; 5 points each)*

On the line provided, write the letter of the *best* answer to each of the following items.

______ **11.** Mercutio can be described as a **foil** to Romeo because —

A he comes from a different social class

B he is much older than Romeo

C he is a Capulet and Romeo is a Montague

D unlike Romeo, he does not take love seriously

______ **12.** An **aside** is spoken —

F among characters in a play

G between a character and the play's author

H by a character to the audience or another character that others onstage are not supposed to hear

J by a character or narrator who explains something about the play directly to the audience

______ **13.** What point does Prince Escalus of Verona make in his **dramatic monologue** to the Montague and Capulet families?

A Anyone who continues the feud between the families will be put to death.

B Montague family members should be invited to the Capulets' party.

C Romeo Montague and Juliet Capulet should be allowed to marry each other.

D Tybalt and Mercutio should duel to see which clan is strongest.

______ **14.** A **tragedy** is defined by all of the following qualities *except* —

F a happy ending results after serious actions and complications

G a main character dies

H a character is responsible for his or her own downfall

J serious actions end unhappily

CONSTRUCTED RESPONSE *(20 points)*

15. On a separate sheet of paper, describe how Shakespeare builds suspense in Act I of *Romeo and Juliet*. Support your ideas with at least two details from the play.

NAME ______ CLASS ______ DATE ______ SCORE ______

SELECTION TEST **Student Edition page 818** LITERARY RESPONSE AND ANALYSIS

The Tragedy of Romeo and Juliet, Act II William Shakespeare

COMPREHENSION *(60 points; 6 points each)*
On the line provided, write the letter of the *best* answer to each of the following items.

______ **1.** Which character speaks the following lines?

"O, speak again, bright angel, for thou art
As glorious to this night, being o'er my head,
As is a wingèd messenger of heaven"

A Mercutio
B Benvolio
C Romeo
D Juliet

______ **2.** Which character speaks the following lines?

"Though
his face be better than any man's, yet his leg excels all
men's; and for a hand and foot, and a body, though
they be not to be talked on, yet they are past compare."

F Tybalt
G Romeo
H Friar Laurence
J Nurse

______ **3.** In the balcony scene, Juliet says, "What's Montague? It is nor hand, nor foot, / Nor arm, nor face. O, be some other name / Belonging to a man. / What's in a name? That which we call a rose / By any other word would smell as sweet."

She means that —

A Montague is an unimportant name in Verona
B Romeo should take her last name when they marry
C Romeo's name is an accident of birth, not an essential part of him
D it is wrong to fall in love with a Montague

______ **4.** Juliet quickly admits her love to Romeo because —

F she wants to marry him
G she is sure his love is true
H she is not a flirt
J he has overheard her thinking aloud about her love for him

______ **5.** What do Juliet and Romeo decide to do about their love?

A They plan to have Friar Laurence marry them.

B The Nurse will lead them out of Verona, away from the Montague and Capulet clans.

C They plan to marry, with their parent's permission, when Juliet turns sixteen.

D The Montagues will hide Juliet in their home after the couple has married.

______ **6.** Tybalt sends a letter to Lord Montague and tells him —

F he is angry because of jokes Mercutio makes about him

G Juliet will marry him with the permission of Lord Capulet

H he has a feud to settle with Lord Montague's son, Romeo

J he will spy for the Montague family if he can marry Rosaline

______ **7.** Mercutio engages Romeo in conversation about fashion in order to —

A let Romeo speak about Juliet's beauty

B convince Romeo to send a letter to the house of Capulet

C have Romeo match wits with him

D prove to Benvolio that Romeo is intelligent

______ **8.** The purpose of the humor rising from the nurse's comic character is to —

F provide relief from the tragedy

G display Shakespeare's wit

H suggest that love has its funny side

J indicate that Juliet's servants are foolish

______ **9.** Friar Laurence scolds Romeo because —

A Romeo is causing trouble by wooing Juliet

B Romeo is so changeable in love

C Juliet is too young to marry

D Romeo has been unfaithful to Rosaline

______ **10.** In Act II, the action focuses on the plans of Romeo and Juliet. When the Nurse brings Juliet the message from Romeo, the Nurse intensifies the moment by —

F going on and on about her pains, thus leaving Juliet in suspense

G refusing to pass on the message until she has been properly tipped

H betraying Romeo and encouraging Juliet to marry Paris

J giving the message to Juliet's mother instead of Juliet herself

NAME ______ CLASS ______ DATE ______ SCORE ______

LITERARY FOCUS *(20 points; 5 points each)*

On the line provided, write the letter of the *best* answer to each of the following items.

______ **11.** When a character delivers a **soliloquy,** he or she —

- **A** directs his or her thoughts to other characters onstage
- **B** expresses private thoughts to the audience
- **C** speaks from behind a curtain or somewhere offstage
- **D** describes an event that is related to but not a part of the dialogue in the play

______ **12.** In the balcony scene, Romeo says to the audience, "Shall I hear more, or shall I speak at this." This form of speech is —

- **F** a monologue
- **G** dramatic irony
- **H** an aside
- **J** a soliloquy

______ **13.** Even though the balcony scene contains some stage directions by Shakespeare, modern directors and actors must —

- **A** change the props and sets as well as some of the action to match the times
- **B** change the original dialogue to fit the kind of stage on which the play will be performed
- **C** research old productions of the play to discover how Shakespeare really meant it to be staged
- **D** interpret the play's dialogue to decide where people are placed onstage and how they should move

______ **14.** **Dramatic irony** occurs —

- **F** whenever Shakespeare stages a fight
- **G** when the audience knows something that the characters in the play do not
- **H** when the friar believes he can unite the feuding families
- **J** when Juliet is insecure about Romeo's true feelings

CONSTRUCTED RESPONSE *(20 points)*

15. Throughout this and other plays by Shakespeare, moments of **dramatic irony** occur. Identify one of these moments. On a separate sheet of paper, explain why it is an example of dramatic irony. Then, explain how the moment affects the audience as they watch the action and listen to the dialogue.

NAME ______________ CLASS ______________ DATE ______________ SCORE ______________

SELECTION TEST **Student Edition page 845** LITERARY RESPONSE AND ANALYSIS

The Tragedy of Romeo and Juliet, Act III William Shakespeare

COMPREHENSION *(60 points; 6 points each)*
On the line provided, write the letter of the *best* answer to each of the following items.

______ **1.** In Scene I, Mercutio speaks the following line: "Tybalt, you ratcatcher, will you walk?" Mercutio wants Tybalt to —

A give up the fight
B join Mercutio for the evening
C fight
D leave quietly

______ **2.** At first, Romeo doesn't want to fight Tybalt because Romeo —

F is a coward
G is now related to Tybalt by marriage
H thinks that Mercutio has a better chance of beating Tybalt
J is on his way to marry Juliet

______ **3.** The prince punishes Romeo by —

A sentencing him to death
B annulling his marriage
C banishing him from Verona forever
D sentencing him to jail

______ **4.** When the prince arrives, Benvolio —

F promises to bring Romeo to the prince
G recounts the events of the killings to the prince
H delivers a message from Romeo to Juliet
J confesses to the killing of Tybalt to the prince

______ **5.** All of the following consequences result from Romeo's killing of Tybalt *except* —

A Juliet decides that Paris is more honorable than Romeo
B Romeo and Juliet cannot reveal their marriage
C Juliet is to be married to Paris almost immediately
D Romeo is banished from Verona

______ **6.** At first, Juliet responds to the news of Tybalt's death with —

F anger toward Tybalt
G anger toward Romeo
H uncontrollable weeping
J anger toward both Romeo and Tybalt

______ **7.** The Nurse helps Juliet by —

A persuading Juliet to tell Lord and Lady Capulet of her marriage to Romeo
B going to Friar Laurence with a ring of Juliet's for Romeo
C never arguing with Juliet and always praising Romeo
D hiding the news about Tybalt and Romeo from Juliet

______ **8.** Which statement is *true* about Paris?

F His interest in Juliet lessens after Tybalt dies.
G He visits the house of Montague and speaks with Benvolio.
H He enjoys puns and games that match people's wits.
J He wishes to marry a woman he has not courted.

______ **9.** Lord Capulet responds to the death of Tybalt by —

A traveling to Mantua in order to murder Romeo himself
B arranging the immediate marriage of Paris and Juliet
C negotiating with the prince for Romeo's banishment
D asking Paris to leave Verona and await further word

______ **10.** All of the following events happen at the conclusion of Act III *except* —

F the Nurse suggests that Juliet forget Romeo and marry Paris
G Juliet refuses to marry Paris
H Lord Capulet scorns his only child and vows to disown her
J Lady Capulet convinces Lord Capulet that Paris should leave Verona

LITERARY FOCUS *(20 points; 5 points each)*

On the line provided, write the letter of the *best* answer to each of the following items.

______ **11.** Because of a **turning point** the rest of the actions in a play —

A do not relate to the original conflict
B foreshadow the ending
C move toward either a happy or unhappy ending
D introduce a new conflict that must also be resolved

______ **12.** The turning point in Romeo and Juliet occurs when —

F Romeo and Juliet marry

G Mercutio is killed

H Romeo kills Tybalt

J Juliet's parents arrange her marriage to Paris

______ **13.** Which of the following events serves as a **complication** to the main conflict of *Romeo and Juliet*?

A At first, Romeo refuses to fight with Tybalt.

B Juliet receives news of Romeo and Tybalt from the Nurse.

C Friar Laurence tells Romeo to leave for Mantua by the next morning.

D Lord Capulet arranges for his daughter to marry Paris.

______ **14.** As Juliet encounters more conflicts and problems, her **character** changes, and she —

F runs away from her problems

G pushes away her elders and threatens suicide

H finds herself unable to make a decision

J confesses that her life with Romeo is ill-fated and wants to leave him

CONSTRUCTED RESPONSE *(20 points)*

15. When she finds Juliet weeping, Lady Capulet assumes that Juliet is still mourning Tybalt's death. On a separate sheet of paper, explain why Shakespeare gives Juliet dialogue filled with double meaning. Support your ideas with at least two details from the play.

NAME ______________________ CLASS ______________________ DATE ______________ SCORE ______________

The Tragedy of Romeo and Juliet, Act IV William Shakespeare

COMPREHENSION *(60 points; 6 points each)*

On the line provided, write the letter of the *best* answer to each of the following items.

______ **1.** What does Paris think of Juliet's state of mind when he visits Friar Laurence?

- **A** She is deep in mourning for Tybalt.
- **B** Her fear of marriage overwhelms her.
- **C** Being disobedient to Lord Capulet has made her feel guilty.
- **D** She has recovered her high spirits well.

______ **2.** What is the *last* thing that happens between Paris and Juliet?

- **F** Juliet tells Paris about Romeo.
- **G** Friar Laurence marries Juliet and Paris.
- **H** Paris kisses Juliet.
- **J** Paris agrees to marry someone other than Juliet.

______ **3.** Friar Laurence thinks Juliet is brave enough to take the sleeping potion because —

- **A** she is unwilling to marry Paris and lose Romeo
- **B** she has said that lying in a tomb is better than life without Romeo
- **C** it is her only hope of escaping marriage to Paris
- **D** if she is brave enough to die, she is brave enough to fake death

______ **4.** Friar Laurence sets a plan in motion. Which of the following details is *not* part of his plan?

- **F** Juliet should consent to marry Paris.
- **G** Juliet should drink the vial of liquid.
- **H** Juliet will wake up alone in the family vault.
- **J** Romeo will take her to Mantua after she wakes up.

______ **5.** Juliet surprises Lord Capulet on her return from Friar Laurence's cell by —

- **A** threatening to take her own life if she must marry Paris
- **B** confessing her secret marriage but promising to have it annulled
- **C** promising to marry Paris on Thursday but not on Wednesday
- **D** agreeing to marry Paris and act as an obedient daughter

______ **6.** While Juliet puts Friar Laurence's plan into action, she asks the Nurse to —

- **F** deliver a message to Romeo in Mantua
- **G** stay with Lady Capulet for the night
- **H** go to speak with Friar Laurence
- **J** play music with Peter and the musicians

______ **7.** In her soliloquy, Juliet admits that —

A she believes in ghosts

B she is afraid

C hiding with her cousin's body would be unbearable

D death is better than losing Romeo

______ **8.** How is Juliet's supposed death discovered?

F The Nurse goes to wake Juliet on her wedding day.

G Paris brings a wedding gift to Juliet's chamber.

H Lord Capulet enters the chamber to speak with his daughter.

J Friar Laurence checks on Juliet in her chambers.

______ **9.** The Capulets, the Nurse, and Paris react to Juliet's supposed death with —

A restrained grief

B regret for how they treated her

C anguished cries of grief

D anger and thoughts of revenge

______ **10.** A possible reason Shakespeare includes the scene between Peter and the musicians is to —

F foreshadow important events

G add more complications to the plot

H illustrate that life goes on amid tragedy

J highlight the violence that exists between characters

LITERARY FOCUS *(15 points; 5 points each)*

On the line provided, write the letter of the *best* answer to each of the following items.

______ **11.** When paraphrasing text, it is most important to —

A shorten the wording

B change the tone so as not to imitate the author

C understand the main idea of the original passage

D summarize only the details of the text

______ **12.** Which of the following statements provides the best paraphrasing of the following passage spoken by Juliet in Act IV?

> "What if it be a poison which the friar
> Subtly hath ministered to have me dead,
> Lest in this marriage he should be dishonored
> Because he married me before to Romeo?"

F What if the friar wants me dead? He's upset because I married Romeo first and now have to marry Paris.

G What if the friar gave me real poison? Maybe he wants me dead because he is afraid his reputation will be ruined. Since the friar has married me to Romeo, how can he marry me to someone else?

H What if this poison the friar gave me doesn't work? How can I let myself be dishonored by marrying someone other than Romeo?

J What if the friar made a mistake and gave me a vial of poison rather than a vial of sleeping potion? The friar is a good man, but he might not be thinking clearly.

______ **13.** At the beginning of Scene 1, why does Friar Laurence say the following **aside** during a conversation with Paris?

> "I would I knew not why it should be slowed—
> Look, sir, here comes the lady toward my cell."

A He does not like Paris, but to be polite, he whispers an insult before going on with more polite conversation.

B He does not want his comment heard by Paris but by the audience, who know more of what's going on than Paris does.

C Because Romeo is hiding in the friar's cell, Friar Laurence addresses Romeo rather than Paris.

D Throughout the play, Shakespeare has the friar alternate between speaking a line of dialogue to a character and speaking a thought aloud to himself.

Constructed Response *(25 points)*

14. In Act IV, we see a side of Juliet that we have not seen before. On a separate sheet of paper, describe what her actions reveal about the growth of her character. Make at least two references to details in the play to support your ideas.

NAME ____________ CLASS ____________ DATE ____________ SCORE ____________

SELECTION TEST **Student Edition pages 895, 911**

LITERARY RESPONSE AND ANALYSIS

The Tragedy of Romeo and Juliet, Act V William Shakespeare
Your Laughter Pablo Neruda
How Do I Love Thee? Elizabeth Barrett Browning

COMPREHENSION *(60 points; 6 points each)*

On the line provided, write the letter of the *best* answer to each of the following items.

______ **1.** During the course of the play, we see Juliet change as she —

A falls more and more deeply in love with Romeo

B becomes extremely confused over what she desires and what others expect

C clashes with her parents over whom she should marry

D becomes more and more determined to be with Romeo

______ **2.** Romeo's servant—not Friar John—brings Romeo news that —

F Juliet is dead

G Juliet needs help

H Juliet must marry Paris

J his banishment is canceled

______ **3.** When Romeo arrives at the tomb, he discovers Paris and —

A they attempt to awaken Juliet

B kills him in a duel

C quarrels with him for a long time

D is jealous and surprised

______ **4.** The prince learns the truth about Romeo and Juliet from —

F Lord Capulet

G a farewell letter Juliet has written

H Friar Laurence

J the Nurse

______ **5.** How does "heaven," or "fate," punish the Capulets and the Montagues for their feud?

A The Prince becomes angry at the two families.

B Their children fall in love but lose their lives as a result of the feud.

C Their children keep secrets from them.

D Both families are disgraced through their children's behavior.

______ **6.** At the play's end both families plan to —

F go into seclusion

G punish the friar for his sins

H hold combined funeral services

J erect a memorial to the lovers

______ **7.** The line "Love goes toward love as schoolboys from their books" includes an example of —

A a pun

B a metaphor

C personification

D a simile

______ **8.** The speaker of "Your Laughter" believes that his love's laughter —

F is violent

G makes him laugh, too

H grows plants

J keeps him alive

______ **9.** Which statement summarizes the speaker's feeling about love in "How Do I Love Thee?"

A Love is something the speaker feels only at certain times and during certain events in her life.

B The speaker wants no more of love after she counts the ways in which she has failed at love in the past.

C The speaker loves someone always, purely, without fear or doubt, even after death.

D The fourteen ways in which the speaker believes a person can love another are identified, one in each line of the poem.

______ **10.** "How Do I Love Thee?" relates to Act V of *Romeo and Juliet* in that it —

F expresses how love exists even after death

G explains how young people are blinded by love

H describes love based on youth and beauty

J tells of love as an everyday, ordinary event

LITERARY FOCUS *(20 points; 5 points each)*

On the line provided, write the letter of the *best* answer to each of the following items.

______ **11.** When Balthasar and Romeo reach the Capulet vault, Balthasar says to the audience:

"For all this same, I'll hide me hereabout.
His looks I fear, and his intents I doubt."

These lines are an example of —

A a dramatic foil

B dynamic character

C a turning point

D an aside

______ **12.** When Romeo hears that Juliet is dead, the **dramatic irony** lies in the fact that —

F Juliet is already wed to Paris

G Romeo feels deep grief

H the audience knows Juliet is not dead

J Juliet lies in the Capulet tomb

______ **13.** The **climax** of the play occurs when —

A Paris is killed

B Juliet stabs herself and dies

C Romeo takes his life

D Romeo is killed

______ **14.** Which of the following sentences *best* states a possible **theme** of the play?

F Children, obey your parents.

G Arranged marriages are the most successful.

H Hatred leads to violence, destruction, and waste.

J Love conquers all.

CONSTRUCTED RESPONSE *(20 points)*

15. On a separate sheet of paper, state the theme of *Romeo and Juliet*, and explain how the play's message might be applied to today's society. Make at least two references to details in the play to support your ideas.

NAME ______ CLASS ______ DATE ______ SCORE ______

SELECTION TEST **Student Edition pages 919, 921** **INFORMATIONAL READING**

Dear Juliet Lisa Bannon
Romeo and Juliet in Bosnia Bob Herbert

COMPREHENSION *(50 points; 10 points each)*
On the line provided, write the letter of the *best* answer to each of the following items.

______ **1.** According to the news article by Lisa Bannon, people write letters to Verona, Italy, because they would like —

A pictures of the medieval town

B to receive advice about their love lives

C to get blueprints for Juliet's balcony

D jobs as tour guides of the Capulet and Montague homes

______ **2.** Which statement about Hala and Omer from "Dear Juliet" relates to the story of Romeo and Juliet?

F In Saudi Arabia as well as Italy, girls marry the men their fathers choose for them.

G In both Italy and Saudi Arabia, buying or selling drugs like heroin is illegal.

H Hala writes to Mr. Tamassia for advice, just as Juliet wrote to Friar Laurence for help about whom to marry.

J Omer's family is the enemy of Hala's family, but Hala and Omer have fallen in love.

______ **3.** In Bob Herbert's article, what about Bosko and Admira is *similar* to Romeo and Juliet ?

A Bosko and Admira come from families on different sides of a war, but they are in love.

B Bosko and Admira have a love relationship without the consent of their families.

C Both Bosnia and Italy are countries in Europe where family feuds run deep.

D Admira, like Juliet, lies to her family about whom she plans to marry.

______ **4.** How is Admira's father similar to or different from Lord Capulet?

F Lord Capulet is very rich and Admira's father is not.

G Both fathers become angry when their daughters act against family wishes.

H Admira's father accepts his daughter's lover.

J Zijo Ismic chooses a husband that Admira agrees to marry.

______ **5.** Bob Herbert concludes that the story of Bosko and Admira is made more tragic by the fact that —

A the couple had almost made it across the bridge to freedom

B it took six days to remove the corpses from the bridge

C ongoing conflicts between religions and ethnic groups seem never ending

D their death was an accident

VOCABULARY DEVELOPMENT *(50 points; 10 points each)*

Write the letter of the choice that is the *best* synonym for the Vocabulary word.

______ **6.** carnage

F bloodshed
G conflict
H imprisonment
J difference

______ **7.** relentless

A failed
B courageous
C moderate
D persistent

______ **8.** esteem

F permission
G respect
H scorn
J indifference

______ **9.** eradicating

A rejoicing
B writing
C explaining
D destroying

______ **10.** dilemma

F problem
G document
H signature
J idea

NAME ______ CLASS ______ DATE ______ SCORE ______

COLLECTION 11 SUMMATIVE TEST

Drama

This test asks you to use the skills and strategies you have learned in this collection. Read this excerpt from a play entitled *The Proposal,* and then answer the questions that follow it.

FROM The Proposal
by Anton Chekhov

Lomov. It's cold . . . I'm trembling all over, just as if I'd got an examination before me. The great thing is, I must have my mind made up. If I give myself time to think, to hesitate, to talk a lot, to look for an ideal, or for real love, then I'll never get married. . . . Brr! . . . It's cold! Natalya Stepanovna is an excellent housekeeper, not bad-looking, well-educated. . . . What more do I want? But I'm getting a noise in my ears from excitement. [*Drinks*] And it's impossible for me not to marry. . . . In the first place, I'm already 35—a critical age, so to speak. In the second place, I ought to lead a quiet and regular life. . . . I suffer from palpitations, I'm excitable and always getting awfully upset. . . . At this very moment my lips are trembling, and there's a twitch in my right eyebrow. . . . But the very worst of all is the way I sleep. I no sooner get into bed and begin to go off when suddenly something in my left side—gives a pull, and I can feel it in my shoulder and head. . . . I jump up like a lunatic, walk about a bit, and lie down again, but as soon as I begin to get off to sleep there's another pull! And this may happen twenty times. . . .
[NATALYA STEPANOVNA *comes in.*]
Natalya Stepanovna. Well, there! It's you, and Papa said, "Go; there's a merchant come for his goods." How do you do, Ivan Vassilevitch!
Lomov. How do you do, honoured Natalya Stepanovna.
Natalya Stepanovna. You must excuse my apron and négligée . . . we're shelling peas for drying. Why haven't you been here for such a long time? Sit down. . . . [*They seat themselves.*] Won't you have some lunch?
Lomov. No, thank you, I've had some already.
Natalya Stepanovna. Then, smoke. . . . Here are the matches. . . . The weather is splendid now, but yesterday it was so wet that the workmen didn't do anything all day. How much hay have you stacked? Just think, I felt greedy and had the whole field cut, and now I'm not at all pleased about it because I'm afraid my hay may rot. I ought to have waited a bit. But what's this? Why, you're in evening dress! Well, I never! Are you going to a ball, or what?—though I must say you look better. . . . Tell me, why are you got up like that?
Lomov. [*Excited*] You see, honoured Natalya Stepanovna . . . the fact is, I've made up my mind to ask you to hear me out . . . Of course you'll be surprised and perhaps even angry, but a . . . [*Aside*] It's awfully cold!
Natalya Stepanovna. What's the matter? [*Pause*] Well?
Lomov. I shall try to be brief. You must know, honoured Natalya Stepanovna, that I have long, since my childhood, in fact, had the privilege of knowing your family. My late aunt and her husband, from whom, as you know, I inherited my land, always had the greatest respect for your father and your late mother. The Lomovs and the Chubukovs have always had the most friendly, and I might almost

say the most affectionate, regard for each other. And, as you know, my land is a near neighbor of yours. You will remember that my Oxen Meadows touch your birchwoods.

Natalya Stepanovna. Excuse my interrupting you. You say, "my Oxen Meadows. . . ." But are they yours?

Lomov. Yes, mine.

Natalya Stepanovna. What are you talking about? Oxen Meadows are ours, not yours!

Lomov. No, mine, honoured Natalya Stepanovna.

Natalya Stepanovna. Well, I never knew that before. How do you make that out?

Lomov. How? I'm speaking of those Oxen Meadows which are wedged in between your birchwoods and the Burnt Marsh.

Natalya Stepanovna. Yes, yes. . . . They're ours.

Lomov. No, you're mistaken, honoured Natalya Stepanovna, they're mine.

Natalya Stepanovna. Just think, Ivan Vassilevitch! How long have they been yours?

Lomov. How long? As long as I can remember.

Natalya Stepanovna. Really, you won't get me to believe that!

Lomov. But you can see from the documents, honoured Natalya Stepanovna. Oxen Meadows, it's true, were once the subject of dispute, but now everybody knows that they are mine. There's nothing to argue about. You see, my aunt's grandmother gave the free use of these Meadows in perpetuity to the peasants of your father's grandfather, in return for which they were to make bricks for her. The peasants belonging to your father's grandfather had the free use of the Meadows for forty years, and had got into the habit of regarding them as their own, when it happened that . . .

Natalya Stepanovna. No, it isn't at all like that! Both my grandfather and great-grandfather reckoned that their land extended to the Burnt Marsh—which means that Oxen Meadows were ours. I don't see what there is to argue about. It's simply silly.

Lomov. I'll show you the documents, Natalya Stepanovna!

Natalya Stepanovna. No, you're simply joking, or making fun of me. . . . What a surprise! We've had the land for nearly three hundred years, and then we're suddenly told that it isn't ours! Ivan Vassilevitch, I can hardly believe my own ears. . . . These Meadows aren't worth much to me. They only come to five dessiatins [13½ acres], and are worth perhaps 300 roubles, but I can't stand unfairness. Say what you will, but I can't stand unfairness. . . .

Lomov. Then you make out that I'm a land-grabber, madam. Never in my life have I grabbed anybody else's land, and I shan't allow anybody to accuse me of having done so. . . . [*Quickly steps to the carafe and drinks more water*] Oxen Meadows are mine!

Natalya Stepanovna. It's not true, they're ours!

Lomov. Mine!

Natalya Stepanovna. It's not true! I'll prove it! I'll send my mowers out to the Meadows this very day!

Lomov. What?

Natalya Stepanovna. My mowers will be there this very day!

Lomov. I'll give it to them in the neck!

Natalya Stepanovna. You dare!
Lomov. [*Clutches at his heart*] Oxen Meadows are mine! You understand? Mine!
Natalya Stepanovna. Please don't shout! You can shout yourself hoarse in your own house, but here I must ask you to restrain yourself!
Lomov. If it wasn't, madam, for this awful, excruciating palpitation, if my whole inside wasn't upset, I'd talk to you in a different way! [*Yells*] Oxen Meadows are mine!
Natalya Stepanovna. Ours!
Lomov. Mine!
Natalya Stepanovna. Ours!
Lomov. Mine!

Vocabulary Skills *(25 points; 5 points each)*

Each of the underlined words below is also underlined in the selection. Re-read those passages in which the underlined words appear, and then use context clues and your prior knowledge to select an answer. On the line provided, write the letter of the word or words that *best* complete each sentence.

______ **1.** Lomov suffers from palpitations, or —

A headaches
B tremblings
C nightmares
D a skin rash

______ **2.** To act like a lunatic is to appear to be —

F crazy
G relaxed
H cautious
J hurried

______ **3.** A dispute is a(n) —

A agreement
B meeting
C argument
D war

______ **4.** To own something in perpetuity is to own it —

F secretly

G forever

H unlawfully

J for a short period of time

______ **5.** Something that is excruciating is —

A unimportant

B bothersome

C intensely painful

D short

COMPREHENSION *(25 points; 5 points each)*
On the line provided, write the letter of the *best* answer to each of the following items.

______ **6.** Which reason does Lomov *not* mention for wanting to marry Natalya?

F He is getting older.

G He needs to lead a quiet life.

H Natalya is an excellent housekeeper

J He is in love.

______ **7.** Which word *best* describes how Lomov feels about proposing to Natalya?

A joyous

B angry

C nervous

D confident

______ **8.** Why is Lomov attired in evening dress?

F He intends to go to a formal dinner after he speaks with Natalya.

G The scene takes place in the early evening.

H He wants Natalya to accompany him to a ball.

J He is trying to make a good impression.

______ **9.** The conflict in this scene takes place between —

A Lomov and Natalya

B Natalya's mowers and Lomov

C Lomov's sense of guilt and his desire for land

D Natalya's and Lomov's relatives

______ **10.** Which word *best* characterizes both Lomov and Natalya?

F patient

G honorable

H stubborn

J hardworking

READING SKILLS AND STRATEGIES: CONSTRUCTED RESPONSE *(10 points)*

Paraphrasing

11. At the beginning of this scene, Lomov reveals his state of mind and discusses his reasons for wanting to get married. Using your own words, paraphrase his monologue.

______

______

______

______

______

______

______

LITERARY FOCUS: CONSTRUCTED RESPONSE *(40 points; 10 points each)*

12. What do we learn about the personalities of Lomov and Natalya from the **dialogue** in this scene? Use examples to support your points.

______

______

______

______

______

______

______

13. How do the **stage directions** in this scene contribute to the characterization of Lomov? What hints do they give the audience about his feelings and his reactions to the situation? Use examples to support your points.

______

______

______

______

______

14. Find an example of **dramatic irony** in this scene. Then, explain how the irony affects the scene and shapes the audience's reactions.

______

______

______

______

______

______

15. Which elements of this scene are characteristic of a **farce**? Explain why each element you have selected is farcical, and support your points with examples from the scene.

______

______

______

______

______

______

NAME ______ CLASS ______ DATE ______ SCORE ______

Consumer and Workplace Documents

On the line provided, write the letter of the *best* answer to each of the following items. *(100 points; 10 points each)*

______ **1.** Which of the following items is *not* a **consumer document**?

- **A** Warranty
- **B** Product information
- **C** Instruction manual
- **D** Memo

______ **2.** Which of the following items is a **workplace document**?

- **F** An employee handbook
- **G** An encyclopedia
- **H** A speech by a former American president
- **J** A thesaurus

______ **3.** You use a **search engine** to —

- **A** find information on the World Wide Web
- **B** create and save a file
- **C** send a document to another person
- **D** cut and paste text in a document

______ **4.** What is a ***Works Cited*** list?

- **F** A list of recommended books
- **G** The books available in a branch of a library
- **H** A list of the sources used in a report
- **J** A list of all the works written by an author

______ **5.** You follow **technical directions** for all of the following activities *except* —

- **A** installing virus-protection software on your computer
- **B** operating a new microwave oven
- **C** reading a short story in an English class
- **D** programming the remote control with your favorite radio stations

______ **6.** The order in which ideas are presented in a **functional document** is called —

F sequence

G chronology

H design

J spacing

______ **7.** **Instructions** that do *not* help you to complete a task might be —

A divided into sections by topic

B missing a step

C printed in several colors

D numbered on each page

______ **8.** The **format** of a functional document —

F elaborates on essential information

G includes no text

H is in alphabetical order

J focuses the reader's attention on key words, sections, and ideas

______ **9.** A **header** in a functional document might include all of the following items *except* a —

A paragraph

B title

C number

D subtitle

______ **10.** **Graphic elements** include all of the following items *except* —

F icons

G photographs

H sentences

J drawings

NAME ______ CLASS ______ DATE ______ SCORE ______

SELECTION TEST **Student Edition page 949** **INFORMATIONAL TEXT**

Reading Consumer Documents

COMPREHENSION *(50 points; 10 points each)*
On the line provided, write the letter of the *best* answer to each of the following items.

______ **1.** The WYSIWYGame Arts warranty states that it is effective *only* if you —
- A are the original purchaser
- B received the product as a gift from the original purchaser
- C complete and mail in the registration card
- D deliver the entire product to WYSIWYGame Arts for inspection

______ **2.** The WYSIWYGame Arts warranty states that the company will replace any defective part without charge to the purchaser for a period of —
- F one year from the date of the original purchase
- G ninety days after the warranty has run out
- H one year and ninety days from the date of the original purchase
- J ninety days from the date of the original purchase

______ **3.** The product information for the game console lists all of the following specifications *except* —
- A an Ethernet port
- B 164 MB of memory
- C an 800-MHz CPU
- D 1920 x 1080 maximum resolution

______ **4.** The safety information states that you should unplug the appliance and contact a qualified service person in all of the following instances *except* if the —
- F game console has been exposed to rain or water
- G power-supply cord or plug has been damaged
- H game console has been installed without ventilation
- J game console has been dropped or the cabinet has been damaged

______ **5.** According to the safety information, all service must be done by —
- A the original consumer purchaser
- B the place of original purchase
- C any electronic dealership
- D qualified service personnel

NAME ______ CLASS ______ DATE ______ SCORE ______

READING INFORMATIONAL TEXT *(50 points; 10 points each)*

On the line provided, write the letter of the *best* answer to each of the following items.

______ **6.** A **warranty** gives details on what happens if the product does not work as promised and —

F lists the prices of replacement parts

G what you must do to receive service

H gives instructions on how to use the product

J gives directions for installation and use

______ **7.** A **contract** includes information —

A on the legal uses of the product

B describing what the product will do

C identifying the features of the product

D about the store where the product was purchased

______ **8.** An **instruction manual** contains instructions on —

F how to use the product

G where to go for service

H the legal uses of the product

J how to fill out the warranty

______ **9.** **Technical directions** provide directions —

A to service locations

B on how to fill out the warranty

C for installation and use

D for several products

______ **10.** When dealing with **consumer documents,** it is important to —

F read everything carefully before throwing out what you don't need

G fill out the warranty and throw away the product information

H read everything carefully before putting the documents in a safe place

J read the contract in case of a lawsuit

SELECTION TEST *Student Edition page 952* INFORMATIONAL TEXT

Following Technical Directions

COMPREHENSION *(50 points; 10 points each)*
On the line provided, write the letter of the *best* answer to each of the following items.

_____ **1.** According to "FAQs About Search Engines," a search engine —
- **A** lists links to browsers on the World Wide Web
- **B** is another name for a browser
- **C** is a Web site that gives technical directions on how to use a computer
- **D** helps you locate information on the World Wide Web

_____ **2.** According to "FAQs About Search Engines," you begin a search request by —
- **F** customizing the browser
- **G** bookmarking favorite sites
- **H** hitting the return key
- **J** typing in a keyword

_____ **3.** According to "FAQs About Search Engines," customizing your browser involves —
- **A** typing in keywords
- **B** asking computer-savvy friends
- **C** finding relevant listings
- **D** following technical directions

_____ **4.** If you want QuickFind 1.0 as your home page, the technical directions tell you to first —
- **F** select Home Page under Browser Options
- **G** copy the URL from the Address window
- **H** click on the Address field on the Home Page
- **J** click on OK at the bottom right

_____ **5.** After having pasted in the new URL according to the technical directions, you finish customizing your browser by —
- **A** selecting Home Page
- **B** clicking on OK
- **C** pulling down the Edit menu
- **D** clicking the Address field

READING INFORMATIONAL TEXT *(50 points; 10 points each)*

On the line provided, write the letter of the *best* answer to each of the following items.

______ **6.** A Web site that enables you to search World Wide Web pages for a specific topic is called a —

- **F** search engine
- **G** browser
- **H** link
- **J** virus

______ **7.** A software program that enables you to access the World Wide Web is called a —

- **A** search engine
- **B** browser
- **C** link
- **D** virus

______ **8.** Informational materials that tell you how to use computers as well as other scientific, mechanical, and electronic products are called —

- **F** government regulations
- **G** technical directions
- **H** product information
- **J** memorandums

______ **9.** All of the following texts are **technical documents** *except* —

- **A** product information
- **B** how-to instructions
- **C** installation instructions
- **D** scientific procedures

______ **10.** FAQs is an abbreviation of —

- **F** Famous Alluded Quotations
- **G** Focused Answers and Questions
- **H** Fair And Quick
- **J** Frequently Asked Questions

NAME ____________________ CLASS ____________________ DATE ____________ SCORE ____________

SELECTION TEST **Student Edition page 956** **INFORMATIONAL TEXT**

Citing Internet Sources

COMPREHENSION *(50 points; 10 points each)*
On the line provided, write the letter of the *best* answer to each of the following items.

______ **1.** According to the citation for "About the New WYSIWYGame Arts Console," when was the source accessed?

- **A** June 7, 2001
- **B** July 27, 2001
- **C** June 27, 2001
- **D** July 7, 2001

______ **2.** The article from an online nonprofit magazine was written by —

- **F** Digital Watchdog
- **G** Lloyd Case
- **H** The Library of Congress
- **J** I. B. Sleuthing

______ **3.** *Building the Ultimate Game PC* is available —

- **A** only online
- **B** only in print
- **C** online and in print
- **D** only by mail order

______ **4.** The note card on consumer information has information from a(n) —

- **F** online source
- **G** print magazine
- **H** technical document
- **J** workplace document

______ **5.** According to the note card on a public document, why is there no print version of the User's Manual for Compiler Version 2.2?

- **A** It is changed too often.
- **B** The software is interactive.
- **C** The hardware is only available online.
- **D** The compiler is user friendly.

READING INFORMATIONAL TEXT *(50 points; 10 points each)*

On the line provided, write the letter of the *best* answer to each of the following items.

______ **6.** An orderly list of works cited in a research report is called a —

F source

G note card

H citation

J bibliography

______ **7.** Which of the following citations is in the correct order?

A Chapter 7,–"Worms in the Garden." Wiggles, Susan. Garden of Eatin'. Savannah, GA: Backyard Publishing, 2002.

B Chapter 7,–"Worms in the Garden." Garden of Eatin'. Savannah, GA: Backyard Publishing, 2002. Wiggles, Susan.

C Backyard Publishing, Savannah, GA: Wiggles, Susan. Chapter 7,– "Worms in the Garden." Garden of Eatin'. 2002.

D Wiggles, Susan. Chapter 7,–"Worms in the Garden." Garden of Eatin'. Savannah, GA: Backyard Publishing, 2002.

______ **8.** In a bibliography, citations are listed —

F alphabetically by title

G in chronological order by date of publication

H alphabetically by the author's last name

J in order of access

______ **9.** Citations of Internet sources require more information than citations of print sources because —

A not everyone has a computer

B online information may be updated daily

C online sources are less reliable than print

D Internet addresses frequently change

______ **10.** Bibliographic citations follow —

F consumer document format

G technical citation style

H the Dewey decimal system

J Modern Language Association style

NAME ______ CLASS ______ DATE ______ SCORE ______

SELECTION TEST **Student Edition page 960** INFORMATIONAL TEXT

Analyzing Functional Workplace Documents

COMPREHENSION *(50 points; 10 points each)*
On the line provided, write the letter of the *best* answer to each of the following items.

______ **1.** According to "WYSIWYGame Arts Shareware Agreement," the user has the right to use the software —

A in perpetuity
B on several computers
C on one computer only
D to generate sales commissions

______ **2.** "WYSIWYGame Arts Shareware Agreement" restricts all of the following activities *except* —

F translating
G reverse programming
H decompiling
J using

______ **3.** Section 4 of "WYSIWYGame Arts Shareware Agreement" tells the user that the software —

A is shareware, not freeware
B has no warranty
C has restrictions
D has limitation of liability

______ **4.** The icon below the title on the WYSIWYGame Arts Web page allows you to —

F upload
G download
H link to another page
J edit the current page

______ **5.** The bulleted, underlined entries on the WYSIWYGame Arts Web page are —

A links
B headers
C downloading options
D format options

READING INFORMATIONAL TEXT *(50 points; 10 points each)*

On the line provided, write the letter of the *best* answer to each of the following items.

______ **6.** The exclusive propriety rights granted to you as the author of a work are called a —

F copyright

G license

H shareware license agreement

J functional workplace document

______ **7.** The design of a **functional workplace document** contains all of the following characteristics *except* —

A graphic elements

B typographic elements

C software elements

D formatting elements

______ **8.** Each major section of a **shareware agreement** usually has all of the following elements *except* —

F a new paragraph

G numerical identification

H footnotes to define difficult words

J a header in boldface capital letters

______ **9.** Two examples of **logical sequence** for a functional workplace document are —

A how-to and by-the-numbers

B point-by-point and by-the-book

C alphabetical and chronological

D step-by-step and point-by-point

______ **10.** The **format** of a document focuses the reader's attention on —

F icons, logos, and pictographs

G white space, borders, and underlining

H key words, sections, and ideas

J capital letters, boldface terms, and FAQs

Evaluating the Logic of Functional Documents

COMPREHENSION *(50 points; 10 points each)*

On the line provided, write the letter of the *best* answer to each of the following items.

______ **1.** What is the problem with the order for downloading the WYSIWYGame Arts Web page?

- **A** The browser will automatically download the file into the folder you have specified.
- **B** The instructions tell you to download without telling you to first select a destination folder.
- **C** Your decompression software will automatically load, decompress the game, and quit.
- **D** The instructions tell users to delete an important file.

______ **2.** Step 2 tells you how to decompress —

- **F** .ZIP format files
- **G** .exe files only
- **H** any file
- **J** browser files

______ **3.** .ZIP files —

- **A** is another name for .exe files
- **B** work with faster game software
- **C** are compressed files
- **D** are decompressed files

______ **4.** The game file has been compressed for —

- **F** faster uploading
- **G** easy installation
- **H** faster downloading
- **J** software protection

______ **5.** Step 5 is out of order for all of the following reasons *except* —

- **A** you cannot decompress game files before you download decompression software
- **B** you can play the game after it has been installed
- **C** you cannot install compressed game software
- **D** you must clean up the directory before you decompress the game files

NAME ______ CLASS ______ DATE ______ SCORE ______

READING INFORMATIONAL TEXT *(50 points; 10 points each)*

On the line provided, write the letter of the *best* answer to each of the following items.

______ **6.** All of the following activities are occasions for using **functional documents** *except* —

F downloading a software game

G putting together a swing set

H using an ATM

J calling for pizza delivery

______ **7.** In order for a functional document to serve its purpose properly, the information has to be presented in a(n) —

A chronological sequence

B alphabetical sequence

C logical step-by-step sequence

D eye-grabbing format

______ **8.** **Logical sequencing** requires that —

F hardware and software be compatible

G you read all of the consumer documents

H all the steps are included and presented in the correct order

J all the steps are logical and easy to follow

______ **9.** Instructions can be misunderstood if a document is *not* —

A written at a third-grade level

B clear and logical

C interactively formatted

D illustrated with diagrams

______ **10.** Documents that are illogically sequenced or have missing steps are —

F easy to follow

G impossible to use

H too technical to understand

J written by technocrats

NAME ______ CLASS ______ DATE ______ SCORE ______

Features of Consumer and Workplace Documents

This test asks you to use the skills and strategies you have learned in this collection. Read this functional document from the Santa Monica Fire Department. Then, answer the questions that follow it.

Fire Extinguishers for the Home

Do you have a portable fire extinguisher? If not, why not? If you do have one, is it the right one for the job, and do you know how to use it? When properly maintained and used, a fire extinguisher can save lives and property by putting out a small fire or controlling it until the fire department arrives.

Portable fire extinguishers, made for personal use, are designed to fight small, confined fires. Even when used to fight a small fire, they are effective only when:

- The extinguisher is of the right type for the fire being fought
- The extinguisher has been properly maintained
- The extinguisher is within easy reach
- The operator knows how to use the extinguisher

Select Your Extinguisher

- It should bear the seal of an independent testing laboratory, such as Underwriters Laboratories (UL) or Factory Mutual (FM). These seals certify that the unit has been type tested and passed for the specified type and size of fire listed.
- It should be labeled as to the type of fire it is intended to extinguish (see "Classes of Fires and Extinguishers" below).
- It must be large enough to put out the fire. The higher the rating on a class A or class B extinguisher, the more fire it can put out.

Classes of Fires and Extinguishers

There are four basic classes of fires, and extinguishers for those fires, grouped according to the type of material involved in fire:

- ***Class A*** fires involve ordinary combustibles such as wood, cloth, paper, rubber, and many plastics. *Class A* extinguishers are water based, often using compressed air to deliver the water. Water acts as a cooling agent to extinguish the fire.
- ***Class B*** fires involve flammable liquids such as gasoline, oil, grease, tar, oil-based paint, lacquer, and flammable gas. *Class B* extinguishers use carbon-dioxide gas, dry chemicals, or foam to cover the fire and exclude air.
- ***Class C*** fires involve energized electrical equipment, including wiring, fuse boxes, circuit breakers, machinery, and appliances. *Class C* extinguishers require the use of nonconductive agents such as carbon dioxide or dry chemicals. Carbon dioxide is the preferred agent, as it leaves no residue to be cleaned up.
- ***Class D*** fires involve combustible metals such as magnesium and sodium. Dry powders are used as the extinguishing medium; they cover the burning material to absorb the heat. Care must be taken not to use an agent that might react with the metal.

ABC Extinguishers: Portable extinguishers labeled "A-B-C" may be used on class A, B, and C fires, but are not acceptable for class D fires.

Extinguisher Sizes
All extinguishers are rated as to the size of fire they are designed to handle. The rating is a number from 1 to 40 for a class A fire and 1 to 640 for a class B fire. For example, a 20-B-rated extinguisher can handle a flammable-liquid fire twice as big as one that a 10-B extinguisher can; the rating will appear on the label.

Installation and Maintenance
Extinguishers should be installed in plain view out of the reach of small children, near an escape route, and away from stoves and heating appliances. Extinguishers require routine care; read your operator's manual. Rechargeable models must be serviced after every use. Disposable models can be used only once and then must be replaced. Following manufacturer's instructions, check the pressure in your extinguishers once a month.

Using Your Extinguisher
Stand about six feet from the fire and follow the four-step PASS method to extinguish the fire. If the fire does not go out immediately, leave the area at once. Even if the fire does go out, you should still call the Fire Department.

- **P**ull the pin out to unlock the operating lever and allow you to discharge the extinguisher. Some extinguishers have other devices, such as a lock latch, that prevent inadvertent operation.
- **A**im low, pointing at the base of the fire.
- **S**queeze the handle or press the lever or button to discharge the extinguishing agent; releasing will stop the discharge.
- **S**weep the nozzle from side to side at the base of the fire until the flames appear to be out. Watch the fire area. If the fire reignites, repeat the process.

Before you begin to fight a fire, be sure that all of the following is true:

- You know what you are doing.
- You have the proper extinguisher, and it is in working order.
- Everyone has left or is leaving the building.
- The fire department has been notified.
- The fire is confined to a small area and is not spreading beyond it.
- You have an unobstructed escape route to which the fire will not spread.

When in doubt, turn around, leave the room, shut the door, and leave the building.

VOCABULARY SKILLS *(25 points; 5 points each)*
The Vocabulary words below are underlined in the selection. Write the letter of the choice that is the *best* synonym for the Vocabulary word.

______ **1.** extinguish

A light
B extinct
C put out
D exit

_____ **2.** combustibles

F combinable

G busted

H explosives

J inert

_____ **3.** energized

A powerless

B oversized

C enough

D electrified

_____ **4.** maintenance

F foremost

G containment

H neglect

J upkeep

_____ **5.** inadvertent

A deliberate

B accidental

C adventuresome

D vertical

COMPREHENSION *(25 points; 5 points each)*
On the line provided, write the letter of the *best* answer to each of the following items.

_____ **6.** To be effective, a portable fire extinguisher should meet all the following conditions *except* —

F the right type for the fire being fought

G properly maintained

H within easy reach

J operated by an unfamiliar user

_____ **7.** Which of the following substances do class A extinguishers use to put out fires?

A Carbon dioxide gas

B Dry chemicals

C Water

D Magnesium

______ **8.** Class C fires are caused by —

- **F** combustible metals
- **G** flammable liquids
- **H** energized electrical equipment
- **J** materials such as wood, paper, plastic, and so on

______ **9.** Extinguishers should *not* be installed —

- **A** in plain view
- **B** near heating appliances
- **C** near an escape route
- **D** above the reach of children

______ **10.** You should check the pressure in your fire extinguisher once a —

- **F** day
- **G** week
- **H** month
- **J** year

READING FUNCTIONAL DOCUMENTS

Understanding the Format of Functional Documents *(10 points)*

11. Under which heading would you learn how to discharge a fire extinguisher?

- **A** "Select Your Extinguisher"
- **B** "Classes of Fires and Extinguishers"
- **C** "Installation and Maintenance"
- **D** "Using Your Extinguisher"

Following Technical Directions *(20 points)*

12. How many steps are there to using a fire extinguisher? What are the steps?

______

______

______

Analyzing the Logic of Functional Documents *(20 points)*

13. Under the heading "Classes of Fires and Extinguishers," what two logical sequences are used to list the types of extinguishers?

End-of-Year Test

Reading and Literary Analysis

DIRECTIONS This story tells about two young men who faced a test of their friendship. Read the story and answer questions 1 through 11.

Damon and Pythias

Damon and Pythias had been the best of friends since childhood. Each trusted the other like a brother, and each knew in his heart there was nothing he would not do for his friend. Eventually the time came for them to prove the depth of their devotion. It happened this way.

Dionysius, the ruler of Syracuse, grew annoyed when he heard about the kind of speeches Pythias was giving. The young scholar was telling the public that no man should have unlimited power over another, and that absolute tyrants were unjust kings. In a fit of rage, Dionysius summoned Pythias and his friend.

"Who do you think you are, spreading unrest among the people?" he demanded.

"I spread only the truth," Pythias answered. "There can be nothing wrong with that."

"And does your truth hold that kings have too much power and that their laws are not good for their subjects?"

"If a king has seized power without permission of the people, then that is what I say."

"This kind of talk is treason," Dionysius shouted. "You are conspiring to overthrow me. Retract what you've said, or face the consequences."

"I will retract nothing," Pythias answered.

"Then you will die. Do you have any last requests?"

"Yes. Let me go home just long enough to say goodbye to my wife and children and to put my household in order."

"I see you not only think I'm unjust, you think I'm stupid as well," Dionysius laughed scornfully. "If I let you leave Syracuse, I have no doubt I will never see you again."

"I will give you a pledge," Pythias said.

"What kind of pledge could you possibly give to make me think you will ever return?" Dionysius demanded.

At that instant Damon, who had stood quietly beside his friend, stepped forward.

"I will be his pledge," he said. "Keep me here in Syracuse, as your prisoner, until Pythias returns. Our friendship is well known to you. You can be sure Pythias will return so long as you hold me."

GO ON

Dionysius studied the two friends silently. "Very well," he said at last. "But if you are willing to take the place of your friend, you must be willing to accept his sentence if he breaks his promise. If Pythias does not return to Syracuse, you will die in his place."

"He will keep his word," Damon replied. "I have no doubt of that."

Pythias was allowed to go free for a time, and Damon was thrown into prison. After several days, when Pythias failed to reappear, Dionysius's curiosity got the better of him, and he went to the prison to see if Damon was yet sorry he had made such a bargain.

"Your time is almost up," the ruler of Syracuse sneered. "It will be useless to beg for mercy. You were a fool to rely on your friend's promise. Did you really think he would sacrifice his life for you or anyone else?"

"He has merely been delayed," Damon answered steadily. "The winds have kept him from sailing, or perhaps he has met with some accident on the road. But if it is humanly possible, he will be here on time. I am as confident of his virtue as I am of my own existence."

Dionysius was startled at the prisoner's confidence. "We shall soon see," he said, and left Damon in his cell.

The fatal day arrived. Damon was brought from prison and led before the executioner. Dionysius greeted him with a smug smile.

"It seems your friend has not turned up," he laughed. "What do you think of him now?"

"He is my friend," Damon answered. "I trust him."

Even as he spoke, the doors flew open, and Pythias staggered into the room. He was pale and bruised and half speechless from exhaustion. He rushed to the arms of his friend.

"You are safe, praise the gods," he gasped. "It seemed as though the fates were conspiring against us. My ship was wrecked in a storm, and then bandits attacked me on the road. But I refused to give up hope, and at last I've made it back in time. I am ready to receive my sentence of death."

Dionysius heard his words with astonishment. His eyes and his heart were opened. It was impossible for him to resist the power of such constancy.

"The sentence is revoked," he declared. "I never believed that such faith and loyalty could exist in friendship. You have shown me how wrong I was, and it is only right that you be rewarded with your freedom. But I ask that in return you do me one great service."

"What service do you mean?" the friends asked.

"Teach me how to be part of so worthy a friendship."

1 The first paragraph of this story MOSTLY provides—

A the crisis or turning point in the story

B the specific obstacles the characters will face

C complications that contribute to rising action

D information to establish characters and background

2 Read this sentence from the selection.

> Eventually the time came for them to prove the depth of their devotion.

The underlined phrase MOSTLY serves to foreshadow—

A Damon's pledge to be held in place of Pythias

B Pythias's request to go home to put his house in order

C Dionysius's demand that Pythias retract his statements

D Dionysius's query about why Pythias is spreading unrest

3 Dionysius was angered because Pythias stated publicly that kings should—

A be overthrown because they are corrupt

B have absolute rule over their people

C use their power according to the will of the people

D step aside and allow the people to govern themselves

4 Read this sentence from the story.

> It was impossible for him to resist the power of such constancy.

The word constancy means about the same thing as—

A deceit

B ambition

C loyalty

D stubbornness

5 Which is the BEST paraphrase of the following statement by Damon: "I am as confident of his virtue as I am of my own existence."

A I care little for my own existence.

B I trust my friend as completely as I trust myself.

C My friend has high morals that are worthy of respect.

D I am not suspicious of my friend's motives.

6 Why was Pythias delayed in returning to his friend who was facing execution?

A Pythias's family begged him not to return to Damon and the king.

B Pythias had no intention of ending his public protests.

C Pythias was afraid to face the executioner.

D Pythias was confronted by perils on land and sea.

GO ON

7 The climax of the story occurs when—

A Pythias is allowed to go free for a time

B Dionysius tells Damon that his time is nearly up

C Damon is led before the executioner

D Pythias staggers into the room

8 In the resolution of the story, readers learn that—

A Dionysius revokes the sentence and tries to learn from the friends

B Pythias retracts his treasonous statements to save his friend

C Damon suffers his friend's sentence, but dies nobly

D Pythias was delayed when his ship was wrecked at sea

9 In this story, Damon and Pythias can BEST be described as—

A corrupt and devious

B devoted and principled

C ruthless and callous

D careless and naïve

10 If the myth is viewed as an allegory, Damon and Pythias would represent faithfulness, and Dionysius would MOST likely represent—

A fear

B anger

C cynicism

D contempt

11 Which statement BEST expresses one theme of this selection?

A A true friend never reveals your secrets.

B A friend will never tell you your faults.

C True friendships are based on complete trust.

D Some people are friends in private but not in public.

Reading and Literary Analysis *(continued)*

DIRECTIONS This article is about a museum exhibit in which you feel as if you are part of the display. Read the article and answer questions 12 through 22.

"Virtual Pompeii"

An alliance of artistry, archaeology, and science, "Virtual Pompeii" allows museumgoers to travel back in time to that ancient Roman city and see it as it was shortly before it was destroyed by the eruption of Mount Vesuvius. Incorporating advanced graphics and a wide range of cutting-edge technologies, this virtual reality production was first presented at San Francisco's M.H. de Young Memorial Museum in 1995. Since then it has been traveling to different museums throughout the country.

The exhibit focuses on a computer-generated re-creation of Pompeii's Temple of Isis. (Isis was an important Egyptian deity whose worship gradually spread across the Mediterranean Sea to Greece and then to Italy.) The reconstructed temple exists within a virtual, or imaginary, space maintained by a computer. The expression "virtual reality" was coined to describe imaginary space applications that are generated by computer and make people feel as if they were really *in* the space, rather than looking in from the outside, as if through a window or a movie screen.

The "Virtual Pompeii" exhibit offers visitors two ways to explore it: individually or as part of a group. Assisted by museum staff, one person at a time wears a head-mounted display that resembles a helmet. Built in to the helmet are headphones, and goggles holding two very small videos, one for each eye. When the user's head moves, the computer dynamically changes the view to create an illusion of "being there." By manipulating a "trackball," the user can navigate through the space. Everything the user sees is projected onto an overhead screen in the exhibit area. The overhead image can be shown in 3-D mode and those watching can don 3-D glasses for a shared virtual reality experience.

Participants who "walk" through the exhibit hear through the headphones the sound of their feet treading the cobblestone streets of ancient Pompeii. They hear a street vendor ask them to buy onions pulled from the ground that morning. Participants who choose to approach Isis's temple will see bald-headed priests in long white robes preparing to open the doors. The virtual reality temple is just as archaeologists believe the real

GO ON

temple must have looked—small, ornate, and decorated with a mixture of Egyptian, Greek, and Roman architectural features.

"Virtual Pompeii" permits viewers to explore the Temple of Isis's colonnaded walkways, courtyards, architectural structures, sculptures, and colorful murals, all reproduced in amazing detail. The sense of reality is heightened by animated figures, including a chanter and a flautist, and by the audio track.

12 What is the author's MAIN purpose in writing this passage?

A to explain what caused the destruction of Pompeii

B to inform readers about a virtual-reality exhibit on Pompeii

C to describe the archaeology of Pompeii

D to persuade readers to visit the actual ruins of Pompeii

13 Which statement BEST summarizes the main idea of the passage?

A Visitors travel to Mount Vesuvius on a tour sponsored by the de Young Museum.

B Visitors can use technology individually or in a group.

C The Temple of Isis, located at Pompeii, was an important religious and architectural site.

D Technology allows visitors to get a sense of early history.

14 The phrase "virtual reality" means—

A an imaginary space created by a computer

B a space that actually exists

C a space that is technologically perfect

D an ethically good space

15 The passage says that the "Virtual Pompeii" exhibit was created by an alliance of artistry, archaeology, and science. Which part of the exhibit did archaeologists probably contribute?

A the development of the technology

B the creation of the audio soundtracks

C how the temple actually looked

D the financial support

16 What does the word deity mean in the following sentence from the passage?

> Isis was an important Egyptian deity whose worship gradually spread across the Mediterranean Sea to Greece and then to Italy.

A an explorer

B a god or goddess

C an important temple

D a believer in Isis

17 **How does an individual experience different sites in "Virtual Pompeii"?**

A The individual looks at an overhead screen.

B The individual manipulates a hand-operated device.

C The individual holds two small video cameras to record and control what the group sees.

D The individual wears two small video cameras to see what the group chooses to experience.

18 **How does a group see the exhibit?**

A in head-mounted displays

B on an overhead screen

C with two small video monitors

D with a trackball

19 **In preparing a report on the ideas in this passage, what would be the MOST relevant question to ask about the museum exhibit?**

A Where does the museum buy the large quantities of 3-D glasses used by visitors?

B Why were there not more animated figures?

C Where can one learn more about the technology used to create this exhibit?

D Why wasn't technology used to forecast the eruption of Mount Vesuvius?

20 **The learning advantage of a virtual reality experience over a traditional classroom approach is that the computer-directed experience—**

A provides participants enough distance from the event to draw objective conclusions

B can easily be conducted right in the classroom

C provides the sense of being there

D aims at concentrating only on factual background

21 **Which sentence is the BEST conclusion about the "Virtual Pompeii" exhibit?**

A The exhibit can be enjoyed by people of all ages.

B The exhibit gives visitors a sense of life in Pompeii.

C The exhibit explains how computer technology works.

D The exhibit enables visitors to describe imaginary places.

22 **For a research paper on the destruction of Pompeii, which would be the BEST source to use?**

A *Vacation Under the Volcano* by Mary Pope Osborne; illustrated by Sal Murdocca

B *Naples: With Pompeii & the Amalfi Coast* by Deni Bown

C *An Illustrated History of Interior Decoration: From Pompeii to Art Nouveau* by Mario Praz

D *The Buried City of Pompeii: What It Was Like When Vesuvius Exploded (I Was There)* by Shelley Tanaka

Reading and Literary Analysis *(continued)*

DIRECTIONS These directions tell how to hook up a video-game system. Read the directions and answer questions 23 through 30.

Ten Easy Steps

Directions for installing the ProFun Video-Game System on your TV

1. Find the Audio/Video (A/V) input jacks, usually located on the back of your TV.
2. Insert the yellow end of the A/V cable into the yellow Video IN jack of the TV.
3. Insert the red end of the A/V cable into the red Audio IN jack of the TV.
4. Insert the white end of the A/V cable into the white Audio IN jack of the TV.

Note: Use a slight twisting motion while pushing the plugs into the input jacks.

5. Insert the black rectangular plug of the A/V cable into the *Multi A/V Out* connection on the back of the ProFun game system.
6. Plug the ProFun game system AC adaptor into an electrical wall outlet.

After the game system is connected to the TV,

7. Insert a game cartridge completely into the game system.
8. Plug the controllers into the front of the ProFun game system. The far left outlet is for Player 1's controller.
9. Slide the power switch to the "ON" position.
10. Turn on the TV and locate the *Input Select* control. It may be called *Input Select*, *AUX*, *Line*, *Line In*, *Input*, *Source*, *Select*, *In*, or *External*. When the game is displayed on the screen, begin playing.

23 **To explain how to install this system, ProFun relies on—**

A personal descriptions of the process
B detailed explanations of the parts
C testimonials from other customers
D a sequence of specific steps

24 **Why does ProFun provide several terms for the *Input Select* control?**

A The term may vary from television to television.
B The term is not identified on the television.
C ProFun is endorsing certain television brands.
D ProFun wants to satisfy speakers of different languages.

25 **If you are Player 1 and your controller will not work, what is the BEST thing to do first?**

A Use the other controller.
B Turn off the television.
C Check to see that the controller is plugged in.
D Call the manufacturer.

26 **It is MOST likely that the directions are in the form of very brief commands in order to—**

A make the installation process easier to understand
B help consumers who can't read very well
C conserve paper for printing the directions
D show that long explanations are not necessary

27 **If the game does not display on the screen, it would be good to do all of the following EXCEPT—**

A look for the jacks in the back of the TV
B make certain that a cartridge is in the system
C make sure that the TV is turned on
D check to see that the A/V connections to the TV are tight

28 **It is MOST likely that the directions say to use a slight twisting motion because the—**

A pieces are made poorly
B pieces are easily broken apart
C cables can be hazardous at this point
D cable plugs will go in more easily

29 **It is important to know what "A/V" means because televisions may—**

A have different labeling systems
B have several different video outputs
C not label the input jacks
D have different inputs for audio and video

30 **What is MOST likely to happen if the color-coded cables are plugged into the correct jacks?**

A The television reception will be improved.
B The game controller will not work as it should.
C The *Input Select* switch will flip up.
D The game will display on the television.

End-of-Year Test

Vocabulary

DIRECTIONS Choose the word or group of words that means the same, or about the same, as the underlined word. Then mark the answer you have chosen.

SAMPLE A

To lob something is to—

A lift it
B remove it
C admire it
D throw it

31 Someone who is serene is—

A intelligent
B confused
C peaceful
D resentful

32 An admonition is a—

A warning
B request
C calamity
D hypothesis

33 If you mar something, you—

A forget it
B damage it
C desire it
D reject it

34 Something that is meager is—

A rebellious
B stubborn
C impartial
D inadequate

35 Conform is another word for—

A investigate
B contradict
C comply
D gather

36 Something that is iridescent is—

A rainbow-colored
B highly original
C irritating
D decomposed

GO ON

End-of-Year Test

Vocabulary

DIRECTIONS Choose the word or words that mean the same, or about the same, as the underlined word. Then mark the space for the answer you have chosen.

SAMPLE B

That problem is a source of great vexation to me.

A comfort
B attraction
C promise
D distress

37 **I do not underestimate the talents of my formidable opponent.**

A commonly accepted
B increasingly uninterested
C strikingly impressive
D completely helpless

38 **My words of loathing left a foul taste in my mouth.**

A relief
B innocence
C solemn feeling
D bitter hate

39 **Because it was important that the message be heard, I reiterated it.**

A deleted
B repeated
C criticized
D reviewed

40 **I was drawn into the vortex of the crisis.**

A whirlpool
B vapor
C charm
D selection

NAME ______ CLASS ______ DATE ______ SCORE ______

ENTRY-LEVEL TEST

Answer Sheet

Reading and Literary Analysis/Vocabulary

1 Ⓐ Ⓑ Ⓒ Ⓓ
2 Ⓐ Ⓑ Ⓒ Ⓓ
3 Ⓐ Ⓑ Ⓒ Ⓓ
4 Ⓐ Ⓑ Ⓒ Ⓓ
5 Ⓐ Ⓑ Ⓒ Ⓓ
6 Ⓐ Ⓑ Ⓒ Ⓓ
7 Ⓐ Ⓑ Ⓒ Ⓓ
8 Ⓐ Ⓑ Ⓒ Ⓓ
9 Ⓐ Ⓑ Ⓒ Ⓓ
10 Ⓐ Ⓑ Ⓒ Ⓓ
11 Ⓐ Ⓑ Ⓒ Ⓓ
12 Ⓐ Ⓑ Ⓒ Ⓓ
13 Ⓐ Ⓑ Ⓒ Ⓓ
14 Ⓐ Ⓑ Ⓒ Ⓓ
15 Ⓐ Ⓑ Ⓒ Ⓓ
16 Ⓐ Ⓑ Ⓒ Ⓓ
17 Ⓐ Ⓑ Ⓒ Ⓓ
18 Ⓐ Ⓑ Ⓒ Ⓓ
19 Ⓐ Ⓑ Ⓒ Ⓓ
20 Ⓐ Ⓑ Ⓒ Ⓓ
21 Ⓐ Ⓑ Ⓒ Ⓓ
22 Ⓐ Ⓑ Ⓒ Ⓓ
23 Ⓐ Ⓑ Ⓒ Ⓓ
24 Ⓐ Ⓑ Ⓒ Ⓓ
25 Ⓐ Ⓑ Ⓒ Ⓓ
26 Ⓐ Ⓑ Ⓒ Ⓓ
27 Ⓐ Ⓑ Ⓒ Ⓓ
28 Ⓐ Ⓑ Ⓒ Ⓓ
29 Ⓐ Ⓑ Ⓒ Ⓓ
30 Ⓐ Ⓑ Ⓒ Ⓓ

Sample A
Ⓐ Ⓑ Ⓒ Ⓓ

31 Ⓐ Ⓑ Ⓒ Ⓓ
32 Ⓐ Ⓑ Ⓒ Ⓓ
33 Ⓐ Ⓑ Ⓒ Ⓓ
34 Ⓐ Ⓑ Ⓒ Ⓓ
35 Ⓐ Ⓑ Ⓒ Ⓓ
36 Ⓐ Ⓑ Ⓒ Ⓓ

Sample B
Ⓐ Ⓑ Ⓒ Ⓓ

37 Ⓐ Ⓑ Ⓒ Ⓓ
38 Ⓐ Ⓑ Ⓒ Ⓓ
39 Ⓐ Ⓑ Ⓒ Ⓓ
40 Ⓐ Ⓑ Ⓒ Ⓓ

NAME ____________________ CLASS ____________ DATE ____________ SCORE ____________

END-OF-YEAR TEST

Answer Sheet

Reading and Literary Analysis/Vocabulary

1 Ⓐ Ⓑ Ⓒ Ⓓ
2 Ⓐ Ⓑ Ⓒ Ⓓ
3 Ⓐ Ⓑ Ⓒ Ⓓ
4 Ⓐ Ⓑ Ⓒ Ⓓ
5 Ⓐ Ⓑ Ⓒ Ⓓ
6 Ⓐ Ⓑ Ⓒ Ⓓ
7 Ⓐ Ⓑ Ⓒ Ⓓ
8 Ⓐ Ⓑ Ⓒ Ⓓ
9 Ⓐ Ⓑ Ⓒ Ⓓ
10 Ⓐ Ⓑ Ⓒ Ⓓ
11 Ⓐ Ⓑ Ⓒ Ⓓ
12 Ⓐ Ⓑ Ⓒ Ⓓ
13 Ⓐ Ⓑ Ⓒ Ⓓ
14 Ⓐ Ⓑ Ⓒ Ⓓ
15 Ⓐ Ⓑ Ⓒ Ⓓ
16 Ⓐ Ⓑ Ⓒ Ⓓ
17 Ⓐ Ⓑ Ⓒ Ⓓ
18 Ⓐ Ⓑ Ⓒ Ⓓ
19 Ⓐ Ⓑ Ⓒ Ⓓ
20 Ⓐ Ⓑ Ⓒ Ⓓ
21 Ⓐ Ⓑ Ⓒ Ⓓ
22 Ⓐ Ⓑ Ⓒ Ⓓ
23 Ⓐ Ⓑ Ⓒ Ⓓ
24 Ⓐ Ⓑ Ⓒ Ⓓ
25 Ⓐ Ⓑ Ⓒ Ⓓ
26 Ⓐ Ⓑ Ⓒ Ⓓ
27 Ⓐ Ⓑ Ⓒ Ⓓ
28 Ⓐ Ⓑ Ⓒ Ⓓ
29 Ⓐ Ⓑ Ⓒ Ⓓ
30 Ⓐ Ⓑ Ⓒ Ⓓ

Sample A

Ⓐ Ⓑ Ⓒ Ⓓ

31 Ⓐ Ⓑ Ⓒ Ⓓ
32 Ⓐ Ⓑ Ⓒ Ⓓ
33 Ⓐ Ⓑ Ⓒ Ⓓ
34 Ⓐ Ⓑ Ⓒ Ⓓ
35 Ⓐ Ⓑ Ⓒ Ⓓ
36 Ⓐ Ⓑ Ⓒ Ⓓ

Sample B

Ⓐ Ⓑ Ⓒ Ⓓ

37 Ⓐ Ⓑ Ⓒ Ⓓ
38 Ⓐ Ⓑ Ⓒ Ⓓ
39 Ⓐ Ⓑ Ⓒ Ⓓ
40 Ⓐ Ⓑ Ⓒ Ⓓ

Answer Key

Answer Key

Entry-Level Test, *page 1*
Reading and Literary Analysis

1. C
2. A
3. D
4. B
5. C
6. C
7. A
8. C
9. A
10. D
11. A
12. D
13. B
14. C
15. C
16. C
17. D
18. C
19. A
20. D
21. C
22. A
23. C
24. B
25. A
26. C
27. B
28. D
29. A
30. D

Vocabulary

Sample A B
31. B
32. D
33. A
34. C
35. D
36. A
Sample B C
37. B
38. A
39. D
40. B

Collection 1

Collection 1 Diagnostic Test
Literature, Informational Text, Vocabulary, *page 13*

1. C
2. H
3. D
4. J
5. A
6. F
7. B
8. J
9. A
10. G

The Most Dangerous Game
by Richard Connell
Selection Test, *page 15*

Comprehension

1. C
2. F
3. D
4. F
5. D
6. H
7. B
8. J
9. A
10. G

Literary Focus

11. A
12. J
13. B
14. F

Vocabulary Development

15. a
16. g
17. b
18. c
19. e
20. i
21. f
22. h
23. j
24. d

Constructed Response

25. Students' responses will vary. A sample response follows:

Aboard a yacht on a tropical night, a man named Rainsford accidentally falls into the sea. He swims until he reaches a strange island he has been warned about. On the island he finds a splendid château where he is greeted by General Zaroff, the owner of the place. Zaroff greets Rainsford warmly as a fellow hunter. He tells Rainsford that he has invented a new kind of game, the most dangerous of all—hunting human beings. Zaroff had bought the island in order to have a place where he could hunt human captives such as sailors. If the "prey" can elude Zaroff for three days, he is freed; but no one has ever successfully done so. Soon Zaroff reveals that Rainsford is to be his next prey. Rainsford is let loose on the island with some food and equipment and uses his immense hunting knowledge to evade Zaroff. However, three of Rainsford's traps fail to stop Zaroff, even though one kills Zaroff's huge servant, Ivan. At last, desperate, Rainsford dives into the sea. Zaroff assumes another victory for himself. Upon returning to the château, Zaroff is surprised by Rainsford in his own bedroom. In a scene not shown, they fight; and it is Rainsford who wakes up the next morning in Zaroff's comfortable bed.

Can Animals Think?
by Eugene Linden

Selection Test, *page 18*

Comprehension

1. D
2. F
3. C
4. H
5. C

Vocabulary Development

6. F
7. B
8. J
9. A
10. G

Dog Star
by Arthur C. Clarke

Selection Test, *page 20*

Comprehension

1. B
2. F
3. C
4. J
5. D
6. G
7. A
8. G
9. B
10. H

Literary Focus

11. A
12. J
13. C
14. F

Vocabulary Development

15. terrestrial
16. stellar
17. desolating
18. misanthropic
19. labyrinthine

Constructed Response

20. Students' responses will vary. A sample response follows:

The use of a flashback in "Dog Star" gives background information by telling the reader who Laika is, how the narrator found Laika, and what kind of life the narrator has had. The flashback explores character by showing the narrator's life through his interactions with Laika and with human beings. Basically, he is capable of warm affection but is uncomfortable around people. These descriptions create an emotional impact by making the reader see and feel the love between the narrator and Laika. Two examples of this love are when the narrator declares that because of Laika he has little need for human companionship and when he says that despite rationality he hesitates before leaving Laika on earth. The flashback creates suspense and mystery by delaying the explanation of what happens after the narrator is awakened by the dream of barking.

Far-out Housekeeping on the ISS
by Ron Koczor

Selection Test, *page 24*

Comprehension

1. B
2. H
3. A
4. G
5. A
6. J
7. B
8. F
9. A
10. J

Answer Key

A Christmas Memory
by Truman Capote

Selection Test, *page 26*

Comprehension

1. D
2. F
3. B
4. H
5. A
6. G
7. B
8. J
9. A
10. H

Literary Focus

11. C
12. G
13. C
14. J

Vocabulary Development

15. suffuse
16. sacrilegious
17. prosaic
18. dilapidated
19. carnage

Constructed Response

20. Students' responses will vary. A sample response follows:

A favorite passage of mine is the one in which Buddy and his friend shell pecans for their fruitcakes. It's set in the kitchen on a November morning after the characters have gathered the nuts in the woods. To me the mood is one of finding joy in the midst of a cold, lonely place. Other people don't seem to be around, but the kitchen is warmed by the fire and filled with the characters' joy and friendship.

There's a contrast between light and dark in this paragraph—the rising moon and the fire on one hand, the growing darkness of the night on the other—that seems to me to show the delicate balance between happiness and loneliness in the characters. The image of the characters' reflections in a dark mirror, mingling with the rising moon, sum that up for me.

In that dark mirror there's a hint of another mood—the bittersweet mood of the adult Buddy looking nostalgically back at his childhood and a few precious moments, fully aware that as the events of the story seeded the rich emotional life that sustained him as a boy, so those same moments, the empty shells of his memories, now feed the transforming fire that makes him a writer.

Collection 1 Summative Test, *page 30*

Vocabulary Skills

1. B
2. F
3. C
4. J
5. B

Comprehension

6. H
7. D
8. F
9. C
10. G

Reading Skills and Strategies

Using Chronological Order

11. The correct order is as follows:

- **4.** The priest tells the boy to avoid large places.
- **3.** The priest rebukes the boy for drawing pictures.
- **10.** The boy becomes a famous artist.
- **8.** The boy is awakened by fighting and screaming.
- **1.** The farmer and his wife ask the priest to take in their son.
- **9.** The boy finds that the mouths of the cats are covered with blood.
- **2.** The priest educates the boy for the priesthood.
- **6.** In the empty temple the boy draws pictures of cats.

7. The boy looks for a small place in which to sleep.
5. The boy travels to the next village in the hope that the priests will take him in.

Predicting

12. G

13. D

Literary Focus: Constructed Response

14. Students' responses will vary. Here is a sample response:

Details You Know That Boy Doesn't Know

The temple is closed up.
A goblin had frightened the priests away.
Brave warriors who tried to kill the goblin were never seen again.
The goblin kept the light burning in the temple to tempt lonely travelers.

Details That Finally Make Boy Suspicious

Temple is gray with dust.
Temple is very large and empty.
The boy remembers the old priest's words.
The boy hears frightening noises at night.

The Old Priest's Warning

The old priest seems to be warning the boy about the temple with the goblin in it. The temple is just such a large space, but the boy remembers the warning and keeps safe because he finds a small space to sleep in, so the huge rat isn't able to get in and harm him.

Collection 2

Collection 2 Diagnostic Test
Literature, Informational Text, Vocabulary, *page 36*

1. B
2. F
3. D
4. F
5. C
6. H
7. A
8. G
9. B
10. J

Thank You, M'am
by Langston Hughes
Selection Test, *page 38*

Comprehension

1. D
2. G
3. B
4. F
5. C
6. F
7. B
8. J
9. A
10. H

Literary Focus

11. C

12. H

13. A

14. G

Constructed Response

15. Students' responses will vary. A sample response follows:

The statement shows that Mrs. Jones is a strong individual, used to making her own decisions and obeying her own values, which are highly moral even if they are not always conventional. She has made up her own mind about Roger's situation and has decided that she can rehabilitate him better than the police can. Her belief in her own ability is shown in the way she brings Roger into her home and speaks as an adult in charge, commanding him to wash his face, questioning him about his activities, and ultimately giving him good advice. She does these things from a sense of shared human need rather than from a sense of superiority, as is shown in her confession that she had in the past done things she was now ashamed of. Additionally, her comment about Roger's face being too dirty to take to the police shows that she has a sense of humor.

Answer Key

Teaching Chess, and Life
by Carlos Capellan

Community Service & You
by T. J. Saftner

Feeding Frenzy
by Peter Ames Carlin and Don Sider

Selection Test, *page 41*

Comprehension

1. A
2. J
3. B
4. H
5. B

Vocabulary Development

6. J
7. A
8. G
9. D
10. F

Helen on Eighty-sixth Street
by Wendi Kaufman

Selection Test, *page 43*

Comprehension

1. C
2. G
3. D
4. H
5. A
6. G
7. D
8. F
9. C
10. J

Literary Focus

11. B
12. H
13. B
14. J

Vocabulary Development

15. odyssey
16. supplication
17. stifled
18. enunciate
19. scourge

Constructed Response

20. Students' responses will vary. A sample response follows:

The passage shows that Old Farfel is a man who has been trying to become intimate with Vita's mother: He "has been coming around a lot lately, taking Mom and me to dinner at Italian places downtown." Farfel's quotation from *Macbeth* shows that he is literate; the descriptions of his laugh and smell show that he is not very appealing—at least not to Vita. In fact, one of the main things the passage shows about Vita is that she dislikes and distrusts Farfel. Calling him Old is an example of her displeasure. (She never accurately states his age, and we don't know if he's forty or seventy.)

In this passage, Vita seems somewhat hostile ("I don't like to be around when he's over"), or perhaps she is merely self-protective and insecure. She also seems witty and imaginative, as demonstrated in the phrases she uses to describe Old Farfel, such as: "He smells like those dark cough drops, the kind that make your eyes tear."

Marigolds
by Eugenia W. Collier

Selection Test, *page 46*

Comprehension

1. B
2. F
3. C
4. G
5. D
6. J
7. B
8. H
9. C
10. F

Literary Focus

11. A
12. J
13. C
14. G

Vocabulary Development

15. clarity

16. placidly

17. impoverished

18. arid

19. futile

Constructed Response

20. Students' responses will vary. A sample response follows:

In interactions with other kids, Lizabeth is pressured into throwing rocks even though at first she had doubts. Later Joey tries to stop her from tearing up the flowers. These two interactions seem to be opposite, but in both cases Lizabeth acts out of a motivation fueled by despair about her life. Lizabeth's interactions with her parents in this story occur only indirectly; she overhears their conversation rather than participating in it; as a result, she learns things that frighten her and hasten her maturity. Similarly, her interaction with Miss Lottie is indirect; its significance lies in what is unsaid rather than in what is said. Like her interaction with her parents, this episode spurs Lizabeth's maturity by giving her an insight into the world around her.

Collection 2 Summative Test, *page 50*

Vocabulary Skills

1. B

2. G

3. C

4. J

5. B

Comprehension

6. F

7. D

8. H

9. A

10. H

Reading Skills and Strategies: Constructed Response

Making Inferences

11. Students' responses will vary. A sample response follows:

The characters live in a world where present-day technology has developed to such an extent that it has completely destroyed the environment as we know it. There are enough similarities between our world and Justin's to suggest that the story's futuristic setting developed out of ours. Similarities include computerized educational programs, expensive sneakers, unctuous sales personnel, and school lunches. However, the characters in this world seem even more removed from nature than we are. City streets are roofed to keep out ultraviolet rays; beaches are off-limits.

Understanding Allusions

12. Students' responses will vary. A sample response follows:

I predict that aliens are going to arrive—an event announced in the first line of the story—and that they are going to put humans in so much danger that the end of the world will seem imminent. In fact, there may be so many aliens that they "flood" the world. Perhaps in response, some human beings will build an "ark" to carry them into space.

Making Inferences About Motivation

13. All four choices are valid possibilities for Molly's motivations. Students' responses will vary. A sample response follows:

Devotion to her son and nostalgia for her past are perhaps the two most obvious choices, and they are constantly present in her thoughts. Her conversation with her son in the morning shows her love and concern, as does her shopping trip.

Literary Focus: Constructed Response

14. Name: Molly Harris

Age: 60

Job or profession: homemaker

Where and when she lives: unidentified city in an unspecified future year, possibly fifty to one hundred years from now

Her inner life (thoughts and feelings): Loves her son and worries about him; worries about the kind of world she and he are living in. (Evidence: worrying that students in her time go to class too little, spend too much time "netted-in.") Also has financial worries. (Evidence: had to cancel subscription to interactive TV channels in order to save for birthday present.) Feels nostalgia for her youth when the environment was less artificial. (Evidence: wishes she could swim at a beach again.)

Her outer life (actions and words): Focuses on being a very good mother. (Evidence: carefully plans her son's school lunch with special treat; conscientiously chooses a birthday present for him that she can ill afford; speaks in a friendly, teasing way to her son; and hugs him.) Weighs her son's tastes more heavily than her own in choice of present. Is not a goody-goody or a Pollyanna, though: rejects birthday presents that are too didactic, not enough fun.

Collection 3

Collection 3 Diagnostic Test

Literature, Informational Text, Vocabulary, *page 56*

1. D
2. F
3. C
4. F
5. B
6. J
7. A
8. H
9. A
10. J

The Interlopers

by Saki

Selection Test, *page 58*

Comprehension

1. C
2. F
3. D
4. G
5. B
6. H
7. C
8. F
9. D
10. H

Literary Focus

11. A
12. H
13. C
14. G

Vocabulary Development

15. succor
16. languor
17. precipitous
18. acquiesced
19. marauders

Constructed Response

20. Students' responses will vary. A sample response follows:

If Saki had used a first-person point of view, he would have severely limited what readers experience. With the first-person point of view, readers would have seen events either through Gradwitz's eyes or Znaeym's eyes but not both. While the first-person point of view would have helped maintain the story's suspense (as readers see all events through only one character's eyes), it also would have made it much harder for the author to trace the growing friendship between the two men equally.

Answer Key

The Necklace
by Guy de Maupassant

Selection Test, *page 61*

Comprehension

1. B
2. G
3. A
4. J
5. C
6. F
7. D
8. H
9. D
10. G

Literary Focus

11. A
12. G
13. C
14. J

Vocabulary

15. b
16. e
17. d
18. a
19. c

Constructed Response

20. Students' responses will vary. A sample response follows:

The author used the third-person-limited point of view to focus on the thoughts of the main character, Mathilde Loisel. This vantage allows the writer to tell us all about Mathilde's longing for a life of wealth and beauty, filled with great parties and social attainment. By selecting this point of view, the writer helps readers identify with Mathilde. As a result, we feel great sympathy for her and see how her life has been ruined by one small mistake. While the tone remains neutral, the author's choice of point of view helps create the story's pathos.

The Cask of Amontillado
by Edgar Allan Poe

Selection Test, *page 64*

Comprehension

1. C
2. F
3. D
4. G
5. B
6. H
7. A
8. F
9. D
10. H

Literary Focus

11. A
12. G
13. C
14. J

Vocabulary Development

15. precluded
16. impunity
17. retribution
18. impose
19. recoiling

Constructed Response

20. Students' responses will vary. A sample response follows:

At the beginning of the story, Montresor explains that Fortunato has wronged him, but he never says how or why. The narrator calmly plots Fortunato's murder, surely the act of a madman. Later, Montresor describes his reaction to Fortunato's mounting panic very matter-of-factly. His calm tone is out of place and reveals that he is insane and thus unreliable as a narrator.

Poe's Final Days
from Edgar A. Poe: Mournful and Never-Ending Remembrance
by Kenneth Silverman

Poe's Death Is Rewritten as Case of Rabies, Not Telltale Alcohol
The New York Times

If Only Poe Had Succeeded When He Said Nevermore to Drink
by Burton R. Pollin and Robert E. Benedetto

Rabies Death Theory
by R. Michael Benitez, M.D.

Selection Test, *page 67*

Comprehension

1. A
2. H
3. C
4. G
5. B
6. J
7. D
8. J
9. A
10. H

Vocabulary Development

11. insensible
12. imposing
13. stupor
14. spectral
15. maligned

Collection 3 Summative Test, *page 70*

Vocabulary Skills

1. D
2. J
3. A
4. F
5. B

Comprehension

6. H
7. A
8. J
9. B
10. G

Reading Skills and Strategies: Constructed Response

Monitoring Your Reading

11. Students' responses will vary. A sample response follows:

Mrs. Zajac, a fifth-grade teacher, demands that her students do their best work. First she tells Clarence that he has to rewrite his paper because he can do a better job. Then she tells Claude to finish his work completely and write clearly and neatly. Next she tells Felipe to get a drink of water to stop his hiccups and then keep his mouth shut. Finally she tells Robert that he must do his work.

Summarizing: A Plot Formula

12. Students' responses will vary. A sample response follows:

Mrs. Zajac wanted . . . her students to learn

but when . . . they do not do their best

she then . . . makes them do the work again

Drawing Conclusions

13. Students' responses will vary. A sample response follows:

She makes her students work hard and redo unsatisfactory work.

She dresses in a professional manner to show respect to her class.

She knows every student by name.

Literary Focus: Constructed Response

14. Students' responses will vary. A sample response follows:

The point of view is first person in the first paragraph and third-person limited in the rest of the passage

The tone is admiring

The voice is personal, friendly

The overall literary effect allows readers to get to know Mrs. Zajac and come to her admire her dedication and competence

Collection 4

Collection 4 Diagnostic Test
Literature, Informational Text, Vocabulary, *page 75*

1. C
2. G
3. B
4. H
5. B
6. F
7. D
8. F
9. A
10. G

The Sniper
by Liam O'Flaherty
Selection Test, *page 77*

Comprehension

1. B
2. G
3. D
4. H
5. A
6. F
7. B
8. G
9. C
10. J

Literary Focus

11. C
12. F
13. A
14. J

Vocabulary Development

15. c
16. e
17. d
18. b
19. a

Constructed Response

20. Students' responses will vary. A sample response follows:

"The Sniper" would not be better told as a novel because the short story form suits its theme and topic. "The Sniper" presents a small but important scene in the life of a Republican sniper. A novel presents many scenes; consequently, the writer would have to pad the story with unnecessary detail. In addition, a novel has many characters, but this story has only three characters. Adding other characters would take away from the surprise ending. Finally, a short story has one theme, but a novel often has several themes. "The Sniper" explores how civil war can turn brother against brother and destroy families. Turning the story into a novel would force the writer to add themes that are not needed to make his point.

Cranes
by Hwang Sunwŏn
Selection Test, *page 80*

Comprehension

1. D
2. F
3. A
4. H
5. D
6. F
7. B
8. J
9. A
10. H

Literary Focus

11. C
12. F
13. A
14. J

Vocabulary Development

Students' responses will vary. A sample response follows:

15. turned toward, presented
16. barrier, obstacle
17. composes, comprises
18. backbone
19. exposure, dangerous place, peril

Constructed Response

20. Students' responses will vary. A sample response follows:

Both "The Sniper" and "Cranes" describe characters with divided loyalties. The Republican soldier in "The Sniper" is pleased when he kills his enemy but horrified when he realizes that his enemy is his brother. In "Cranes," Sŏngsam bitterly resents how his childhood playmate Tŏkchae betrayed the villagers by becoming the vice-chairman of the Farmers Communist League. Nonetheless, Sŏngsam remembers their friendship and helps Tŏkchae escape. Both stories show that our loyalties are not clear-cut. Especially in times of war, people can find themselves torn between two very hard choices.

A Country Divided
***from* One Belfast Boy**
by Patricia McMahon

Lives in the Crossfire
***from* Children of "the Troubles"**
by Laurel Holliday

Internment
by Margaret McCrory

Peace Isn't Impossible
by George J. Mitchell

Selection Test, *page 83*

Comprehension

1. B
2. H
3. C
4. J
5. D

Vocabulary Development

6. designate
7. absorb
8. reunification
9. divergent
10. coerced

Liberty
by Julia Alvarez

Exile
by Julia Alvarez

An American Story
by Anthony Lewis

Ex-Refugee Is Nominated for Justice Post by Dena Bunis and Anh Do

Selection Test, *page 85*

Comprehension

1. D
2. F
3. A
4. H
5. B
6. F
7. A
8. J
9. D
10. H

Literary Focus

11. C
12. F
13. B
14. J

Vocabulary Development

15. c
16. d
17. b
18. e
19. a

Constructed Response

20. Students' responses will vary. A sample response follows:

Both Julia Alvarez and Anthony Lewis selected genres that allowed them to accomplish their purposes. Alvarez's story allows readers to experience the narrator's sense of displacement, confusion, and fear. Stories help readers *understand* a writer's theme and insight about life. Alvarez's poem allows readers to visualize the experience. A poem helps readers *feel* the narrator's emotions keenly. By reading the story and the poem together, readers get a more complete view of the narrator's experience of immigrating to America. Lewis's article makes readers *think about* the issue of immigrating and becoming an American. He is not as concerned with conveying a theme or an emotion.

Collection 4 Summative Test, *page 88*

Vocabulary Skills

1. B
2. G
3. C
4. J
5. D

Comprehension

6. H
7. B
8. F
9. D
10. J

Reading Skills and Strategies: Constructed Response

Making Inferences about Motivation

11. Students' responses will vary. A sample response follows:

    Goal—wants to live in a home like Christy Sanders's; **Motivation**—overall desire for better things; **Outcome**—She is motivated to become a writer.

    Goal—wants culture in her life; **Motivation**—desire to find beauty in life; **Outcome**—She visits libraries and art museums when she attends college.

    Goal—wants to be someone important; **Motivation**—desire not to feel inferior; **Outcome**—After a time spent repeating other people's ideas, she finds her own voice.

Comparing and Contrasting Themes

12. Students' responses will vary. A sample response follows:

    Main character: "The Best Gift of My Life"—the narrator, Cynthia Rylant; **"Daily"**—the narrator, Naomi Shihab Nye

    Character's motives: "The Best Gift of My Life"—to escape from her small town; **"Daily"**—to link her chores to the world

    What character learns: "The Best Gift of My Life"—to find her own voice; **"Daily"**—to share her appreciation of chores

    Theme: "The Best Gift of My Life"—Work can make a person special; **"Daily"**—Chores make people the same.

Connecting Literature to Current Events

13. Students' responses will vary. A sample response follows:

    The New Orleans Symphony visited Beaver, West Virginia, when Cynthia Rylant was a teenager. This concert was her first exposure to any form of culture, and it awakened in her a hunger for beauty. It made her want a life "beyond Saturdays at G. C. Murphy's department store and Sundays with the Baptist Youth Fellowship." The experience marked a turning point in her life because it awakened her desire to "be someone else" and gave her the courage to try to be a writer.

Literary Focus: Constructed Response

14. Students' responses will vary. A sample response follows:

    Genre: "The Best Gift of My Life"—autobiography; **"Daily"**—poetry

    Purpose: "The Best Gift of My Life"—to get readers to think about the role of culture; **"Daily"**—to get readers to see and feel the importance of everyday tasks

    Theme: stated or implied: "The Best Gift of My Life"—stated in last paragraph; **"Daily"**—implied

    How genre is used to develop the theme: "The Best Gift of My Life"—with facts and examples; **"Daily"**—with imagery, figurative language, and sound devices

    Theme: "The Best Gift of My Life"—"I wanted to be someone else, and that turned out to be the worst curse and the best gift of my life." **"Daily"**—Everyday, hands-on tasks connect the doer to the world.

Collection 5

Collection 5 Diagnostic Test

Literature, Informational Text, Vocabulary, *page 94*

1. B
2. F
3. C
4. G
5. D
6. J
7. D
8. H
9. A
10. H

The Gift of the Magi

by O. Henry

Selection Test, *page 96*

Comprehension

1. D
2. H
3. B
4. G
5. C
6. J
7. D
8. H
9. A
10. H

Literary Focus

11. A
12. J
13. C
14. F

Vocabulary Development

15. B
16. F
17. C
18. G
19. D

Constructed Response

20. Students' responses will vary. A sample response follows:

Situational irony is a form of irony in which events not only take us by surprise but are the opposite of what we might expect. In "The Gift of the Magi," a twist of fate turns an entire situation on its head, resulting in a series of events for which we—as well as the story characters—are unprepared. This kind of situational irony is called a surprise ending. We are completely unprepared for the fact that Jim's present to Della—a set of combs for her long, beautiful hair—is useless to her. Further, we don't find out until Jim's disclosure that, in order to buy Della the combs, he sold his watch. The sale makes Della's gift to him—a watch chain—as useless as the combs. The situational irony lies in our expectation that Della's gift to Jim would be perfect. As it turns out, she and he couldn't have made worse practical choices. Nevertheless, O. Henry and we know that their sacrifice is the real and the best gift.

The Lady, or the Tiger?

by Frank R. Stockton

Selection Test, *page 100*

Comprehension

1. B
2. G
3. D
4. J
5. C
6. F
7. B
8. G
9. D
10. H

Literary Focus

11. D
12. G
13. A
14. G

Vocabulary Development

15. impartial
16. retribution
17. dire
18. exuberant
19. deliberation

Constructed Response

20. Students' responses will vary. A sample response follows:

In this story the author sets up a situation that demands resolution, but he refuses to give us a satisfying answer. This ambiguity challenges readers to think for themselves. By failing to give readers a sense of closure, the author ensures the story's effectiveness; he knows that its ideas will continue to haunt us until well after the last word has been read. We continue to wonder if the princess's jealousy is more powerful than the wish to save the life of her lover, and we continue to wonder about the poor man's fate. Further, we may wonder if chance is—as the king has stated—truly "impartial and incorruptible." The fact that the author leaves the ending ambiguous implies that people must come to their own conclusions about fate and human nature.

A Defense of the Jury System
by Thomas M. Ross, Esq.

Selection Test, *page 103*

Comprehension

1. A
2. J
3. A
4. J
5. D

Vocabulary Development

6. advocates
7. irrational
8. affluent
9. superficial
10. obscure

The Road Not Taken
by Robert Frost

Selection Test, *page 105*

Comprehension

1. D
2. G
3. D
4. G
5. A
6. H
7. A
8. G
9. D
10. G

Literary Focus

11. C
12. G
13. B
14. J

Constructed Response

15. Students' responses will vary. A sample response follows:

The title "The Road Not Taken" is ambiguous. Does it refer to the road the narrator took—or the one he *didn't* take? A poem's title is always significant. In this case, "The Road Not Taken" might refer to either road—the road the narrator passed up (it was the road not taken) or the one he actually took (the road "less traveled by" was also a road not taken by other people). Seen in this light, the important thing to the narrator seems *not* to be the road he chose but the road he had to pass up in order to make that choice. The poet seems to be saying that a necessary consequence of making a choice is that it can't be made again because "way leads on to way." Once chosen, a path must be followed to its logical conclusion. The title expresses the idea that the choices we pass up are as important as the ones we make—perhaps even more important. In saying that choosing the road less traveled has "made all the difference," the poet is saying that one decision has the power to change the entire course of a life.

Collection 5 Summative Test, *page 108*

Vocabulary Skills

1. C
2. J
3. C
4. F
5. D

Comprehension

6. G
7. B
8. H
9. A
10. J

Reading Skills and Strategies:

Constructed Response

Making Inferences

11. Students' responses will vary. A sample response follows:

From the tone of the poem, it can be inferred that the speaker is issuing a warning to those who turn away from their heritage. The unspoken "you" to whom the poem is addressed cares too much about keeping up with the times to pay attention to the "voices of dead relatives." These young, modern people, it can be inferred, are also the people who wield weapons and make war—without the benefit of the knowledge and wisdom of their elders.

12. Students' responses will vary. A sample response follows:

In the poem the speaker advises against forgetting the "secret name" that can be heard in one's dreams. This secret name, spoken by "dead relatives," is the name of one's original family, religion, tribe, country, or the name one has been given at birth. The speaker criticizes those who give up traditional clothes for the sake of fashion. It can be inferred that the speaker puts into this category those who have changed or altered their names out of embarrassment, indifference, or ignorance. In effect, to forget this secret name is to forget who you really are. In a too modern world only those elder, familial voices know and can remind you of your true identity.

Literary Focus: Constructed Response

13. Students' responses will vary. A sample response follows:

The tone of the poem is somber and cautionary. The statement "it is dangerous" is repeated throughout the poem and establishes the tone. The lines in Spanish at the end sound like the beginning of a prayer, and praying is something one might do in response to feeling threatened in a dangerous environment. The rhythm of the poem is not bouncy, and there is no end rhyme. The lines are short, but the sentences are long, adding to the solemn tone. This tone contrasts starkly with the tone with which the trappings of modern life are described —a take-a-chance attitude, excitement, catchy music, trendiness, and an attitude of embracing the future as superior to the past. For the speaker the familiar is best and safest—traditional clothes, old-time religion, and family values.

Collection 6

Collection 6 Diagnostic Test

Literature, Informational Text, Vocabulary, *page 112*

1. C
2. J
3. C
4. F
5. A
6. G
7. D
8. H
9. A
10. G

The Scarlet Ibis

by James Hurst

Selection Test, *page 114*

Comprehension

1. C
2. J
3. A
4. F
5. B
6. J
7. C
8. H
9. B
10. H

Literary Focus

11. B
12. G
13. D
14. F

Vocabulary Development

15. doggedness
16. imminent
17. precariously
18. reiterated
19. infallibility

Constructed Response

20. Students' responses will vary. A sample response follows:

In this story the scarlet ibis is a symbol for the narrator's brother. Both Doodle and the ibis die as a result of their inability to cope with the world. An ibis can live only in its natural habitat; when it finds itself far from home, it cannot survive. The ibis in the story has been forced from its natural surroundings, eventually finding its way to a tree outside the narrator's home. The ibis dies, too weak to survive. Like the ibis, the narrator's brother, Doodle, is special and too weak to survive. By using the ibis as a symbol, the author emphasizes Doodle's uniqueness and shows how this quality is also what challenges him. Like the ibis, Doodle dies because he is not suited to his surroundings. The ibis as a symbol for Doodle reminds me that rare beauty is all too often fragile.

The Grandfather
by Gary Soto

Selection Test, *page 117*

Comprehension

1. D
2. H
3. D
4. G
5. A
6. F
7. C
8. J
9. C
10. H

Literary Focus

11. C
12. G
13. A
14. H

Vocabulary Development

15. gurgle
16. hovered
17. meager
18. sulked
19. meager

Constructed Response

20. Students' responses will vary. A sample response follows:

Gary Soto uses the image of the avocado tree to symbolize his family's history. Both his grandfather and the tree were fresh and new as Americans: Grandfather arriving as a young man from Mexico; the avocado tree planted in the yard as part of this new American life. Grandfather nurtures the tree as he nurtures the family and patiently waits for it to bear fruit—just as he patiently waits for his grandson to grow up.

When the author is a teenager, the tree begins to bear fruit just as the author begins to develop his intellect. The black spot on the first fruit symbolizes the trouble that lies ahead—the author and his brother start to spend less time with the family.

As the tree begins to bear fruit steadily, the family continues to grow and prosper in America. The fruit of the tree provides nourishment as well as income. By the time of Grandfather's death, the family understands that they will continue to flourish as long as they nurture future generations the way Grandfather had nurtured the avocado tree he had planted.

The Golden Kite, the Silver Wind
by Ray Bradbury

Selection Test, *page 120*

Comprehension

1. B
2. F
3. D
4. H
5. A
6. G
7. C
8. H
9. A
10. G

Literary Focus

11. D
12. H
13. C
14. J

Vocabulary Development

15. c
16. e
17. a
18. b
19. d

Constructed Response

20. Students' responses will vary. A sample response follows:

Two charity organizations are collecting cans of food for the needy. As each charity goes about collecting donations, each begins to criticize the other in order to get all the donations for itself. Eventually, the charities even accuse each other of selling the food, keeping the money, and spending it on fancy cars and flashy clothes.

If the charities understood this story, they would work together toward their common goal. For instance, one group might collect donations while the other might distribute them.

Weapons of the Spirit
by Albert Einstein

Letter to President Roosevelt
by Albert Einstein

On the Abolition of the Threat of War
by Albert Einstein

The Arms Race
by Albert Einstein
Selection Test, ***page 123***

Comprehension

1. C
2. J
3. A
4. G
5. B

Vocabulary Development

6. G
7. D
8. F
9. C
10. F

Collection 6 Summative Test, *page 125*

Vocabulary Skills

1. D
2. F
3. B
4. H
5. C

Comprehension

6. G
7. B
8. F
9. D
10. G

Reading Skills and Strategies: Constructed Response

Making Generalizations about an Allegory

11. Students' responses will vary. A sample response follows:

In the tale a clever wanderer tricks a rich man at his own game. The poor wanderer is smart and generous; instead of keeping the wealth for himself, he distributes it among the poor. So it is the poor people of the area who win in the end. The selfish and arrogant rich man ends up a loser. The wanderer simply continues on with the life he has chosen. The universal message is twofold: First, people who use their abilities to help others are the true winners. Second, the same qualities—greed and arrogance—that enabled the rich man to gain wealth are responsible for his losing it all. These messages are universal because they can apply to all people everywhere.

Literary Focus: Constructed Response

12. Students' responses will vary. A sample response follows:

As the last line implies, the lizard is used to represent "sorrow . . . regret" and "self-pity." The lizard may have been chosen to represent these qualities because it makes a sound like the sound people make when they experience sorrow and regret. Moreover, the lizard, like the once wealthy man, has no possessions.

13. Students' responses will vary. A sample response follows:

cranes: protectors or indicators of wealth; the cranes that spread their wings over the rich man's property

lizard: person trapped by greed and regret, like the rich man who is condemned by his selfishness and arrogance to live trapped in a lizard's body

chipped coconut-shell cup: simplicity and peacefulness, as the life of the wanderer is simple and peaceful. The fact that the cup is chipped, a flaw that does not diminish its usefulness, indicates that function should be more important than beauty.

Collection 7

Collection 7 Diagnostic Test

Literature, *page 131*

1. B
2. G
3. B
4. J
5. C
6. H
7. C
8. G
9. A
10. F

A Blessing
by James Wright

Selection Test, *page 133*

Comprehension

1. C
2. J
3. D
4. F
5. A
6. F
7. C
8. H
9. A
10. H

Literary Focus

11. D
12. G
13. A
14. H

Constructed Response

15. Student's responses will vary. A sample response follows:

A person cannot visibly blossom like a plant with flowers. But blossoming is a positive, healthy, and possibly happy occasion for a plant. A plant in blossom is a metaphor for the happiness the speaker feels while out in nature with the two ponies. The experience he has in nature makes him feel deeply happy, in touch with his feelings and surroundings. For the speaker, that kind of love of life is like the opening, embracing love of life that a new blossom symbolizes.

Woman Work
by Maya Angelou

Daily
by Naomi Shihab Nye

Selection Test, *page 136*

Comprehension

1. A
2. H
3. D
4. H
5. B
6. H
7. A
8. J
9. C
10. F

Literary Focus

11. D
12. H
13. B
14. J

Constructed Response

15. Student's responses will vary. A sample response follows:

Both "Woman Work" and "Daily" tell about women who do chores in and around their homes everyday. The speaker of "Woman Work" is tired of her chores, whereas the speaker of "Daily" finds the wonder of being alive in the chores she performs. The mood of exhaustion in "Woman Work" is expressed when the speaker pleads for snowflakes to "Cover me with white / Cold icy kisses and / Let me rest tonight." Her hope is that nature will bring her rest and peace, because her work makes her so tired and weary. The mood of wonder in "Daily" is expressed when the speaker says, "The hands are churches that worship the world." The speaker means that like a church, which is a sacred building full of the wonder of faith in things beyond our world, her hands are sacred tools of everyday work and activity in the natural world.

in Just-
by E. E. Cummings

Selection Test, *page 139*

Comprehension

1. D
2. F
3. C
4. G
5. C
6. H
7. A
8. G
9. B
10. F

Literary Focus

11. B
12. J
13. D
14. H

Constructed Response

15. Student's responses will vary. A sample response follows:

E. E. Cummings uses words, no punctuation, and the arrangement of words on the page to help a reader experience spring in a new and different way. He combines words to make new, playful ones, such as *mudluscious*, which describes the muddy puddles that children love to play in. He breaks lines cleverly and uses extra spaces in the poem whenever he wants the reader to pause or even skip ahead, like a child at play. Usually poets use punctuation marks to indicate how and when to pause. When E. E. Cummings adds spaces between the words in the phrase "whistles far   and wee," the reader senses the distance traveled by the sound of the balloonman's whistle—and that far-reaching sound attracts children to come out and play happily in the spring air. In all, Cummings makes me see separate things as a unit—"eddieandbill" are one, a pair, and he makes me see familiar units, like "far and wee," as independent parts that may even be replaceable.

Haiku
by Miura Chora, Chiyo, Matsuo Bashō, and Kobayashi Issa

Selection Test, *page 142*

Comprehension

1. A
2. H
3. D
4. G
5. B
6. F
7. C
8. J
9. C
10. G

Literary Focus

11. B
12. J
13. A
14. H

Constructed Response

15. Student's responses will vary. A sample response follows:

In his haiku, Bashō tells about an experience he had at a pond. Like all haiku, this one has three lines. The first line gives the setting—"The old pond." The second line describes something that happens at the pond—"A frog jumps in." The activity in this setting suggests that it is a warm month of the year. Then the last line surprises the reader with the unique way in which the speaker experiences the setting and activity. It states, "Sound of water." With this line the poet shows how something old, such as the pond, can become lively and fresh when it is seen in a new way.

The form of the poem also reinforces the mood, because the short lines of few words and strong punctuation mimic the quick, discrete series of events that the haiku commemorates. Thus, the form re-creates the mood of surprise.

Answer Key

Once by the Pacific
by Robert Frost

Country Scene
by Hồ Xuân Hu'o'ng

Selection Test, *page 145*

Comprehension

1. B	**6.** G
2. H	**7.** D
3. D	**8.** G
4. G	**9.** C
5. A	**10.** G

Literary Focus

11. A	**13.** D
12. H	**14.** G

Constructed Response

15. Student's responses will vary. A sample response follows:

"Country Scene" is a lyric poem in which the speaker expresses the emotions stirred by a waterfall's desolate surroundings. The lyric form gives the poet the best way to approximate the fleeting and variable quality of emotions, for no strict structure imposes itself on the poet's flowing impressions. As the poet relates thoughts on the activities and scenes of country life, their transitory quality becomes obvious. In the lyric form these thoughts need not be complete; an ellipsis is perfect to create the emotional impression that the poet needs to convey. Similarly the lyric form permits variety; hence, the poet does not use parallel construction when listing the elements of the scene.

Tiburón
by Martín Espada

Selection Test, *page 148*

Comprehension

1. D	**6.** F
2. G	**7.** C
3. D	**8.** G
4. H	**9.** D
5. A	**10.** H

Literary Focus

11. C	**13.** B
12. F	**14.** J

Constructed Response

15. Student's responses will vary. A sample response follows:

"Tiburón" describes a simple scene on a city street: A long red car is stalled, and its hood is open. The situation is ordinary. The figure of speech—a simile—allows the reader to view the scene through new eyes. The simile compares the stalled car and its open hood to "a prize shark / mouth yanked open." When you read this simile, you are entertained by the fact that both shapes are similar. The idea of a shark gives the inoperable car a power it doesn't really have. The poet then imagines the radio of the car as a fisherman's radio swallowed by the shark. These figures of speech make the poem's tone playful and lively. They help the reader see an ordinary situation in an extraordinary way.

Answer Key

Folding Won Tons In
by Abraham Chang

On "Folding Won Tons In"
by Abraham Chang

Selection Test, *page 151*

Comprehension

1. B	**6.** G
2. H	**7.** D
3. A	**8.** F
4. G	**9.** D
5. C	**10.** F

Literary Focus

11. B	**13.** C
12. F	**14.** G

Constructed Response

15. Student's responses will vary. A sample response follows:

In this poem's simile, newborns huddled together are compared to the line of fresh won tons the speaker has just made by hand. The newness of the won tons is like that of newborns. Newborns are also like fresh blossoms, which the speaker has likened the won tons to. The idea of newborns and flowers lends a hopeful tone to the poem.

"Hope" is the thing with feathers
by Emily Dickinson

Internment
by Juliet S. Kono

Selection Test, *page 154*

Comprehension

1. A	**6.** G
2. H	**7.** C
3. B	**8.** F
4. G	**9.** C
5. D	**10.** G

Literary Focus

11. A	**13.** D
12. H	**14.** H

Constructed Response

15. Student's responses will vary. A sample response follows:

Dickinson compares the idea of hope to a bird. In the poem, Dickinson describes different ways in which birds act, both literally and through personal interpretation. For example, a bird literally "sings the tune without the words," but only in the poet's imagination does a bird perch "in the soul." The comparison is, in my opinion, quite appropriate: Birds are beautiful creatures that can survive the toughest situations, like storms and gales. In this way, birds are like the hope that people carry within them through thick and thin. Hope, like a bird, is both beautiful and strong. Both hope and birds can survive whatever people do to them, positive or destructive. Most amazingly, hope—like birds—makes its qualities, such as beauty and song, available to people without asking for anything in return.

Fog
by Carl Sandburg

Fire and Ice
by Robert Frost

Selection Test, *page 157*

Comprehension

1. C	**6.** G
2. F	**7.** C
3. A	**8.** H
4. G	**9.** D
5. D	**10.** F

Literary Focus

11. B	**13.** D
12. G	**14.** F

Constructed Response

15. Student's responses will vary. A sample response follows:

The main idea in "Fire and Ice" is that hate and desire are equally destructive emotions. Frost believes that a person consumed by desire is as destructive as fire that destroys the world. He says, "From what I've tasted of desire / I hold with those who favor fire." But Frost also believes that a person consumed by hate is as destructive as ice that destroys the world. He says, "I think I know enough of hate / To say that for destruction ice / Is also great." Frost feels that one emotion, when it is unchecked, is just as destructive as the other. He ends the poem by saying that ice as a destructive force "would suffice." In other words, one method of destruction is equal to the other, and any emotion allowed to go haywire is destructive to humans.

The Seven Ages of Man
by William Shakespeare
Selection Test, *page* 160

Comprehension

1. C	**6.** G
2. J	**7.** A
3. A	**8.** H
4. H	**9.** D
5. B	**10.** H

Literary Focus

11. B	**13.** D
12. H	**14.** F

Constructed Response

15. Student's responses will vary. A sample response follows:

According to Shakespeare, there are seven "acts" to life, in which each "player" plays a part: the infant, the schoolboy, the lover, the soldier, the justice, the shrunken oldster, and finally, the second childhood "sans teeth, sans eyes, sans taste, sans everything." It is an apt comparison in that life has a beginning, middle, and end, just like a play—a play that tells the story of life. In life as in a play, we do play "many parts," for as we move through life, each of us changes, physically and emotionally. We change so much that we may become unrecognizable to those who once knew us well.

Women
by Alice Walker
Selection Test, *page 163*

Comprehension

1. C	**6.** G
2. H	**7.** B
3. B	**8.** H
4. F	**9.** A
5. D	**10.** J

Literary Focus

11. A	**13.** C
12. H	**14.** J

Constructed Response

15. Student's responses will vary. A sample response follows:

The tone of the poem mirrors the speaker's respect and awe for what the women have accomplished. Through images of fierce admiration, the speaker helps the reader infer the struggle these poor working women have gone through to reach their goal, the education of their children. When the speaker uses the word *armies* instead of *children*, the reader feels the tough fight the women were involved in. When, in the implied metaphor, the women are said to lead their armies "Across mined / Fields / Booby-trapped / Ditches / To discover books," the hardships in reaching their goal are made clear to the reader. In the end, even without the ability to read or write, the women have achieved an impressive victory for future generations. The poem is a testimony to the character and fortitude of the women.

Boy at the Window
by Richard Wilbur

Selection Test, *page 166*

Comprehension

1. D	**6.** F
2. G	**7.** B
3. A	**8.** H
4. G	**9.** A
5. C	**10.** G

Literary Focus

11. C	**13.** B
12. F	**14.** F

Constructed Response

15. Student's responses will vary. A sample response follows:

In the first stanza a boy is upset that a snowman cannot come inside from "A night of gnashings and enormous moan." This personification of the wind's night allows the reader to experience the fear the small boy feels for the snowman's well-being. The second stanza shares the attitude of the snowman, who "is, nonetheless, content, / Having no wish to go inside and die." Snowmen are objects and do not have feelings or wishes—and they melt rather than die. Later in the stanza the snowman takes pity on the boy. As some snow melts near its eye, the speaker describes "A trickle of the purest rain, a tear." Just as the boy is expressing his fear of the cold through his personification of the wind's night, so Wilbur is expressing his own feelings of sympathy for the boy through the personification of the snowman.

I Wandered Lonely as a Cloud
by William Wordsworth

I Never Saw Daffodils so Beautiful
by Dorothy Wordsworth

Selection Test, *page 169*

Comprehension

1. A	**6.** J
2. H	**7.** C
3. A	**8.** G
4. J	**9.** D
5. A	**10.** F

Literary Focus

11. C	**13.** A
12. J	**14.** H

Constructed Response

15. Student's responses will vary. A sample response follows:

The poem has four iambic feet per line. This pattern makes the poem sound like a song. A happy, lively tone is created through the poem's rhythm. For example, the iambic phrase "Along the margin of a bay," describes the location of the daffodils with an energetic rhythm. In another example, the idea the poet expresses as "What wealth the show to me had brought" is a far more exciting, positive, and joyous way to remember daffodils than saying in prose something simple like, "Those daffodils were nice."

The Courage That My Mother Had
by Edna St. Vincent Millay

Selection Test, *page 172*

Comprehension

1. C	**6.** G
2. H	**7.** D
3. A	**8.** H
4. G	**9.** A
5. C	**10.** G

Literary Focus

11. D
12. F
13. B
14. J

Constructed Response

15. Student's responses will vary. A sample response follows:

In "The Courage That My Mother Had," every other line of each stanza rhymes. When you read these rhymes, you can't help but raise your voice slightly in a way that you wouldn't if a nonrhyming word were used. The rhymes lend an upbeat tone to the poem even though the speaker is discussing the fact that her mother has passed away. The last word in the first stanza is *hill*, which rhymes with *still*. If the word *mountain* or *land* took the place of *hill*, a person's voice would not rise to match the vowel sounds of *still* in a previous line. The rhyme brings more energy and attention to the idea it expresses. In the second stanza, the word *spare*, which rhymes with *wear*, is upbeat sounding. It surprises the reader, though, by making him or her think about what the speaker truly cherishes about her mother.

Ballad of Birmingham
by Dudley Randall

Selection Test, *page 175*

Comprehension

1. B
2. F
3. B
4. H
5. D
6. G
7. C
8. H
9. C
10. F

Literary Focus

11. C
12. G
13. A
14. J

Constructed Response

15. Student's responses will vary. A sample response follows:

The ballad is far more vivid than a newspaper article about the 1963 bombing of the Birmingham church. A newspaper article would present facts about the event. The ballad helps the reader feel present in the life of one of the girls who became a victim. The rhythms, which carry the words along like music, and the patterns of rhyme in each stanza add a dramatic tone to the story. For instance, "No, baby, no, you may not go" contains trochees (two stressed syllables followed by one unstressed syllable) that bring out the drama in the mother's answer. The dialogue between mother and daughter makes the reader feel closer to the tragedy than he or she would feel by reading the mere facts in a newspaper article.

The Gift
by Li-Young Lee

Selection Test, *page 178*

Comprehension

1. A
2. J
3. B
4. G
5. A
6. H
7. D
8. H
9. C
10. G

Literary Focus

11. C
12. J
13. C
14. F

Constructed Response

15. Student's responses will vary. A sample response follows:

Even though you pause briefly according to the punctuation, the line breaks help you group ideas the way the poet has experienced the subject of the poem. The poet also creates some surprises with the tiny, extra pauses the reader must make between lines. For example, the next-to-last sentence ends in the next-to-last line of the poem, so the reader pauses more than if the next sentence began right after the period. This distinct pause heightens the impact of the last line, "I kissed my father," which comes as a tender surprise to the reader and adds to the affectionate tone of the poem.

Legal Alien / Extranjera legal
by Pat Mora

Selection Test, *page 181*

Comprehension

1. A	**6.** G
2. H	**7.** C
3. D	**8.** F
4. G	**9.** B
5. D	**10.** F

Literary Focus

11. B	**13.** B
12. J	**14.** G

Constructed Response

15. Student's responses will vary. A sample response follows:

The speaker of the poem is a Mexican American. By living the experience that the poem tells about, the speaker provides first-hand information about what it is like to speak both Spanish and English and to live by traditions both Mexican and American. Clearly the speaker knows English and Spanish, because there is a Spanish phrase in "Legal Alien." In addition, the poem appears in a Spanish version, "Extranjera legal." The poet writes about the difficulty of being Mexican to Americans and American to Mexicans in lines like "(their eyes say, 'You may speak / Spanish but you're not like me')." This line refers to the way Mexicans view the speaker as being more American than Mexican even though she is both. The speaker's understanding of her situation and her feelings of frustration creates the tone of conflict the poem conveys.

The Base Stealer
by Robert Francis

American Hero
by Essex Hemphill

Selection Test, *page 184*

Comprehension

1. C	**6.** J
2. H	**7.** D
3. B	**8.** H
4. J	**9.** B
5. A	**10.** G

Literary Focus

11. B	**13.** B
12. H	**14.** G

Constructed Response

15. Student's responses will vary. A sample response follows:

The speaker of "The Base Stealer" loves to watch the base runner steal a base during a baseball game. He observes the base stealer closely and uses alliterative phrases like "he teeters, skitters, tingles, teases" to communicate his enjoyment of watching the base stealer in action. Similes compare the base stealer to an "ecstatic bird" hovering between two bases. In another instance, when the base stealer has not yet committed to running for the next base, he's described as "taut like a tightrope-walker." The sound devices and images together create the tone of respect and admiration as well the thrilling feeling the speaker has as he watches a base stealer in action.

Collection 7 Summative Test, *page 187*

Vocabulary Skills

1. A	**4.** H
2. F	**5.** D
3. D	

Comprehension

6. F
7. C
8. G
9. D
10. F

Reading Skills and Strategies:

Constructed Response

Describing Poetic Form

11. Students' responses will vary. A sample response follows:

The poem is written in two-line stanzas, or couplets. The meter of the poem is four feet per line. Most feet are iambic—a foot that contains an unstressed followed by a stressed syllable. Take, for example, the first line: "Across the years he could recall." Some lines contain anapests—two unstressed syllables followed by a stressed syllable. Some contain spondees—two stressed syllables. Other lines contain different combinations of stressed and unstressed syllables among the poem's iambs.

12. Students' responses will vary. A sample response follows:

The father would best be described as dependable; to the boy, the father's presence means protection, safety, love, and security.

13. Students' responses will vary. A sample response follows:

This poem is written in rhymed couplets. Such a form is especially appropriate to describe this father. The steady, predictable rhymed stanzas are a good match for this steady and dependable man. Thus, the poet has given readers the security of a predicable form just as the father has given a stable home to the boy.

Literary Focus: Constructed Response

14. Students' responses will vary. A sample response follows:

The metaphor in this poem compares the flame of a lit match with the heart of the boy's father. The father treats his son so lovingly and kindly that the boy believes the glow of the flame is a heart, the "bare heart." His father's real heart is the "hidden heart," mentioned in the same line. The metaphor extends as it repeats directly or through implication in other lines of the poem. In another example, the glow of the match, "showed a look upon a face / Too tender for the day to trace." In these lines, the glow of the match takes on a feeling of love and warmth; the reader knows that the speaker experiences it as the "bare heart" his father shows to him.

15. Diction: sire, kindled, semblance, heart, tender, shone

Form: lyric

Rhythm/rhyme: meter with four feet, mostly iambs; rhyming couplets

Figurative language: extended metaphor implies the match flame is bare heart while the father's heart is a hidden, or secret, heart

Voice of speaker: reverent, awed, worshipful, serious

Tone: reverent and full of loving respect

Collection 8

Collection 8 Diagnostic Test

Literature, Informational Text, Vocabulary, *page 192*

1. B
2. F
3. A
4. G
5. C
6. J
7. B
8. G
9. D
10. J

Answer Key

A Sound of Thunder
by Ray Bradbury

from Jurassic Park
by Michael Crichton

Selection Test, *page 194*

Comprehension

1. C
2. J
3. A
4. J
5. B
6. J
7. D
8. F
9. A
10. H

Literary Focus

11. B
12. H
13. A
14. G

Vocabulary Development

15. e
16. a
17. c
18. b
19. d

Constructed Response

20. Students' responses will vary. A sample response follows:

Bradbury effectively uses figurative language and diction to create a mood, or atmosphere, in this story. The "alternate future" is the result of human error. To emphasize Eckels's humanity, the author describes him in lavish, sensory detail—Eckels not only speaks, but he *feels* himself speaking. The mood of the prehistoric setting is created through sensory details ("far birds' cries blew on a wind, and the smell of tar and an old salt sea, moist grasses, and flowers the color of blood") and figurative devices, such as simile ("Sounds like music and sounds like flying tents filled the sky"). When we read about the death of the dinosaur, we see the impact of his death. By contrast, the death of the butterfly seems irrelevant.

Rising Tides
by Bob Herbert

An Arctic Floe of Climate Questions
by Robert Cooke

Selection Test, *page 197*

Comprehension

1. C
2. G
3. A
4. J
5. C

Vocabulary Development

6. g
7. a
8. j
9. a
10. h

To Da-duh, in Memoriam
by Paule Marshall

Selection Test, *page 199*

Comprehension

1. B
2. F
3. D
4. H
5. C
6. J
7. A
8. H
9. D
10. G

Literary Focus

11. B
12. G
13. D
14. H

Vocabulary Development

15. formidable
16. admonished
17. unrelenting
18. austere
19. truculent

Constructed Response

20. Students' responses will vary. A sample response follows:

Paule Marshall writes long, flowing sentences with a variety of interesting, sometimes difficult words. Every so often she adds commentary in parentheses within a sentence. She uses vivid comparisons and sensory language to describe Da-duh and her life in Barbados. Her use of figurative language, complicated diction, and elaborate sentence structure can be seen in the following example:

"I had suddenly become her anchor, for I felt her fear of the lorry with its asthmatic motor (a fear and distrust, I later learned, she held of all machines) beating like a pulse in her rough palm."

She compares the sound of a truck motor with the sound someone with asthma might make. She describes herself as an anchor for her grandmother. She includes extra information about her grandmother in parentheses. In addition, Marshall shows us the dialect her grandmother used—for example, "They's canes father, bo."

How to Eat a Guava
from When I Was Puerto Rican
by Esmeralda Santiago

The Tropics in New York
by Claude McKay

Selection Test, *page 203*

Comprehension

1. D
2. F
3. C
4. G
5. C
6. J
7. C
8. F
9. C
10. G

Literary Focus

11. B
12. G
13. D
14. F

Constructed Response

15. Students' responses will vary. A sample response follows:

The theme of "The Tropics in New York" is homesickness and how it can strike a person at any time. As the speaker looks out a window in New York City, he can't help but think of the beauty of his native home's tropical landscape. That vision makes him sad and homesick, as is emphasized by the poem's somber mood. In the first two stanzas sensory images allow the reader to envision a beautiful tropical landscape. In the last stanza the speaker expresses his yearning for the tropics: "A wave of longing through my body swept, / And, hungry for the old, familiar ways, / I turned aside and bowed my head and wept."

Figurative language helps endow the images with a sacred quality. The word *parish* in the first stanza alerts the reader to an importance verging on that of religion. Then, in the second stanza, skies give a figuative "benediction" to "nun-like hills."

Collection 8 Summative Test, *page 206*

Vocabulary Skills

1. B
2. F
3. D
4. F
5. B

Comprehension

6. G
7. A
8. H
9. B
10. H

Reading Skills and Strategies:
Constructed Response

Comparing and Contrasting

11. Students' responses will vary. A sample response follows:

City: fast, crowded, house cats, harried

Country: slow, solitude, mousers, dignity

Literary Focus: Constructed Response

12. Students' responses will vary. A sample response follows:

A cone-shaped mountain in the Glendora countryside is described as having been "caressed by sunrays that danced on the brown stones, making them sparkle like jewels." The glimmering light mentioned in this figure of speech creates a mood of near-perfection and tranquillity. At the end of the story, when Mrs. Heaslip attempts to pet the new kitten, it looks at her with "two flaring eyes" and utters a "savage hiss, then the sound of spitting." The mood of serenity is transformed into one of violence and aggression.

13. Students' responses will vary. A sample response follows:

Liam O'Flaherty has a formal writing style that includes multisyllabic, descriptive words with a variety of sentence structures, including many that are complicated. For example, rather than simply state that many people feel stress from living in a crowded city, O'Flaherty writes, "In the city, among the multitude of human beings, there had been no repose, no dignity." Interestingly, the main conflict of the story—the fact that mice live in the house—is presented by O'Flaherty in a simple sentence that is also an entire paragraph. By momentarily changing his writing style, he emphasizes the conflict, surprising the reader just as the characters are surprised by this situation in the story. O'Flaherty also uses simple, straightforward sentences to create realistic dialogue.

14. Students' responses will vary. A sample response follows:

Tone is the author's attitude toward a subject. In this story, Liam O'Flaherty pokes fun at the characters, who are too urban for their own good. Their foolish idea about the perfect tranquillity of the countryside is a fool's dream. Life is as difficult and cruel in the country as it is in the city, O'Flaherty tells us. People have to fight for survival no matter where they live. The Heaslips, stressed out from urban congestion and construction, think they'll have a calm life in the countryside—until they are faced with the situation of mice. O'Flaherty's gentle sarcasm about the couple's ignorance is apparent in his descriptions of the Heaslip's pet cat from the city, about which he says, "The struggle for existence meant nothing to it. It was as innocuous as an old maiden lady with a fixed income."

15. Students' responses will vary. A sample response follows:

Diction: multi-syllabic, difficult words, such as *multitude, gesticulating, innocuous*

Sentence structure: variety of sentence lengths and structures, formal

Tone: cynical

Mood: peaceful at first, then more menacing, then cruel and violent

Collection 9

Collection 9 Diagnostic Test

Literature, Informational Text, Vocabulary, *page 212*

1. D
2. H
3. A
4. J
5. B
6. F
7. B
8. H
9. A
10. G

American History
by Judith Ortiz Cofer

Volar
by Judith Ortiz Cofer

Selection Test, *page 214*

Comprehension

1. C
2. G
3. C
4. F
5. B
6. G
7. D
8. F
9. C
10. G

Literary Focus

11. D
12. J
13. A
14. F

Vocabulary Development

15. enthralled

16. literally

17. solace

18. infatuated

19. vigilant

Constructed Response

20. Students' responses will vary. A sample response follows:

El Building in Paterson, New Jersey, is described as being a home for new immigrants from Puerto Rico. The building sounds like a jukebox. (Cofer suggests that music drowns out the suffering of the immigrants.) El Building is significant in the story because it provides a vantage point for Elena. Sitting on the fire escape, she is able to see first the Jewish family and then Eugene's family in the house next door. When Elena visits Eugene's house and looks back at her building, she perceives it as a prison. In "Volar" the reader learns that Judith Ortiz Cofer and her family lived in a building very much like El Building. Cofer's family had a "tiny apartment" from which she dreamed of flying away in the form of Supergirl, a heroine from a favorite comic book.

In both selections the buildings serve as symbols of limitation. The rooms are small; they allow only the imagination to fly. Economically, the tenants are stuck there; they cannot even afford plane fare to Puerto Rico. The unkempt appearance of the building figuratively mirrors society's view of the residents as unworthy, and therefore, it limits their participation in mainstream life.

A Warm, Clear Day in Dallas
from John F. Kennedy
by Marta Randall

Address to Congress, November 27, 1963
by Lyndon B. Johnson

Students React to President Kennedy's Death
from Children and the Death of a President

Selection Test, *page 218*

Comprehension

1. A
2. G
3. C
4. G
5. A

Vocabulary Development

6. f
7. d
8. j
9. c
10. f

Beware of the Dog
by Roald Dahl

Wounded and Trapped
by Ernie Pyle

Selection Test, *page 220*

Comprehension

1. D
2. H
3. C
4. J
5. B
6. G
7. D
8. J
9. A
10. G

Literary Focus

11. C
12. F
13. B
14. G

Vocabulary Development

15. e
16. c
17. a
18. b
19. d

Constructed Response

20. Students' responses will vary. A sample response follows:

Germany was an enemy of Britain and the United States. The United States and Britain worked together as allies during the war. France was occupied by the Germans, so when British pilots flew over France, they faced great danger. When Peter Williamson hears Junkers 88 engines, he becomes frightened and uncomfortable because he knows those planes are the aircraft used by Germany. When the British pilot of "Wounded and Trapped" is discovered by Americans, he happily greets them because they are allies. When Peter looks out of his hospital room window and reads a sign written in French, he understands that he is in enemy territory, since France was occupied by Germany for much of World War II.

Collection 9 Summative Test,

page 224

Vocabulary Skills

1. C

2. J

3. B

4. F

5. C

Comprehension

6. H

7. A

8. G

9. A

10. J

Reading Skills and Strategies: Constructed Response

Using Prior Knowledge

11. Students' responses will vary. A sample response follows:

Food: coffee, cherry pie, cigars

Technology: TV, ironing, doorbell, tractors, thermos

Activities: stacking dishes, answering the phone, cleaning glasses, meeting
Language: contractions, nicknames, incomplete sentences, idioms

Other: baby sitters, neighborhood disagreements

Literary Focus: Constructed Response

12. Students' responses will vary. A sample response follows:

The strongest response is H. The neighbors have agreed to act together against one family, but at least one neighbor—Arthur—is having second thoughts, which he attempts to talk to Frank about. The issue is prejudice. The neighbors are trying to keep the doors of the neighborhood from opening to admit a family different from them in some way—most likely race or ethnicity. The laws of the United States do not necessarily back Arthur's concerns because the civil rights laws did not pass until 1965.

13. Students' responses will vary. A sample response follows:

If the author of *Thunder on Sycamore Street* were prejudiced and believed that people should not live in integrated neighborhoods, the conflict in the play would be quite different. In Reginald Rose's play one person—Arthur—expresses doubts about his neighborhood's decision to bar a family. Someone who did not believe in integration in 1956 would not include Arthur or would attempt to make Arthur seem wrong for his doubts—not just wrong in the eyes of Frank and other prejudiced neighbors, but wrong in the eyes of the audience, too.

14. Students' responses will vary. A sample response follows:

Theme: Neighborhoods should be open to all families.

Historical influence: In 1956, neighborhoods were not always integrated. Laws did not protect families from prejudice or discrimination.

Frank feels free to act on his feelings of prejudice and bar the family from his neighborhood.
Arthur is a lone voice for fairness.

Biographical influence: The theme of the play indicates that Rose believed in integration.
The conflict shows that Rose was against discrimination.
Arthur's lone voice against the neighborhood plan is Rose's voice rising against prejudice.
Rose used his play to point out an important social issue in the United States in 1956.

Collection 10

Collection 10 Diagnostic Test

Literature, Informational Text, Vocabulary, *page 233*

1. B
2. F
3. D
4. G
5. A
6. J
7. A
8. G
9. C
10. H

from the Odyssey, Part One: The Wanderings

by Homer
translated by Robert Fitzgerald

Selection Test, *page 235*

Comprehension

1. B
2. H
3. D
4. J
5. C
6. G
7. C
8. F
9. B
10. H

Literary Focus

11. D
12. J
13. B
14. J

Vocabulary Development

15. g
16. h
17. j
18. e
19. b
20. a
21. c
22. f
23. i
24. d

Constructed Response

25. Students' responses will vary. A sample response follows:

Circe reveals that Scylla takes six men from every ship that passes her. Also, Teiresias and Circe prophesize that the crew will die if they raid the cattle of Helios and that Odysseus will return to Ithaca alone. Given the Greek view of fate, Odysseus may believe that losing six men to Scylla is inevitable and, more logical, that telling them so would cause panic. It could also be argued that Odysseus, always a clever strategist, realizes that he needs his crew's labor more than they need his leadership. If Odysseus is right about his crew's attitude, his decision is certainly pragmatic, if not morally sound. If he had not withheld information, the fate of his crew would not have changed, but he would have joined them at the bottom of the ocean, never to see home again.

from the Odyssey, Part Two: Coming Home

by Homer
translated by Robert Fitzgerald

Selection Test, *page 239*

Comprehension

1. C
2. J
3. B
4. H
5. B
6. G
7. D
8. F
9. C
10. H

Literary Focus

11. A
12. F
13. B
14. F

Vocabulary Development

15. h
16. b
17. i
18. a
19. d
20. j
21. g
22. f
23. e
24. c

Constructed Response

25. Students' responses will vary. A sample response follows:

    The only character in these passages who is heroic in the classical sense of the word is Odysseus. Telemachus shows signs of heroism, but he is really in the shadow of his father. In a modern sense, Penelope shows considerable heroism. She manages to keep the suitors at bay for some time, although it is not clear just how long they have been at the palace. Her fidelity to her husband for the twenty years that Odysseus is away shows some heroism. Also, her testing of Odysseus by telling the servant to move the bed—in order to make sure that the gods are not playing a trick on her—shows some of the characteristics of heroism. Certainly, the ruse demonstrates that she can match wits with Odysseus.

Where I Find My Heroes
by Oliver Stone

Heroes with Solid Feet
by Kirk Douglas

Selection Test, *page 243*

Comprehension

1. C
2. J
3. B
4. J
5. C

Vocabulary Development

6. defers
7. emaciated
8. emulate
9. annihilate
10. advocate

The Fenris Wolf
retold by Olivia Coolidge

Selection Test, *page 245*

Comprehension

1. D
2. G
3. D
4. G
5. C
6. J
7. D
8. G
9. A
10. G

Literary Focus

11. B
12. G
13. D
14. F

Constructed Response

15. Students' responses will vary. A sample response follows:

    Scandinavian culture viewed good and evil differently than other cultures. Scandinavians regarded evil as a potential part of everything and everyone. They tolerated Loki because he was handsome, and we know they valued beauty in men: Their god of beauty, Balder, was male. They also admired Loki for his intelligence, which they knew they needed. When the gods first see the Fenris Wolf, Loki's offspring, they hope that his good side may be stronger than his evil side and that he may be tamed. The story suggests that Scandinavians may not have trusted cleverness, but they knew it was needed for survival, at least until the unavoidable end of everything.

Collection 10 Summative Test, *page 248*

Vocabulary Skills

1. B
2. H
3. A
4. G
5. D

Comprehension

6. H
7. B
8. J
9. A
10. H

Reading Skills and Strategies: Constructed Response

Monitoring Your Comprehension

11. Students' responses will vary. A sample response follows:

    First, Odysseus spots land and thinks he is home safe. But when he swims toward shore, he sees that there is no beach, only sheer cliffs and rocks. Concluding that there is no point in trying to go ashore, Odysseus considers swimming down the coast, outside the breakers. If he chooses that option, another storm could drive him out to sea again, and he could be eaten by a shark. Swept against the rocks and out to sea, Odysseus finally decides to swim along the coast until he comes to the mouth of a river.

Literary Focus: Constructed Response

12. Students' responses will vary. A sample response follows:

    Sunrise: Direct Quotation—"shining ringlets in the East"; **Appeal to Sense**—sight

    Sea: Direct Quotation—"trampling roar of sea on rock, / where combers, rising shoreward, thudded down / on the sucking ebb—all sheeted with salt foam"; **Appeal to Sense**—sound, sight

    Land: Direction Quotation—"the mouth of a calm river / at length came into view, with level shores / unbroken, free from rock, shielded from wind—"; **Appeal to Sense**—sight, touch

13. Students' responses will vary. A sample response follows:

    An epic is written about a hero, who is usually on a quest or journey. The language of an epic is elevated; the tone is lofty. The *Odyssey* is the model for the epic of the long journey. Its hero, Odysseus, is known for his physical strength and mental prowess. He overpowers and outthinks his opponents. An example of the lofty tone is found in the following lines: "What of my sailing, then, from Troy? / What of those years / of rough adventure, weathered under Zeus?"

14. Seafaring people were a significant part of Homer's audience. They knew well the danger of the ocean. No doubt, they knew of people who had been in Odysseus's position: adrift in the surf and in danger of sharks, currents, and rocks. One can easily imagine an excited audience shouting, "What about sharks?" as Homer describes the hero's dilemma. Other listeners might have been sadly remembering how a family member was lost under the waves. For these people, an octopus was not merely something they had heard about; they had seen, caught, eaten, and perhaps even been attacked by this creature. The silent prayer muttered by Odysseus as the current drags him would have elicited vivid memories for many. In this excerpt, the events accurately mirror the survival issues of this historical period.

Collection 11

Collection 11 Diagnostic Test

Literature, Informational Text, Vocabulary, *page 253*

1. B
2. H
3. A
4. H
5. A
6. G
7. C
8. J
9. D
10. F

Answer Key

Visitor from Forest Hills
from Plaza Suite
by Neil Simon

Selection Test, *page 255*

Comprehension

1. C
2. G
3. B
4. J
5. B
6. F
7. C
8. G
9. A
10. G

Literary Focus

11. B
12. F
13. C
14. J

Vocabulary Development

15. interminable
16. torrent
17. despondently
18. volatile
19. incredulously

Constructed Response

20. Students' responses will vary. A sample response follows:

Roy is a man who becomes easily frustrated and then explodes with anger. He is also a man who is concerned about money. So when his daughter refuses to come out of the bathroom when it is time for her to get married, Roy can't understand his daughter's problem, gets angry, and yells about money. To talk with Mimsey, Roy tries to break down the bathroom door with his arm. The door won't open, and Roy loudly complains that he has broken his arm. His broken arm, though, does not keep him from wiggling his fingers or using his arm normally. When Roy decides to climb outside onto the seventh-floor ledge to get in through the bathroom window, his jacket rips in half. On top of it all, Roy becomes wet and bedraggled because it began to rain when he climbed onto the ledge.

The Tragedy of Romeo and Juliet, the Prologue, Act I
by William Shakespeare

Selection Test, *page 258*

Comprehension

1. C
2. F
3. B
4. J
5. A
6. H
7. C
8. G
9. A
10. H

Literary Focus

11. D
12. H
13. A
14. F

Constructed Response

15. Students' responses will vary. A sample response follows:

Shakespeare builds suspense with a number of details in the scene at the Capulet party. Romeo and his friends arrive at the party wearing masks so that no Capulet is aware that members of the Montague clan are among the guests. Tybalt, though, recognizes Romeo's voice. In addition, Romeo dances with Juliet and kisses her, even though she does not know who he is or what family he is from. Thus, readers are kept in a constant state of suspense, wondering what will happen if Romeo is discovered and what Juliet's reaction will be when she learns his identify. Only at the end of the scene does the Nurse inform Juliet that she has danced with and kissed Romeo Montague.

Answer Key

The Tragedy of Romeo and Juliet, Act II
by William Shakespeare

Selection Test, *page 261*

Comprehension

1. C
2. J
3. C
4. J
5. A
6. H
7. C
8. F
9. B
10. F

Literary Focus

11. B
12. H
13. D
14. G

Constructed Response

15. Students' responses will vary. A sample response follows:

Dramatic irony occurs when the audience knows something that the characters do not know. One moment of dramatic irony occurs in Scene 6 when Friar Laurence brings Romeo and Juliet together in marriage. He speaks to Romeo (just as Juliet is arriving) about love, but those lines also tell the audience what will happen in the play. Romeo is too involved in his love affair to see himself or his beloved in these words of warning. The friar warns Romeo that love that is too passionate turns destructive. The audience knows that this play is a tragedy and that the love of Romeo and Juliet will come to a bad end. The friar even foreshadows the death of the lovers when he begins his speech, "These violent delights have violent ends."

The Tragedy of Romeo and Juliet, Act III
by William Shakespeare

Selection Test, *page 265*

Comprehension

1. C
2. G
3. C
4. G
5. A
6. J
7. B
8. J
9. B
10. J

Literary Focus

11. C
12. H
13. D
14. G

Constructed Response

15. Students' responses will vary. A sample response follows:

Juliet uses words with double meanings to mourn for her cousin Tybalt and remain true to her love for Romeo, her secret husband. When Lady Capulet labels Romeo the "villain" who killed Tybalt, Juliet says, "Villain and he be many miles asunder— / God pardon him! I do, with all my heart; / and yet no man like he doth grieve my heart." Juliet seems to agree with her mother's opinion of Romeo, but the audience knows what Juliet is really saying: Romeo is not a villain. True, Romeo does grieve her here, but not for Tybalt's death; she grieves Romeo's absence. Juliet later exclaims about Romeo, "To wreak the love I bore my cousin / Upon his body that hath slaughtered him!" She means she would transfer the love she had for Tybalt to Romeo, not in blows but in kisses.

The Tragedy of Romeo and Juliet, Act IV
by William Shakespeare

Selection Test, *page 268*

Comprehension

1. A
2. H
3. D
4. H
5. D
6. G
7. B
8. F
9. C
10. H

Literary Focus

11. C
12. G
13. B

Constructed Response

14. Students' responses will vary. A sample response follows:

At the beginning of the play, Juliet is a meek, obedient girl. When she marries Romeo in secret, her life changes. From that point on, she makes bold decisions based on her love for Romeo, not the good of the Capulet family. When Tybalt dies, Juliet uses words with double meanings to keep her love of Romeo a secret from her mother. Later, Juliet becomes bolder. She tells her father that she will not marry Paris or anyone else. When her father threatens to disown her, Juliet holds to her position and keeps her marriage to Romeo a secret. With the help of Friar Laurence, she plans to fake her own death just before her wedding day. She goes ahead with the plan even though the idea of taking a sleeping potion and waking in the family vault frightens her. Her love has made her deceitful, scheming, assertive, and bold.

The Tragedy of Romeo and Juliet, Act V
by William Shakespeare

Your Laughter
by Pablo Neruda

How Do I Love Thee?
by Elizabeth Barrett Browning

Selection Test, *page 271*

Comprehension

1. D
2. F
3. B
4. H
5. B
6. J
7. D
8. J
9. C
10. F

Literary Focus

11. D
12. H
13. B
14. H

Constructed Response

15. Students' responses will vary. A sample response follows:

The interaction between the Capulet and Montague families when Romeo and Juliet fall in love show that feuds lead to destruction and tragedy. In the play six people die within the span of a few days. These deaths affect families other than those involved in the feud, especially the family of the prince. Friar Laurence's career is ruined even if the prince decides not to punish him. If Romeo and Juliet had spoken truthfully and directly to their parents of their love or of their plans to marry, some of these deaths—including their own—could have been prevented. The actions and decisions of the young couple serve as a chilling warning to those who, even today, would find themselves embroiled in bitter disputes or rapt in forbidden love.

Dear Juliet
by Lisa Bannon

Romeo and Juliet in Bosnia
by Bob Herbert

Selection Test, *page 274*

Comprehension

1. B
2. J
3. A
4. H
5. C

Vocabulary Development

6. f
7. d
8. g
9. d
10. f

Collection 11 Summative Test, *page 276*

Vocabulary Skills

1. B
2. F
3. C
4. G
5. C

Comprehension

6. J
7. C
8. J
9. A
10. H

Reading Skills and Strategies:

Constructed Response

Paraphrasing

11. Students' responses will vary. A sample response follows:

    It's cold in here, and I'm shaking all over. You'd think I was about to take a test! I need to make a decision. If I think too much about it or wait to find a woman I love, I'll never marry. Why would I want a better wife than Natalya? She's a good housekeeper, fairly good-looking, and smart. Now my ears are ringing! Anyway, I have to marry. I'm already thirty-five, and I need to settle down. I get the shakes, and I'm always getting upset. Right now my lips are quivering, and my right eyebrow is twitching. The worst thing is I can't sleep. As soon as I start to fall asleep, I get this spasm on my left side and jump out of bed. I'm like a crazy person. It happens all night long.

Literary Focus: Constructed Response

12. Students' responses will vary. A sample response follows:

    The opening of the dialogue reveals that Lomov is a nervous man. For example, as he is about to propose, he admits that Natalya may get angry at him for what he is about to say. Then he loses his confidence and begins talking to himself. However, in the second half of the scene, his stubbornness is revealed in his argument with Natalya over the land. In contrast, Natalya is impatient and confident at the start. When Lomov is unable to get to the point, she prods him and impatiently asks, "What's the matter?" Later she interrupts him in the middle of his proposal and confidently argues that the Oxen Meadows belong to her family.

13. Students' responses will vary. A sample response follows:

    Chekhov uses the stage directions to show how nervous and unsure Lomov is. Lomov drinks water whenever he feels especially nervous, as we see during his opening monologue and later during his stressful argument with Natalya. At the end of the scene, during the argument about Oxen Meadows, the stage directions indicate that he clutches his heart and yells at Natalya. These last two actions show that he is losing his composure and is upset that the conversation is going badly.

14. Students' responses will vary. A sample response follows:

    After Lomov's monologue the audience knows that he has come to Natalya's home to propose to her. Natalya, however, doesn't know why he is there. The audience's knowledge of Lomov's plan makes the quarrel that erupts between Lomov and Natalya surprising and frustrating, as well as comical.

15. Students' responses will vary. A sample response follows:

    This scene contains two elements of a farce. First, the fact that an argument related to an old family feud erupts in the middle of a marriage proposal seems ridiculous. Second, the scene contains physical comedy. The awkward pauses in Lomov's monologue and his need to drink water when he is nervous are examples of physical comedy.

Collection 12

Collection 12 Diagnostic Test

Informational Text, *page 282*

1. D
2. F
3. A
4. H
5. C
6. F
7. B
8. J
9. A
10. H

Reading Consumer Documents

Selection Test, *page 284*

Comprehension

1. C
2. J
3. B
4. H
5. D

Reading Informational Text

6. G
7. A
8. F
9. C
10. H

Following Technical Directions

Selection Test, *page 286*

Comprehension

1. D
2. J
3. D
4. G
5. B

Reading Informational Text

6. F
7. B
8. G
9. A
10. J

Citing Internet Sources

Selection Test, *page 288*

Comprehension

1. B
2. J
3. C
4. F
5. A

Reading Informational Text

6. J
7. D
8. H
9. B
10. J

Analyzing Functional Workplace Documents

Selection Test, *page 290*

Comprehension

1. C
2. J
3. B
4. G
5. A

Reading Informational Text

6. F
7. C
8. H
9. D
10. H

Evaluating the Logic of Functional Documents

Selection Test, *page 292*

Comprehension

1. B
2. F
3. C
4. H
5. B

Reading Informational Text

6. J
7. C
8. H
9. B
10. G

Answer Key

Collection 12 Summative Test, *page 294*

Vocabulary Skills

1. C
2. H
3. D
4. J
5. B

Comprehension

6. J
7. C
8. H
9. B
10. H

Reading Functional Documents

Understanding the Format of Functional Documents

11. D

Following Technical Directions

12. 4 —**1.** Pull the pin. **2.** Aim low. **3.** Squeeze the handle. **4.** Sweep the nozzle from side to side at the base of the fire until the flames appear to be out.

Analyzing the Logic of Functional Documents

13. The types of extinguishers are listed alphabetically and from the kind used for the most-common type of fire to the sort used for the least-common type of fire.

End-of-Year Test, *page 299*

Reading and Literary Analysis

1. D
2. A
3. C
4. C
5. B
6. D
7. D
8. A
9. B
10. C
11. C
12. B
13. D
14. A
15. C
16. B
17. B
18. B
19. C
20. C
21. B
22. D
23. D
24. A
25. C
26. A
27. A
28. D
29. D
30. D

Vocabulary

Sample A D
31. C
32. A
33. B
34. D
35. C
36. A
Sample B D
37. C
38. D
39. B
40. A

Skills Profile

Skills Profile

Student's Name ______________________ Grade ____________

Teacher's Name ______________________ Date ____________

For each skill, write the date the observation is made and any comments that explain the student's development toward skills mastery.

SKILL	NOT OBSERVED	EMERGING	PROFICIENT
Literature			
Analyze the characteristics of different forms of dramatic literature such as comedy, tragedy, drama, and dramatic monologue.			
Compare and contrast similar themes across genres.			
Analyze influences on characters (such as internal and external conflicts and motivation) and the way those influences affect the plot.			
Determine characters' traits from what the characters say about themselves.			
Compare and contrast works that express a universal theme, and provide evidence to support that theme.			
Analyze the development of time and sequence, including the use of foreshadowing and flashback.			
Analyze various literary devices, including figurative language, imagery, allegory, and symbolism.			
Identify ambiguities, contradictions, and ironies in the text.			
Analyze the way voice, tone, persona, and choice of narrator affect characterization and plot.			

NAME ______________________ CLASS ______________

SKILL	NOT OBSERVED	EMERGING	PROFICIENT
Analyze the function of dialogue, scene design, soliloquies, asides, and character foils in dramatic literature.			
Evaluate the aesthetic qualities of style, including the effect of diction, figurative language, tone, and mood.			
Analyze the way a work of literature relates to the themes and issues of its historical period. (Historical approach)			
Informational Text			
Analyze the way authors use the structure and format of workplace documents to achieve their purposes.			
Prepare a bibliography of reference materials using a variety of consumer, workplace, and public documents.			
Generate relevant research questions after reading about an issue.			
Synthesize the content from several sources or works by a single author on a single issue.			
Analyze and elaborate on ideas presented in primary and secondary sources.			
Follow technical directions to use technology.			
Evaluate the logic of functional documents.			
Evaluate the credibility of an author's argument by examining generalizations, the scope of the evidence, and the intentions of the author.			
Vocabulary			
Identify the literal and figurative meanings of words, and understand word derivations.			

NAME ______________________ CLASS ______________

SKILL	NOT OBSERVED	EMERGING	PROFICIENT
Distinguish between the denotative and connotative meanings of words.			
Use knowledge of Greek, Roman, and Norse mythology to understand the origin and meaning of new words.			